Mastercam® 2018

Lathe Training Tutorial

To order more books:

Call 1-800-529-5517 or

Visit www.emastercam.com or

Contact your Mastercam dealer

Mastercam 2018 Lathe Training Tutorial

Copyright: 1998 - 2018 In-House Solutions Inc. All rights reserved

Software: Mastercam 2018

Author: Mariana Lendel

ISBN: 978-1-77146-646-2

Revision Date: May 29, 2017

Tutorial	Geometry Functions	Surface and Toolpath Creation
#1	**Rectangle** **Line Parallel** **Chamfer Entities** **Fillet Entities** **Trim Entities**	**Face** **Roughing** **Finish**
#2	**Line Endpoints (Polar Line)** **Line Parallel** **Line Endpoints (Horizontal)** **Divide/delete** **Trim 2 Entities** **Fillet**	**Face** **Roughing** **Finish** **Groove - Multiple Chains** **Drilling**
#3	**Import a Parasolid File** **Turn Profile**	**Face** **Drill** **Canned Rough ID** **Canned Finish ID** **Rough OD** **Finish OD** **Groove - Straight grooves** **Groove - Angled Grooves** **Cutoff**
#4	**Rectangle** **Parallel Line** **Line Endpoints** **Trim Divide** **Trim 2 Entities**	**Face** **Roughing** **Finish** **Drill** **ID Rough** **ID Finish** **ID Groove - Multiple Chains** **Cutoff**

Tutorial	Geometry Functions	Surface and Toolpath Creation
#5	Line Endpoints Arc Tangent Dynamic Relief Groove Chamfer	Face Rough OD Finish OD Groove Thread Drill Stock Flip Face Rough OD Finish OD Groove Thread Drill
#6	Rectangle Parallel Line Line Endpoints Fillet Trim Chamfer Relief Groove Line Tangent to Two Arcs Rotate Bolt Circle Translate Copy	Face Rough OD Finish OD Groove Thread Center Drill Stock Advance Lathe Tailstock Groove Cutoff
#7	Import a SolidWorks File Turn Profile	Create standard toolpaths geared towards VTL machines. Face Rough OD Finish OD Drill Rough ID Finish ID Groove ID Change Tool Definitions Thread

Table of Contents

GETTING STARTED

Objectives:

✓ Starting Mastercam.
✓ The student will learn about the Graphical User Interface (GUI).
✓ The student will learn how to navigate through Mastercam.

STEP 1: STARTING MASTERCAM

For Windows 7

- ◆ Select the **Start** button.
- ◆ Select **All Programs** and click on **Mastercam 2018**.

For Windows 8

- ◆ Select the **Start** button.
- ◆ Click on the drop down arrow to open **Apps.**
- ◆ Find and click on **Mastercam 2018**.

For Windows 10

- ◆ Select the **Start** button.
- ◆ Click on the drop down arrow to open **Apps.**
- ◆ Find and click on **Mastercam 2018**.

- ◆ To start the software, from the **Desktop**, click on the shortcut icon as shown.

STEP 2: GUI - GRAPHICAL USER INTERFACE

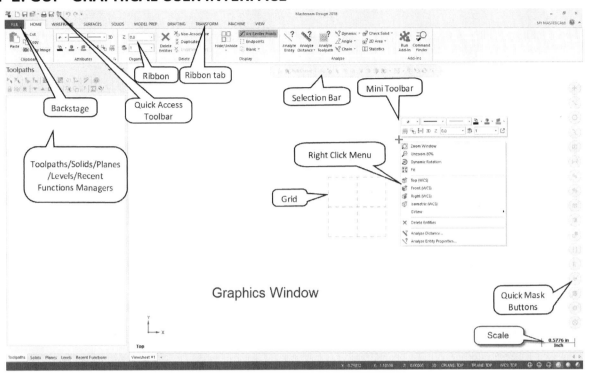

Quick Access Toolbar	QAT contains a fully customizable set of functions that can be quickly accessed by the user.
Backstage (File)	Allows you to manage files. You can insert information about files, start a new file, open an existing one or merge files together. You can also save, convert or print files as well as access the help resources.
Tabs	Contain all the functionality within Mastercam.
Ribbon	Displays the commands available for a selected Tab.
Selection Bar	Allows you to set the AutoCursor modes and to switch between wireframe or solid selections.
Quick Mask Buttons	Lets you select all entities of a specific type. Clicking on the left side of the button or right side of the button toggles between select all or only.
Right Click Menu	The right click menu allows quick access to functions such as zoom, graphic views or recent functions used. A mini toolbar will also appear that allows you to quickly change the attributes.
Toolpaths/Solids/ Planes Manager	Lists the history of the toolpath operations and solids.
Graphics Window	Workspace area in Mastercam where the geometry is displayed.
Scale	Shows you a scale of the object on the screen.

WCS: TOP T/C plane:	Displays the current WCS and T/C plane information.

STEP 3: NAVIGATE THROUGH MASTERCAM

In this step you will learn how to use the ribbon tabs in Mastercam to create the geometry.

3.1 Using the Wireframe tab to select the command to create Line Endpoint

- ◆ Left click on **WIREFRAME.**
- ◆ Left click on **Line Endpoints** as shown in Figure: 3.1.1.

Figure: 3.1.1

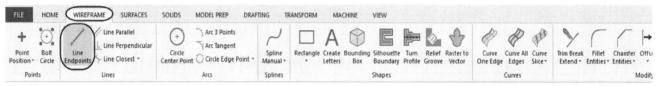

- ◆ Once you select **Line Endpoints** the **Line Endpoints** panel appears on the screen as shown.

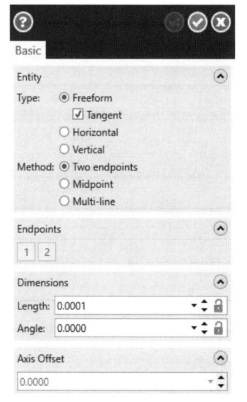

Sketching a line

- To sketch a line left click on two locations on the screen.

Creating a line knowing the endpoint coordinates

- To make a line knowing the two endpoint coordinates, select the **AutoCursor Fast Point** icon from the **General Selection** toolbar.

- In the coordinates field that opens in the upper left corner enter the coordinates of the first endpoint as shown.

- Press **Enter** to continue.
- Select the **AutoCursor Fast Point** icon again and enter in the coordinates of the second endpoint and then press **Enter**.

Create a line knowing an endpoint, the length and the angle

- You can also press the **Space bar** or select the **AutoCursor Fast Point** icon and enter the coordinates of the first endpoint, then enter the **Length** and **Angle** if necessary.
- To continue making lines choose the **OK and Create New Operation** button from the dialog box or press **Enter**. 
- To exit the current command select the **OK** button or press the **Esc** button. 
- To undo the last command, from the **QAT** (Quick Access Toolbar) select the **Undo** button.  The undo button can be used to go back to the beginning of the geometry creation or to the last saved point of the file.

  Mastercam also has a **Redo** button  for your convenience.

3.2 Function Prompt

Prompts the user to execute a command.

- Example: this prompt is used in the **Line Endpoints** command. Specify the first endpoint

NOTE: To find a command, from the **HOME** ribbon, select the **Command Finder** icon and type the function name in the field that opens up.

For example, to find the **Polygon** command type "polygon" in the text field.

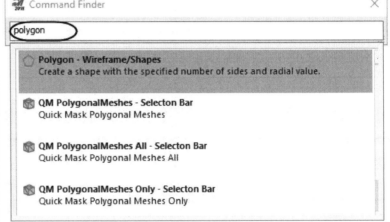

From the list, select the desired command.

STEP 4: SET THE ATTRIBUTES

Mastercam attributes include point style, line style, line thickness, color and level. Before starting to create geometry you should set the attributes.

4.1 'Attributes' Group

Point Style	Displays and sets the system point style.
Line Style	Displays and sets the system line style.
Line Width	Displays and sets the current system line width.
Color	Assigns the current color to wireframe, solid and surface entities. To change the current color click in the specific color field and select a color from the color pallet. To change an existing geometry color, select the geometry first and then click in the color field and select a color from the color pallet.
Clear Colors	When performing a transform function, Mastercam creates a temporary group from the originals (red) and a result group (purple) from the transformed entities. These system groups appear in the Groups dialog box. However, they stay in effect only until you use the **Clear Colors** function or perform another transform function.
2D / 3D Construction Mode	Toggles between 2D and 3D construction modes. In 2D mode all geometry is created parallel to the current Cplane at the current system Z depth. In 3D mode you can work freely in various Z depths, unconstrained by the current system Z depth and Cplane setting.

4.2 'Organize' Group

Z Depth	Sets the current construction depth. To set this click on the Z depth in the status bar at the bottom of the page. Select the drop down arrow and pick one from the most recently used list or click the **Z:** label and pick a point in the graphics window to use the Z depth value of.
Level	Sets the main level you want to work with in the graphics window. To change the current working level type the level number in the box.

Change the Wireframe Color

• Click on the drop down arrow next to the **Wireframe Color** field as shown.

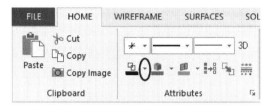

• Select the desired color from the dialog box as shown.

NOTE: Any geometry on your screen will remain in the previous system color. This change will only affect the geometry you create going forward.

To change the color of existing geometry, select the entities first and then click on the drop down arrow next to the **Wireframe Color** icon and select the desired color.

The same method can be applied for any other attribute that you want to set or change.

STEP 5: MANAGER PANELS

5.1 The Toolpaths Manager

- The **Toolpaths Manager** displays all the operations for the current part as shown in Figure: 5.1.1.
- You can sort, edit, regenerate, verify and post any operations.

- For more information on the **Toolpaths Manager**, please refer to the **Help** icon.

Figure: 5.1.1

- The **Toolpaths Manger, Solids Manager** or **Planes Manager** can be hidden to gain more space in the graphics area for creating geometry. Use the **Auto Hide** icon to close all **Toolpaths, Solids, Planes** and **Levels Manager** panels.

- The panels will be hidden to the left of the **Ribbon** as shown.

- To un-hide them, click on one of the managers to open it and click again on the **Auto Hide** icon a shown.

- Selecting the **X** (Close icon) instead of the **Auto Hide** icon will close the manager panels. To re-open them, from the **VIEW ribbon,** select **Toolpaths, Solids, Planes** or **Levels** as shown.

STEP 6: SETTING MASTERCAM TO IMPERIAL

In this step you will learn how to switch the system to imperial and how to set the imperial system as your default. You will have to select the **Backstage** options and select the system configuration.

6.1 Setting Mastercam to imperial for the current session only

NOTE: You may need to switch Mastercam to run in Imperial mode.

FILE
- **Configuration.**
- Select the drop down arrow beside **Current** as shown in Figure: 6.1.1.
- Select **mcamxm.config <English>** as shown.

Figure: 6.1.1

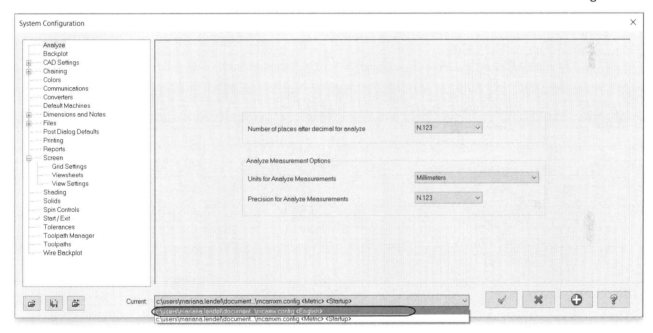

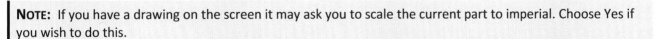

- Select the **OK** button to exit the **System Configuration** dialog box.

NOTE: If you have a drawing on the screen it may ask you to scale the current part to imperial. Choose Yes if you wish to do this.

6.2 Setting Mastercam to imperial as a default

> **NOTE:** If you wish to always work in Imperial mode, follow these steps to save imperial as your current configuration file.

FILE
- **Configuration.**
- Select **Start/Exit** from the configuration topics.
- Select the drop down arrow below **Configuration** in the **Startup settings** area as shown in Figure: 6.2.1.
- Select **mcamxm.config <English>** as shown.

Figure: 6.2.1

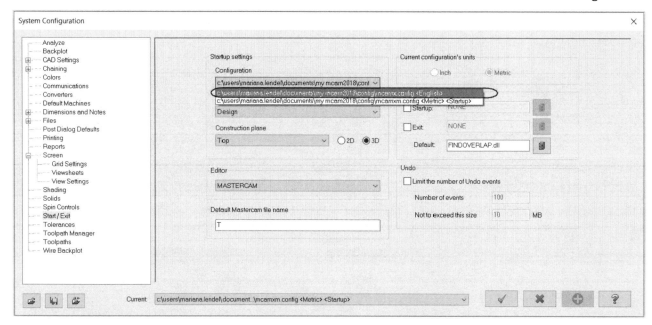

- Select the **OK** button to exit the **System Configuration** dialog box.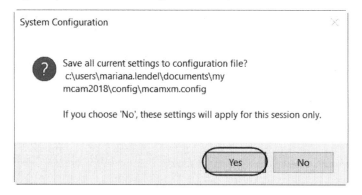
- Mastercam will then prompt you to save these settings to your current configuration file, select **Yes**.

STEP 7: SET THE GRID

Before beginning to create geometry, it is highly recommended to enable the **Grid**. The grid will show you where the origin is and the orientation of the grid gives you a quick preview of the plane you are working in.

FILE
* **Configuration.**
* Select **Screen** from the configuration **Topics.**
* Select the plus sign (+) beside **Screen** as shown in Figure: 7.0.1.

Figure: 7.0.1

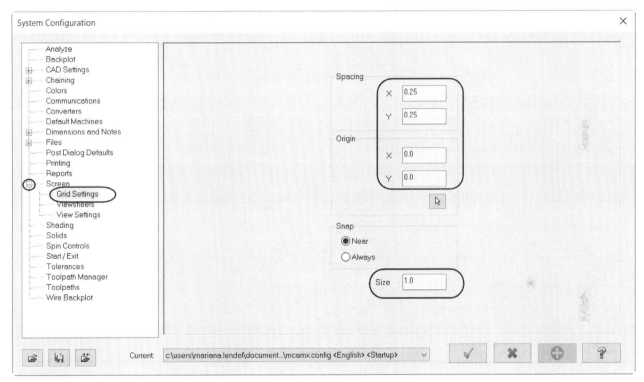

* In **Grid Settings** change the **Spacing** to **X = 0.25 and Y = 0.25**.
* Set the **Size** to **1.0**.

* Choose the **OK** button to exit.
* To see the **Grid** in the graphics window, from the **VIEW ribbon**, enable **Show Grid** as shown.

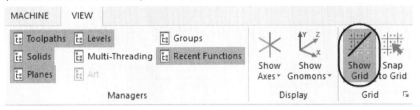

* The **Grid** should appear in the graphics window.

TUTORIAL #1

OVERVIEW OF STEPS TAKEN TO CREATE THE FINAL PART:

From drawing to CAD model:
* The student should examine the drawing on the following page to understand what part is being created in the tutorial.
* From the drawing we can gain an idea of how to create the geometry in Mastercam.

Create the 2D CAD Model used to generate Toolpaths from:
* The student will create the upper profile of the part. Only half of the geometry is needed to create the necessary toolpaths to machine the part.
* Geometry creation commands such as Line Endpoints, Line Parallel, Rectangle, Fillet Entities, and Trim will be used.

Create the necessary toolpaths to machine the part:
* The student will set up the stock size to be used and the clamping method used.
* A Facing toolpath will be created to remove material from the face of the part.
* A Roughing toolpath will be created to remove the bulk of material in preparation for a finish toolpath.
* A Finish toolpath will be created to machine the leftover material from the roughing operation.

Backplot and Verify the file:
* The Backplot will be used to simulate a step by step process of the tool's movements.
* The Verify will be used to watch a tool machine the part out of a solid model.

Post Process the file to generate the G-code:
* The student will then post process the file to obtain an NC file containing the necessary code for the machine.

  This tutorial takes approximately twenty minutes to complete.

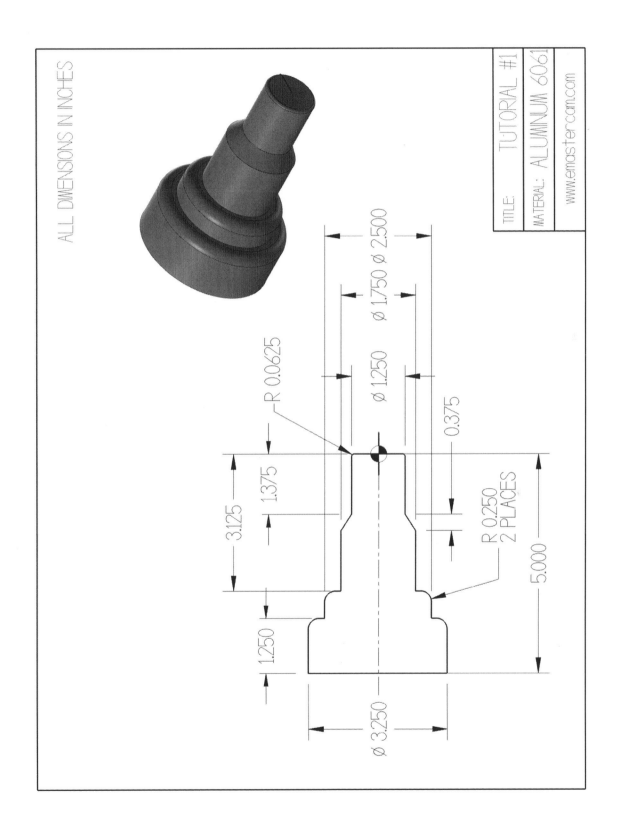

GEOMETRY CREATION

STEP 1: SETTING UP THE GRAPHIC USER INTERFACE

Please refer to the **Getting Started** section to set up the graphical user interface accordingly. In this step you will learn how to hide the manager panels to gain more space in the graphics window.

1.1 Hide the manager panels

VIEW

♦ From the **Managers** group, enable all four managers as shown.

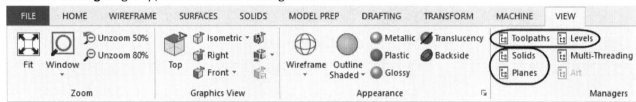

♦ The panels should be on the left side of the graphics window as shown.

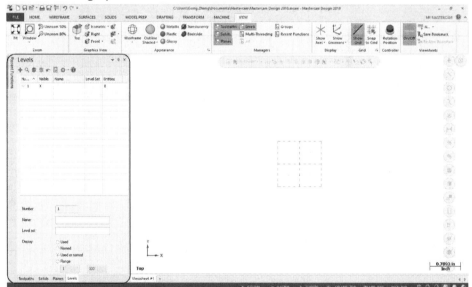

> **NOTE:** It does not matter which panel is currently opened. It could be the **Toolpaths**, the **Solids**, the **Planes** or the **Levels** panel as shown.

♦ To hide all panels, click on the **Auto Hide** icon as shown <u>Figure: 1.1.1</u>.

Figure: 1.1.1

Levels
+ ♦ ...

• The panels will be hidden to the left of the graphics window as shown.

• To un-hide them temporarily, click on one of the managers to open it as shown.

STEP 2: CREATE A RECTANGLE

In this step you will learn how to create a rectangle given the width, the height, and the anchor position.

Step Preview:

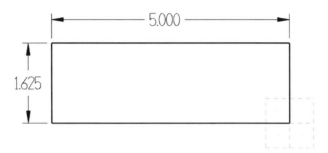

2.1 Create the 5" by 1.625" rectangle

WIREFRAME

♦ From the **Shapes** group, select **Rectangle.**

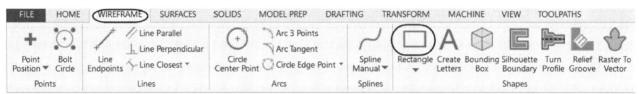

> **NOTE:** Select the rectangle icon as shown. If you click too close to the drop down arrow, a fly-out list of commands appears and you can select the top Rectangle command.

- Enter the **Width** and the **Height** and press **Enter**.

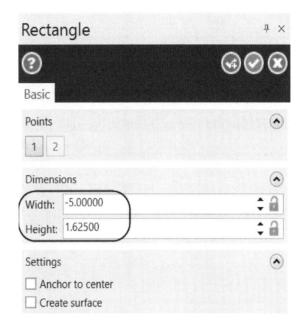

- To select the position of the base point, from the **General Selection** toolbar, click on the drop down arrow next to **AutoCursor** as shown.

- From the fly-out menu select **Origin**.

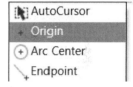

- To see the entire rectangle, right mouse click in the graphics window and select **Fit** as shown.

NOTE: To fit the geometry to the screen you can also press **Alt + F1**.

• A preview of the geometry should look as shown.

NOTE: The geometry should appear in a cyan blue color which is the color for live entities.

While the rectangle is live you can adjust the dimensions or select a new base point.

• Select the **OK** button to exit the **Rectangle** command.

• The geometry should look as shown.

NOTE: While creating geometry for this tutorial, if you make a mistake, you can undo the last step using the

Undo icon ↺ or by pressing **Ctrl + Z**. You can undo as many steps as needed. If you delete or undo a step by

mistake, just use the **Redo** icon ↻ or press **Ctrl + Y**.

To delete unwanted geometry, select the geometry first and then press **Delete** from the keyboard.

To zoom or unzoom, move the cursor to the center of the geometry and scroll up or down on the mouse wheel.

STEP 3: CREATE THE PARALLEL LINES

In this step you will learn how to create parallel lines to existing lines given the distance between the lines. We are creating the lines to use as part of the geometry as well as the construction lines.

Step Preview:

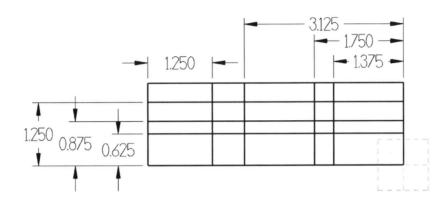

WIREFRAME

◆ From the **Lines** group, select **Line Parallel.**

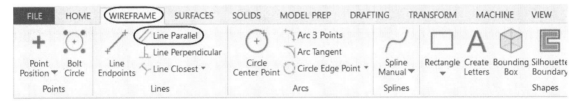

◆ [Select a line]: Select **Entity A** as shown.

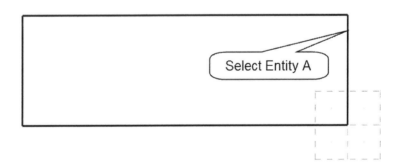

Select Entity A

◆ [Select the point to place a parallel line through]: Pick a point to the left of the selected line.

Pick a point here

NOTE: The color of the geometry is cyan which means that the entity is "live" and you can still change the line parameters if needed.

◆ In the **Line Parallel** panel, enter the **Distance 1.375.**
◆ Press **Enter** to move the line to the proper distance.

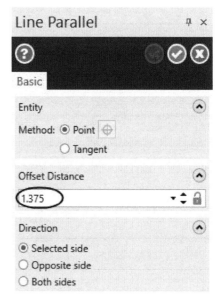

NOTE: To continue using the same command you can either select the **OK and Create New Operation** button

or press **Enter**. To exit the command you can either start a new command or select the **OK**

button.

◆ Press **Enter** to continue.

◆ [Select a line]: Select **Entity B** as shown.

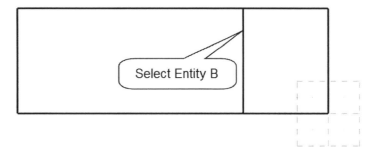

Select Entity B

◆ [Select the point to place a parallel line through]: Pick a point to the left of the selected line.
◆ Enter the **Distance 0.375**.
◆ Press **Enter** to move the line to the proper distance.

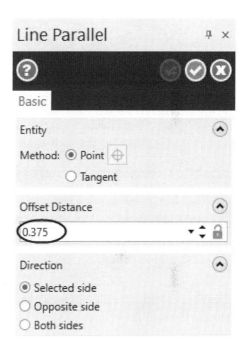

◆ Press **Enter** to continue.
◆ [Select a line]: Select **Entity A** again as shown.

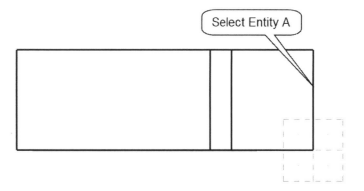

Select Entity A

◆ [Select the point to place a parallel line through]: Pick a point to the left of the selected line.

- Enter the **Distance 3.125.**
- Press **Enter** to move the line to the proper distance.

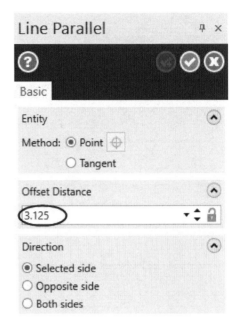

- Press **Enter** to continue.
- [Select a line]: Select **Entity C** as shown.

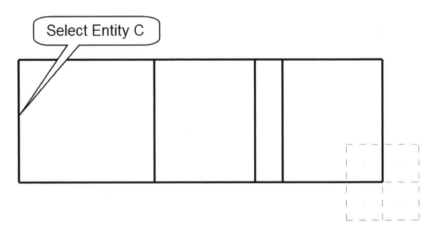

Select Entity C

- [Select the point to place a parallel line through]: Pick a point to the right of the selected line.

• Enter the **Distance 1.25.**
• Press **Enter** to move the line to the proper distance.

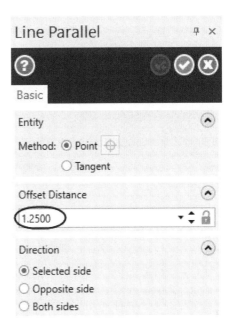

• Press **Enter** to continue.
• [Select a line]: Select **Entity D** as shown.

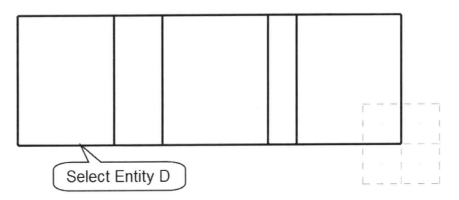

• [Select the point to place a parallel line through]: Pick a point above the selected line.

• Enter the **Distance 0.625.**

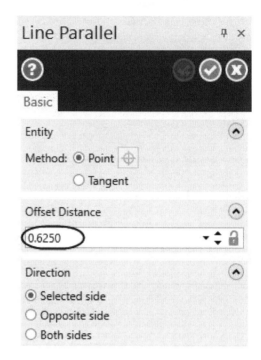

• Press **Enter** to move the line to the proper distance.
• Press **Enter** to continue.
• [Select a line]: Select **Entity D** again as shown.

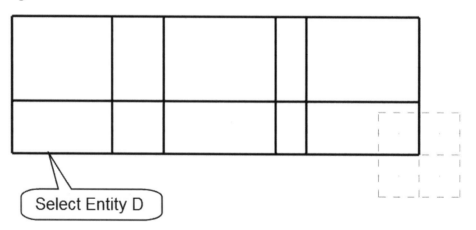

Select Entity D

• [Select the point to place a parallel line through]: Pick a point above the selected line.

• Enter the **Distance 0.875.**

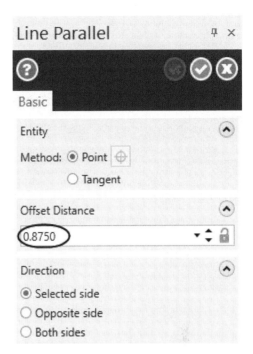

• Press **Enter** to move the line to the proper distance.
• [Select a line]: Select **Entity D** again as shown.

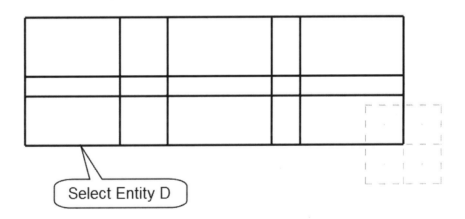

Select Entity D

• [Select the point to place a parallel line through]: Pick a point above the selected line.

- Enter the **Distance 1.250.**

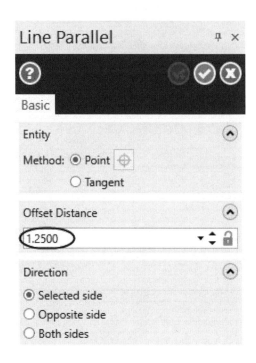

Line Parallel   ⊓ ×

Basic

Entity   ⌃
   Method: ⦿ Point ⊕
            ○ Tangent

Offset Distance   ⌃
   1.2500   ▾ ⬍ 🔒

Direction   ⌃
   ⦿ Selected side
   ○ Opposite side
   ○ Both sides

- Select the **OK** button to exit the command.
- The part should appear as shown.

STEP 4: CREATE LINE ENDPOINT

In this step you will use the line endpoints command to create a line connected to the intersection point of two construction lines.

Step Preview:

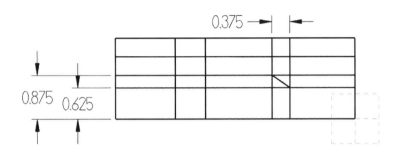

WIREFRAME

- From the **Lines** group, select **Line Endpoints.**

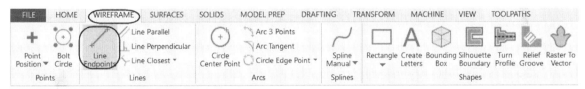

- [Specify the first endpoint]: Click the intersection between the two lines at **Point A** as shown.

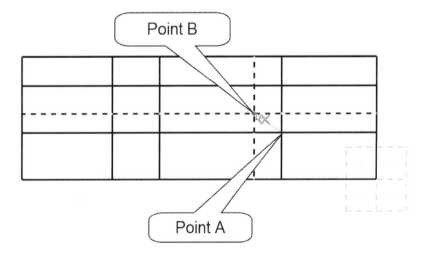

- [Specify the second endpoint]: Click the intersection between the two lines at **Point B** as shown.

- Select the **OK** button to exit the command.

STEP 5: CREATE THE FILLETS

In this step we will use the create fillet command to simultaneously create a fillet and trim two entities.

Step Preview:

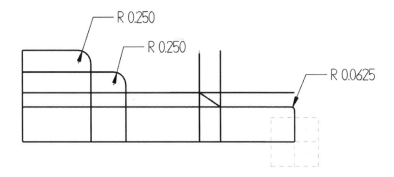

WIREFRAME
• From the **Modify** group, select **Fillet Entities**.

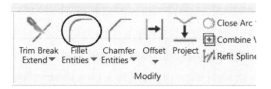

• Enter the **Radius 0.25** and make sure that the rest of the parameters in the window are set as shown.

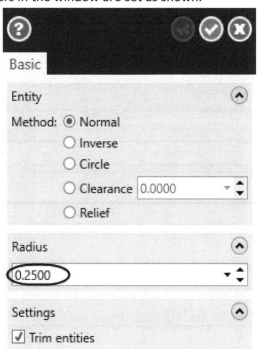

♦ [Select an entity]: Select **Entity A** as shown in <u>Figure: 5.0.1</u>.
♦ [Select another entity]: Select **Entity B** as shown in <u>Figure: 5.0.1</u>.

Figure: 5.0.1

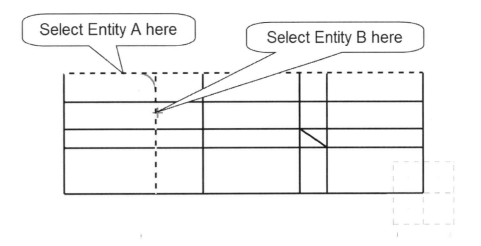

♦ [Select an entity]: Select **Entity C** as shown in <u>Figure: 5.0.2</u>.
♦ [Select another entity]: Select **Entity D** as shown in <u>Figure: 5.0.2</u>.

Figure: 5.0.2

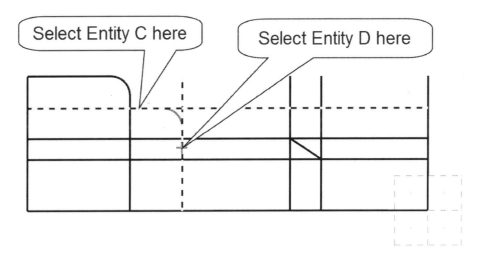

♦ Press **Enter** to finish the fillet.

• Change the **Radius** to **0.0625** and make sure that the rest of the parameters in the window are set as shown.

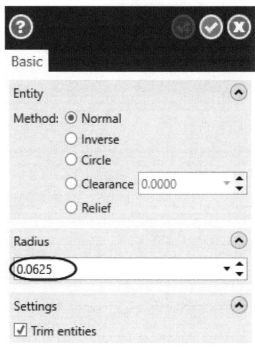

• [Select an entity]: Select **Entity E** as shown in Figure: 5.0.3.
• [Select another entity]: Select **Entity F** as shown in Figure: 5.0.3.

Figure: 5.0.3

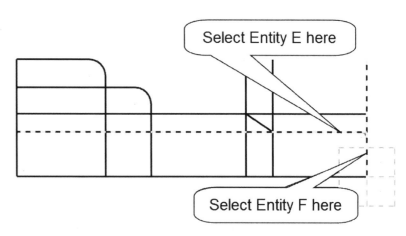

• Select the **OK** button to exit the command.

STEP 6: TRIM THE GEOMETRY

This step shows you how to trim two entities using the trim command. To trim two entities to their intersection, enable the **Trim 2 entities** button and click on the first entity that you want to trim or extend on the side that you want to keep after trimming and then click on the entity you want to trim or extend to. Always ensure that you select the entities on the side that you want to keep after trimming.

Step Preview:

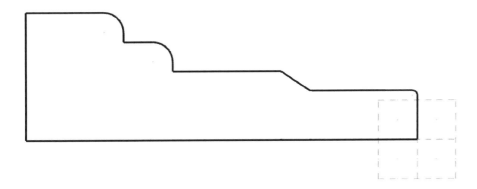

6.1 Use the trim two entities command

WIREFRAME

◆ From the **Modify** group, select **Trim Break Extend.**

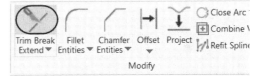

◆ Enable the **Trim 2 entities** button.

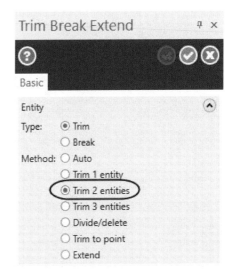

- [Select the entity to trim/extend]: Click on **Entity A** as shown in <u>Figure: 6.1.1</u>.
- [Select the entity to trim/extend to]: Click on **Entity B** as shown in <u>Figure: 6.1.1</u>.

NOTE: Mastercam's auto-preview feature displays the results of the selected function as you move the mouse over the final entity selection. A solid line represents what will be created. A dashed line represents what will be removed.
It is very important to select the entities at the locations shown in <u>Figure: 6.1.1</u>.

Figure: 6.1.1

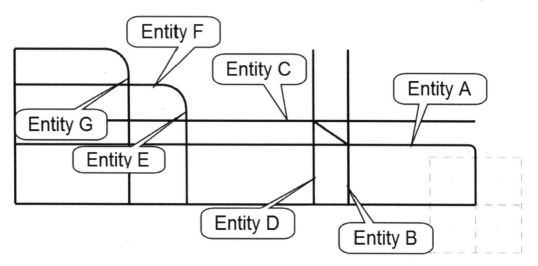

- [Select the entity to trim/extend]: Click on **Entity C** as shown in <u>Figure: 6.1.1</u>.
- [Select the entity to trim/extend to]: Click on **Entity D** as shown in <u>Figure: 6.1.1</u>.
- [Select the entity to trim/extend]: Click on **Entity E** as shown in <u>Figure: 6.1.1</u>.
- [Select the entity to trim/extend to]: Click on **Entity C** as shown in <u>Figure: 6.1.1</u>.
- [Select the entity to trim/extend]: Click on **Entity G** as shown in <u>Figure: 6.1.1</u>.
- [Select the entity to trim/extend to]: Click on **Entity F** as shown in <u>Figure: 6.1.1</u>.

6.2 Delete the 2 leftover lines

• In the **Trim Break Extend** panel, enable **Divide/delete.**

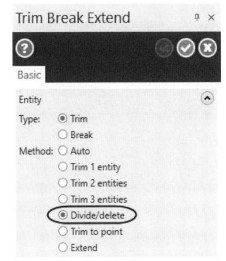

• [Select the curve to divide / delete]: Select **Entity A** and **Entity B** as shown.

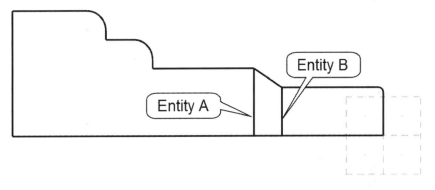

• Select the **OK** button from the toolbar.

• The part should appear as shown in <u>Figure: 6.2.1</u>.

Figure: 6.2.1

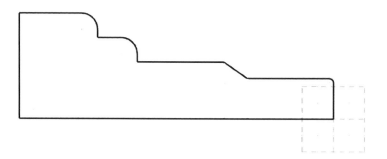

NOTE: To create the toolpaths for a lathe part you only need half of the geometry. Lathe parts are revolved parts that are obtained by rotating a plane curve around some straight line (the **X axis**) that lies on the same plane.

STEP 7: SAVE THE FILE

FILE
• **Save As.**

• Click on the **Browse** icon as shown.
• Find a location on the computer to save your file.
• File name: "Your Name_1".

TOOLPATH CREATION

PART SETUP:

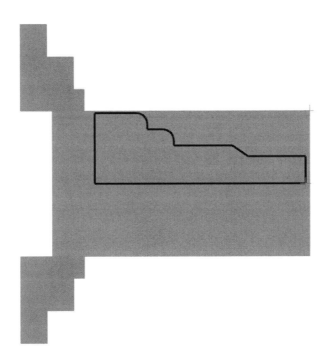

SETUP SHEET:

TYPE:	General Turning Tool	FLUTE LENGTH:
DIA OFFSET:		OVERALL LENGTH:
HOLDER:		CORNER RAD:
NUMBER:	1	# OF FLUTES:
LENGTH OFFSET:		

T0101: General Turning Tool - OD ROUGH RIGHT - 80 DEG.

TYPE:	General Turning Tool	FLUTE LENGTH:
DIA OFFSET:		OVERALL LENGTH:
HOLDER:		CORNER RAD:
NUMBER:	21	# OF FLUTES:
LENGTH OFFSET:		

T2121: General Turning Tool - OD FINISH RIGHT - 35 DEG.

STEP 8: SELECT THE MACHINE AND SET UP THE TOOL SETTINGS AND THE STOCK

In this step you will learn how to select a machine, assign tool numbers, tool offset numbers, and default values for feeds, speeds, and other toolpath parameters. You will also learn how to define the stock and chuck jaws using the lathe machine groups.

- The **Toolpaths Manager** will be hidden to the left of the graphics window as shown.

- To lock it, click on the **Toolpaths** tab and then click on the **Auto Hide** icon a shown.

- The **manager panels** will be translated to the **lower left corner** of the graphics window.

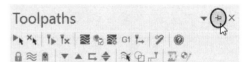

> **NOTE:** If a **Machine Group** already exists in the Toolpaths Manager, skip the next step.

8.1 Select the machine

NOTE: If another machine is already selected, from the **Machine** ribbon in the **Machine Type** group select **Design**. Then in the **Toolpaths Manager**, click on the **Delete all operations, groups and tools** icon to remove the existing **Machine Group**.

♦ Press **Alt + F1** to fit the geometry to the screen.

MACHINE
♦ From the **Machine Type** area, click on the drop down arrow below **Lathe** and select **Default**.

NOTE: Once you select the **Lathe Default** the ribbon bar changes to reflect the toolpaths that could be used with **Lathe** machine.

♦ Select the plus sign (+) in front of **Properties** in the **Toolpaths Manager** panel to expand the **Toolpaths Group Properties**.

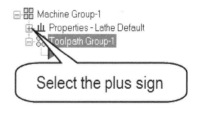

♦ Select **Tool settings** to set the tool parameters.

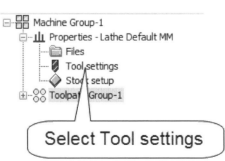

◆ Change the parameters to match the screenshot in <u>Figure: 8.1.1</u>.

Figure: 8.1.1

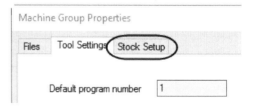

Default program number is used to enter a number if your machine requires a number for a program name.

Assign tool numbers sequentially allows you to overwrite the tool number from the library with the next available tool number. (First operation tool number 1; Second operation tool number 2, etc.)

Warn of duplicate tool numbers allows you to get a warning if you enter two tools with the same number.

Override defaults with modal values enables the system to keep the values that you enter.

Feed Calculation set to **From tool** uses the feed rate, plunge rate, retract rate and spindle speed from the tool definition.

◆ Select the **Stock Setup** tab.

◆ Choose the **Properties** button to set up the stock for the **Left Spindle**.

◆ Define the stock by setting the stock geometry (Cylinder) and entering the stock dimensions.

◆ Ensure you enable **Use Margins** and enter the values as shown in Figure: 8.1.2.

Figure: 8.1.2

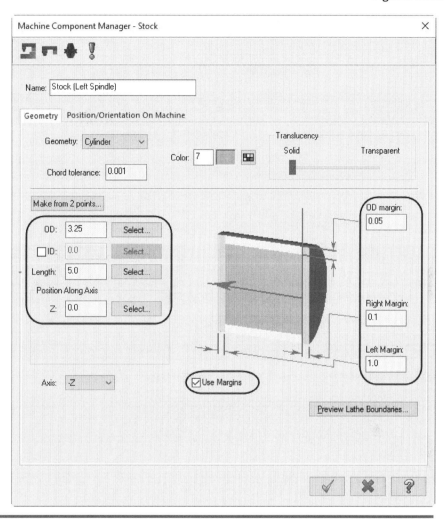

OD is used to enter the outer diameter of the final part. You can also click on the **Select** button and pick a point from the geometry. **Length** is used to enter the length of the finished part. Again you can click on the **Select** button and pick a point from the geometry.

Use Margins allows you to add extra stock to the final part size. **OD margin** allows you to enter a value as a radius value that will be added to the final part to define the stock's outer diameter. **Left margin** allows you to add a value to the stock's left side. **Right margin** allows you to add a value to the stock's right side.

NOTE: The **stock** model that you create can be displayed with the part geometry when viewing the file or the toolpaths, during backplot, or while verifying toolpaths. You can create stock on the left or right spindle.

◆ Select the **OK** button to exit the **Machine Component Manager - Stock** dialog box.

◆ Ensure that **Left Spindle** is selected and then select the **Properties** button in the Chuck Jaws area as shown.

◆ Make the necessary changes to define the chuck size, the clamping method and the stock position. Ensure that you choose the clamping method **OD #1** as shown.

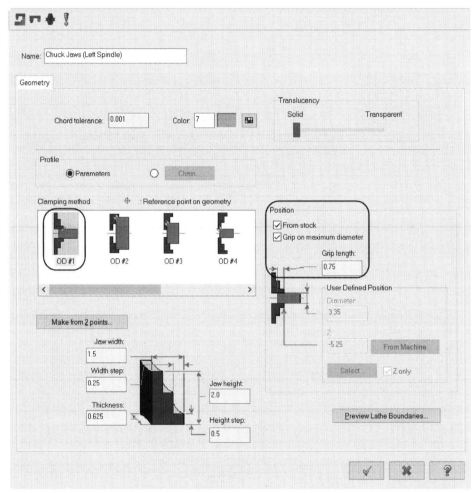

Position parameters determine where the reference point is in relation to the stock.

From stock positions the chuck jaw on the stock using the selected clamping method's reference point. You can choose how much of the stock the jaw grips.

◆ Select the **OK** button to exit the **Machine Component Manager - Chuck Jaws** dialog box.

◆ Set the **Display Options** as shown.

◆ Select the **OK** button to exit the **Machine Group Properties** dialog box.
◆ Press **Alt + F1** to fit the drawing to the screen.
◆ The stock should look as shown in Figure: 8.1.3.

Figure: 8.1.3

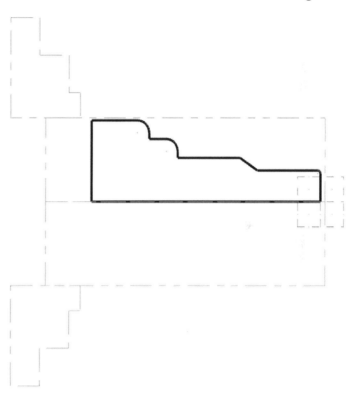

NOTE: The stock is not geometry and cannot be selected.

STEP 9: FACE THE PART

Face toolpaths allow the user to quickly clean the stock from one end of the part and create an even surface for future operations. Note that we do not have to chain any geometry to create the toolpath because of the extra material we specified on the right face in the stock setup. You can also select points to dictate where Mastercam will create the facing operation.

Toolpath Preview:

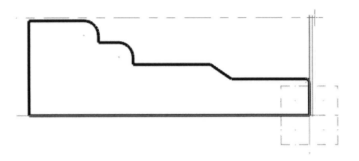

TURNING

♦ From the **General** group, select the **Face** icon.

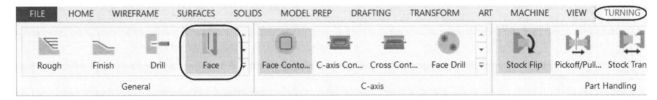

• Select the **OD Rough Right - 80 Degree** tool and enter the comment as shown.

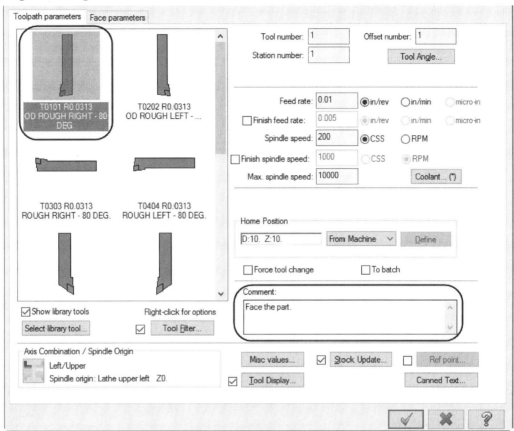

NOTE: The **Feed rate** and the **Spindle speeds** are based on the **Mastercam Tool Definitions**. They can be changed at any time based on the material that you are going to machine.

• Next you will have to set parameters in the **Face parameters** page.

NOTE: If you accidentally click on the **OK** button [✓] before you set the parameters in all of the pages the toolpath has, from the **Toolpaths Manager**, click on **Parameters** as shown.

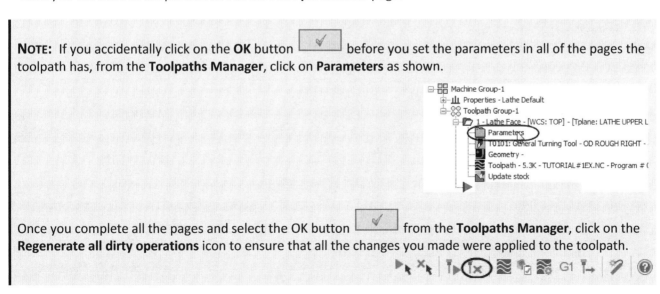

Once you complete all the pages and select the OK button [✓] from the **Toolpaths Manager**, click on the **Regenerate all dirty operations** icon to ensure that all the changes you made were applied to the toolpath.

♦ Select the **Face parameters** tab and make all of the necessary changes as shown.

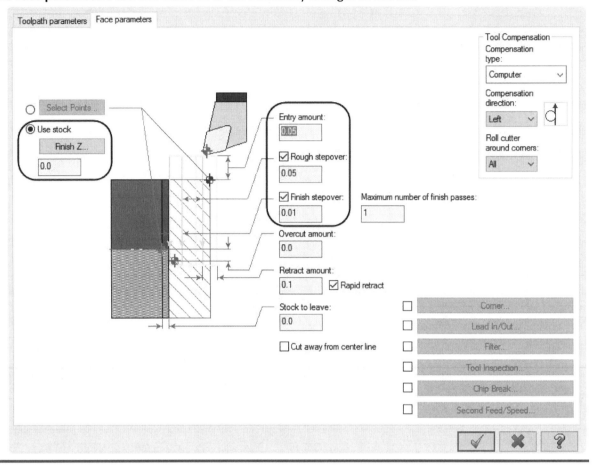

Entry amount sets the height at which the tool rapids to or from the part.

Rough stepover sets the roughing pass value.

Finish stepover sets the finish pass value.

Overcut amount determines how far past the center of the part the tool will cut.

Retract amount determines the distance the tool moves away from the face of the part before it moves to the start of the next cut.

Stock to leave sets the remaining stock after the tool completes all passes.

Cut away from the center line sets the tool to start cutting closest to the center line and cut away from the center line at each pass.

♦ Once you have entered in all of the information select the **OK** button to exit the **Lathe Face** dialog box.

NOTE: If you exit the toolpath in the middle of setting the parameters, in the **Toolpaths Manager** you will have a red X on the Face Toolpath as shown in Figure: 9.0.1. This indicates that you modified the toolpath and you need to update it. You will have to select the **Regenerate all dirty operations** icon each time you change something in the toolpath parameters.

Figure: 9.0.1

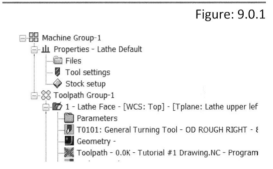

STEP 10: BACKPLOT THE TOOLPATHS

Backplotting shows the path the tools take to cut the part. This display lets you spot errors in the program before you machine the part. As you backplot toolpaths, Mastercam displays additional information such as the X, Y, and Z coordinates, the path length, the minimum and maximum coordinates and the cycle time.

♦ Make sure that the toolpath is selected (signified by the green check mark on the folder icon). If the operation is not selected, choose the **Select all operations** icon.

♦ Select the **Backplot selected operations** icon.

- In the **Backplot** dialog box enable the **Display with color codes**, **Display tool, Display holder** and **Display rapid moves** icons as shown.

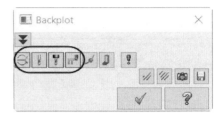

- To fit the workpiece to the screen, if needed, right mouse click in the graphics window again and select **Fit** or press **Alt + F1**.

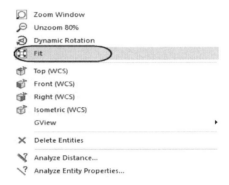

- You can step through the **Backplot** by using the **Step forward** or **Step back** buttons.
- You can adjust the speed of the backplot with the **Run speed slider**.
- Select the **Play** button to run **Backplot**.
- The toolpath should look as shown <u>Figure: 10.0.1</u>.

Figure: 10.0.1

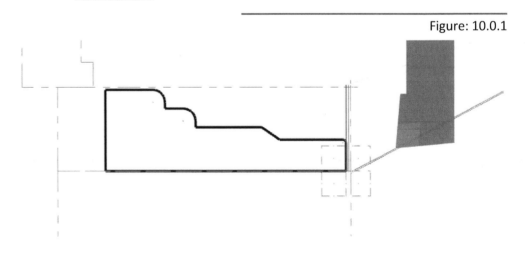

- Select the **OK** button to exit **Backplot**.

STEP 11: SIMULATE THE TOOLPATH IN VERIFY

Verify shows the path the tools take to cut the part with material removal. This display lets you spot errors in the program before you machine the part. As you verify toolpaths, Mastercam displays additional information such as the X, Y, and Z coordinates, the path length, the minimum and maximum coordinates and the cycle time. It also shows any collisions between the workpiece and the tool.

♦ From the **Toolpaths Manager**, select the **Verify selected operations** icon as shown.

> **NOTE:** Mastercam launches a new window that allows you to check the part using **Backplot** or **Verify**.

♦ In **Mastercam Simulator**, **Verify** should be enabled and change the settings as shown.

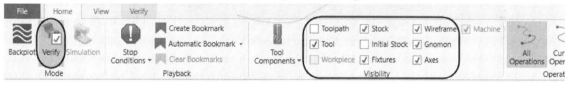

♦ Select the **Play** button to run **Verify**.
♦ To see the part from an **Isometric** view right mouse click in the graphics window and select **Isometric** as shown.

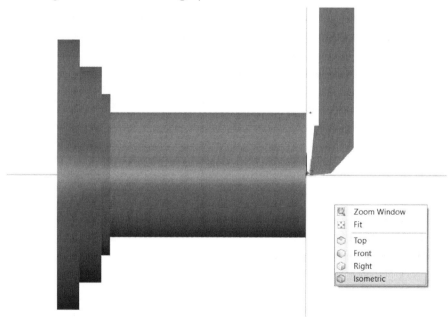

- To fit the workpiece to the screen, right mouse click in the graphics window again and select **Fit**.

- The part should look as shown in Figure: 11.0.1.

Figure: 11.0.1

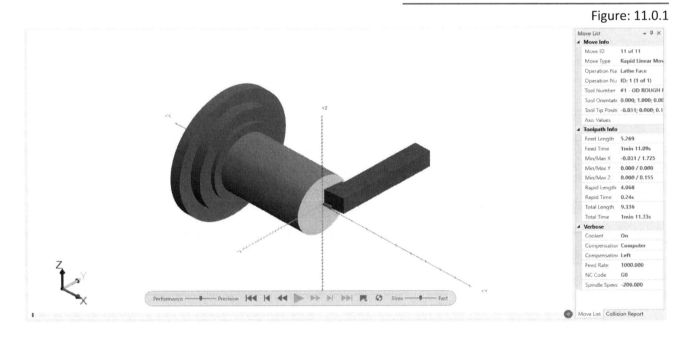

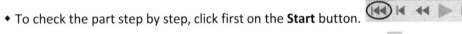

NOTE: To rotate the part, move the cursor to the center of the part and click and hold the mouse wheel and slowly move the mouse in one direction.
To zoom in or out scroll up or down as needed.

- To check the part step by step, click first on the **Start** button.

- Click on **Step Forward** to see the tool moving one step at a time.

• The part should look as shown after several steps.

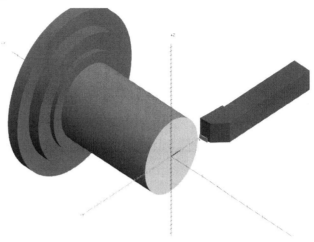

• Click on **Step Forward** until the toolpath is completed.

• To go back to the Mastercam window, minimize the **Mastercam Simulator** window as shown.
• Press **Alt + T** to remove the toolpath display.

STEP 12: ROUGH THE PART

Rough toolpaths quickly remove large amounts of stock in preparation for a finish pass. Roughing passes are typically straight cuts parallel to the **Z axis**.

Toolpath Preview:

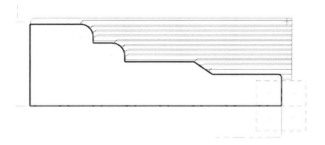

TURNING
• From the **General** group, select **Rough.**

• Leave the default settings in the **Chaining** dialog box.

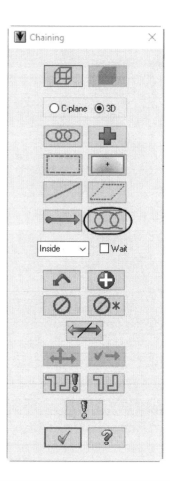

NOTE: The chaining mode is **Partial** by default. You will have to select the first entity and the last entity of the contour.

♦ Select **Entity A** (the fillet) as shown in <u>Figure: 12.0.1</u>.

> **NOTE:** Make sure that the chaining direction is **CCW**, otherwise select the **Reverse** button in the **Chaining** dialog box.

Figure: 12.0.1

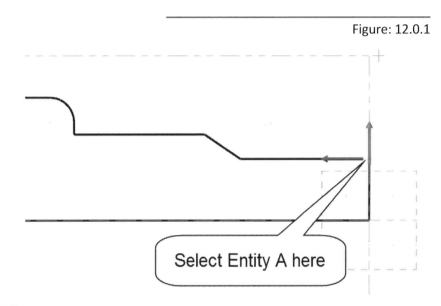

Select Entity A here

♦ Select **Entity B** as shown <u>Figure: 12.0.2</u>.

Figure: 12.0.2

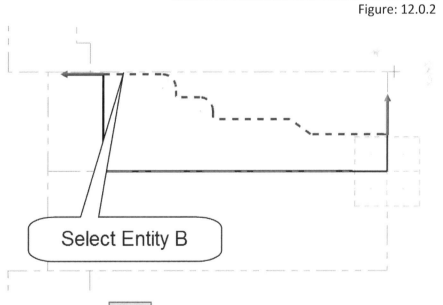

Select Entity B

♦ Select the **OK** button to exit the **Chaining** dialog box.

◆ In the **Toolpath parameters** tab, select the same tool that we used in the facing operation and make all of the necessary changes as shown.

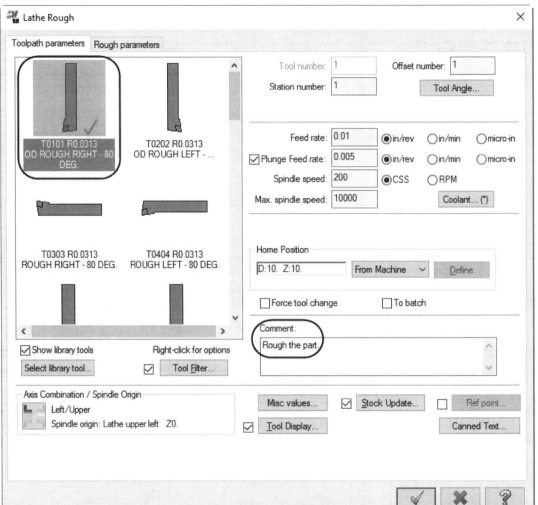

• Select the **Rough parameters** tab and make any necessary changes as shown.

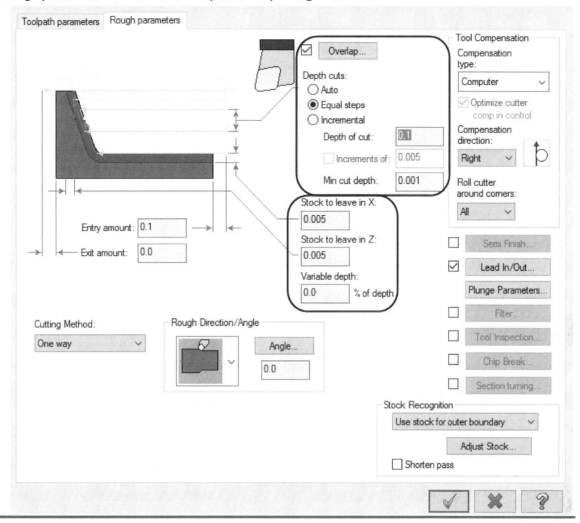

Depth of cut sets the amount of material to be removed during each pass.

Equal steps sets the **Depth of cut** value to the maximum amount of material that the tool can remove at each pass to ensure equal passes.

Minimum cut depth sets the minimum cut that can be taken per pass.

Stock to leave in X sets the remaining stock in the **X axis** after the tool completes all passes.

Stock to leave in Z sets the remaining stock in the **Z axis** after the tool completes all passes.

Entry amount sets the height at which the tool rapids to or from the part.

- Select the **Overlap** button to establish how much the tool overlaps the previous cut. Specify an **Overlap amount** of **0.05** as shown.

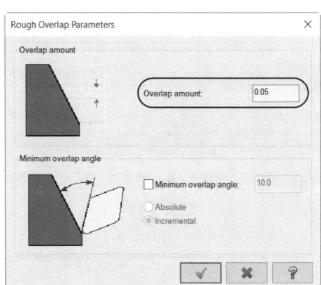

Rough Overlap Parameters lets you select options to determine how much the tool overlaps the previous cut before making the next cut.

Overlap amount sets the overlap amount as a distance.

Minimum overlap angle sets the angle at which Mastercam will start overlapping cuts.

- Select the **OK** button to exit the **Rough Overlap Parameters** dialog box.
- Select the **Lead In/Out** button and choose the **Lead out** tab to extend the end of the contour as shown.

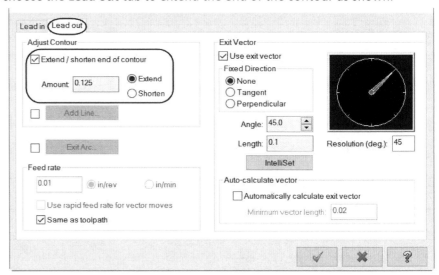

Adjust Contour allows you to extend or shorten the contour by an amount or by adding a line. We are extending the lead out to ensure that the part is completely machined.

Feed rate allows you to specify a custom feed rate for the Lead In/Out.

Exit Vector allows you to create a tangent arc move or perpendicular move to start the toolpath. You can also manually define an entry/exit vector or let the system automatically calculate a vector for you.

♦ Select the **OK** button to exit the **Lead In/Out** dialog box.
♦ In the **Rough parameters** tab, change the **Stock Recognition** to **Use stock for outer boundary** as shown.

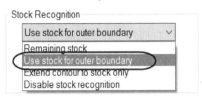

♦ Select the **OK** button to exit the **Lathe Rough** dialog box.

12.1 Backplot the toolpath

♦ Once the operation has been regenerated, **Backplot** the toolpath.
♦ See **page 49** to review the procedure. The toolpath should look as shown in Figure: 12.1.1.

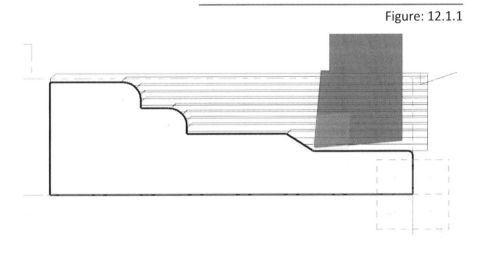

Figure: 12.1.1

♦ Select the **OK** button to exit **Backplot**.

12.2 Verify the toolpaths

◆ To verify all toolpaths, from the **Toolpaths Manager**, choose the **Select all operations** icon.

◆ Select the **Verify selected operations** icon.

◆ Select the Verify tab, and enable Color Loop as shown.

◆ This option will change the material removal color. This can be set based on the operation or on the tool number used to machine the part. This makes it easier to spot if you forgot to leave the stock on in the finish operations.
◆ See **page 51** to review the procedure.

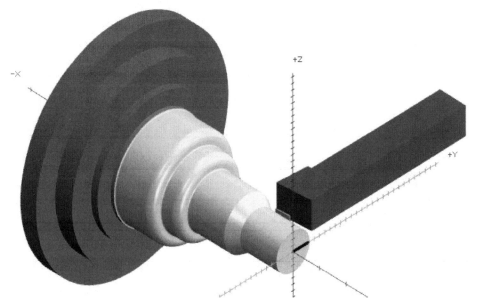

◆ To return to the Mastercam window, minimize the **Mastercam Simulator** window as shown.

STEP 13: FINISH THE PART

The **Finish Toolpath** follows the contour of the chained geometry. Typically a finish toolpath follows a roughing toolpath.

Toolpath Preview:

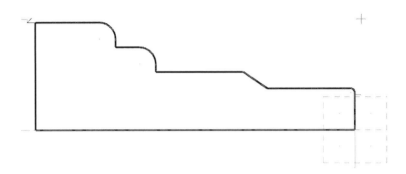

• Select **Toggle display on selected operations** to turn the toolpath display off.

NOTE: You can also use **Alt + T** to toggle the toolpath display on or off.

TURNING

• From the **General** group, select **Finish**.

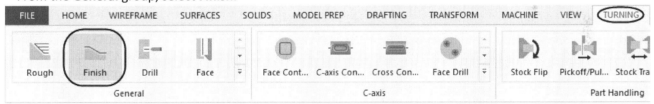

◆ Select the **Last** button in the **Chaining** dialog box as shown.

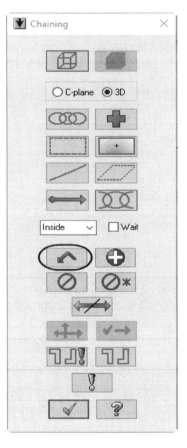

The **Last** button will automatically select the last chain that we used in the roughing toolpath.

◆ Select the **OK** button to exit the **Chaining** dialog box.

◆ Select the **OD 55 Degree Right** tool from the tool list and enter the comment as shown.

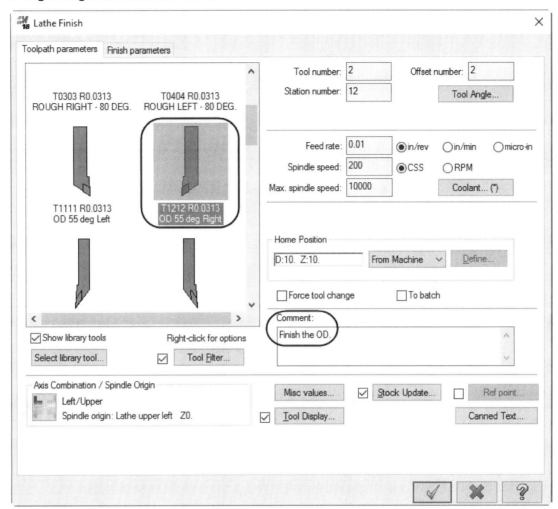

NOTE: The **Feed rate** and **Spindle speed** are based on the **Mastercam Tool Definition.**

• Select the **Finish parameters** tab and make sure the parameters match the screenshot below.

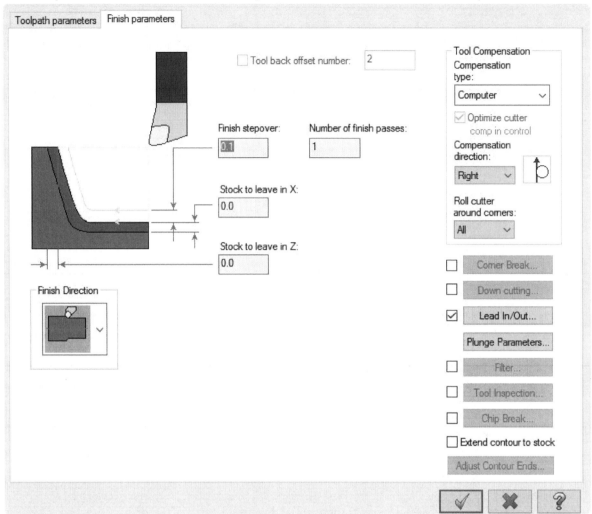

• Select the **Lead In/Out** button, choose the **Lead out** tab, and extend the end of the contour by **0.125**.

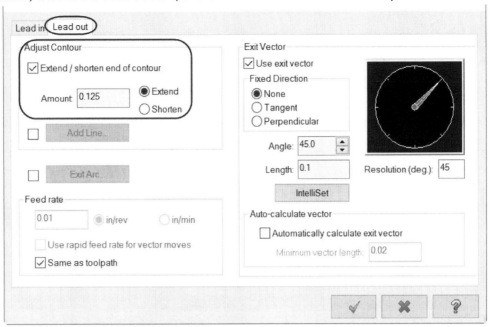

• Select the **OK** button to exit the **Lead In/Out** dialog box.

• Select the **OK** button to exit the **Lathe Finish** dialog box.

13.1 Backplot the toolpath

• Once the operation has been regenerated, **Backplot** the toolpath.
• See **page 49** to review the procedure.

See **page 49** to review the procedure.

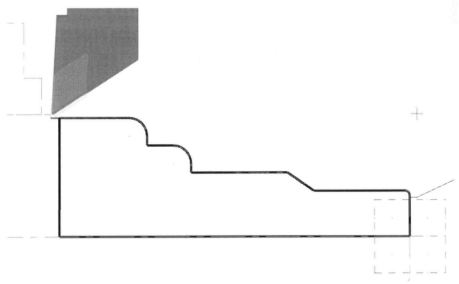

• Select the **OK** button to exit **Backplot**.

13.2 Verify the toolpaths

• To verify all toolpaths, from the **Toolpaths Manager**, choose the **Select all operations** icon.

• See **page 51** to review the procedure.

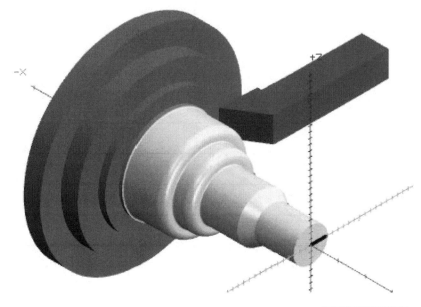

• To return to the Mastercam window, minimize the **Mastercam Simulator** window as shown.

STEP 14: POST THE FILE

Posting refers to the process where the toolpaths in Mastercam are converted to a format that can be understood by the machine's controller, specifically the G-code. In most cases, every machine will require its own post processor customized to produce code formatted to meet the machine's exact requirements.

• Ensure all operations are selected. If they are not, use the **Select all operations** icon in the **Toolpaths Manager**.

• Select the **Post selected operations** icon from the **Toolpaths Manager**.

> **NOTE:** The HLE/Demo version of Mastercam does not support post processing. The G1 button does not work and no G-code can be created in the HLE/Demo version.

• In the **Post processing** dialog box, make the necessary changes as shown in Figure: 14.0.1.

Figure: 14.0.1

NC File enabled allows you to keep the NC file and to assign the same name as the MCAM file.

Edit enabled allows you to automatically launch the default editor.

• Select the **OK** button to continue.
• Save the NC file.

• The **Mastercam Code Expert** window will be launched and the NC program will appear as shown.

```
1    %
2    O0001
3    (PROGRAM NAME - TUTORIAL 1)
4    (DATE=DD-MM-YY - 10-01-17 TIME=HH:MM - 10:27)
5    (MCX FILE - C:\USERS\GONG.ZHANG\DOCUMENTS\MASTERCAM\TUTORIAL 1.MCAM)
6    (NC FILE - C:\USERS\GONG.ZHANG\DOCUMENTS\MASTERCAM\LATHE\TUTORIAL 1.NC)
7    (MATERIAL - STEEL INCH - 1030 - 200 BHN)
8    G20
9    (TOOL - 1 OFFSET - 1)
10   (OD ROUGH RIGHT - 80 DEG.  INSERT - CNMG-432)
11   ( FACE THE PART. )
12   G0 T0101
13   G18
14   G97 S221 M03
15   G0 G54 X3.45 Z.055 M8
16   G50 S3600
17   G96 S200
18   G99 G1 X-.0625 F.01
19   G0 Z.155
20   X3.45
21   Z.01
22   G1 X-.0625
23   G0 Z.11
24   X3.45
25   Z0.
26   G1 X-.0625
27   G0 Z.1
28   ( ROUGH THE PART. )
29   X3.1594
30   Z.205
```

• Select the **"X"** box at the upper right corner to exit the editor.

STEP 15: SAVE THE UPDATED MCAM FILE

REVIEW EXERCISE - STUDENT PRACTICE

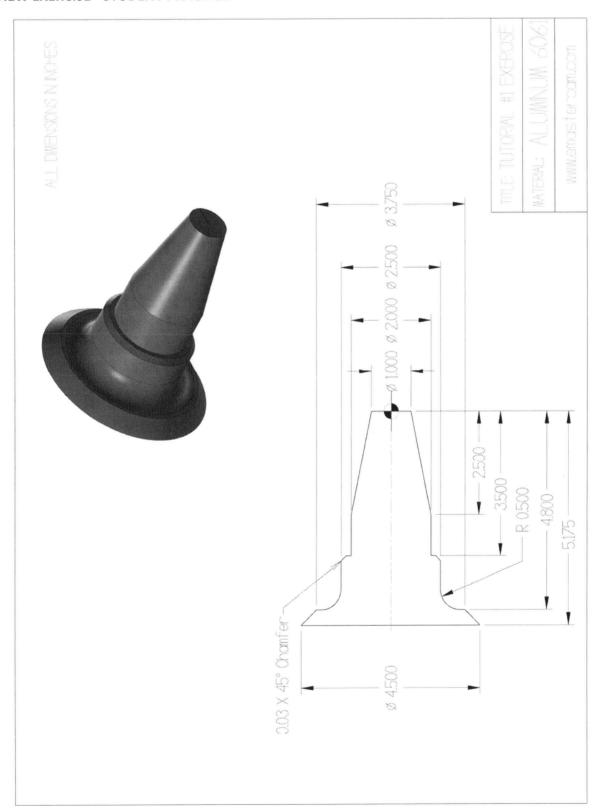

ALL DIMENSIONS IN INCHES

TITLE: TUTORIAL #1 EXERCISE

MATERIAL: ALUMINUM 6061

www.emastercam.com

Ø 3.750
Ø 2.500
Ø 2.000
Ø 1.000
2.500
3.500
R 0.500
4.800
5.175
0.03 X 45° Chamfer
Ø 4.500

CREATE THE GEOMETRY FOR TUTORIAL #1 EXERCISE

Use these commands to create the top half of the geometry.

* Rectangle.
* Line Parallel.
* Fillet Entities.
* Chamfer Entities.
* Trim Break Extend.
* Delete Entities.

CREATE THE TOOLPATHS FOR TUTORIAL #1 EXERCISE

Create the Toolpaths for Tutorial #1 Exercise as per the instructions below.

Set the machine properties including the stock.
Remove the material on the face of the part.
* Use the Stock setup to define the face operation.
* Use the OD Rough Right Tool.
* Enable Rough Stepover.
* Also add a finish cut.

Rough and finish the OD of the part.
* Chain the outside profile CCW.
* Use the OD Rough Right Tool.
* Use Lead In/Out and extend the contour so that the tool does not hit the chuck.
* Use stock for outer boundary.

Finish the OD of the part.
* Use the last command in the chaining dialog box.
* Use the OD Finish Right Tool.
* Use Lead In/Out and extend the contour so that the tool does not hit the chuck.

NOTES:

Mastercam. 2018

TUTORIAL #1 QUIZ

◆ Why should you create a facing operation?

◆ What is a roughing toolpath used for?

◆ What does backplotting your toolpath allow you to see?

◆ What does toolpath verification represent?

◆ What does a post processor do?

Lathe Training Tutorial

Mastercam. 2018

TUTORIAL #2

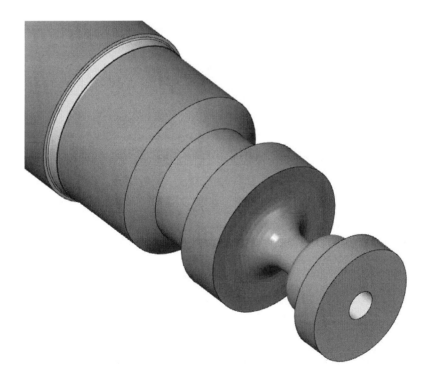

OVERVIEW OF STEPS TAKEN TO CREATE THE FINAL PART:

From drawing to CAD model:
* From the drawing we can gain an idea of how to create the geometry in Mastercam.
* Angled lines need to be created, as well as vertical and horizontal lines, to generate the grooves.

Create the 2D CAD Model used to generate Toolpaths from:
* The student will create the upper profile of the part. Only half of the geometry is needed to create the toolpaths necessary to machine the part.
* The student will create all of the necessary construction lines and trim the unneeded wireframe.
* The student will learn how to create lines given their endpoint locations and how to create a line with a given angle and length.

Create the necessary Toolpaths to machine the part:
* The student will set up the stock size and the clamping method.
* The OD of the part will be faced, roughed, and finished.
* Two grooving toolpaths will be created: one using the width of the tool and one by a chain.
* Drill toolpaths will also be created to center drill and drill the part.

Backplot and Verify the file:
* The Backplot will be used to simulate a step-by-step process of the tool's movements.
* The Verify will be used to watch a tool machine the part out of a solid model.

Post Process the file to generate the G-code:
* The student will then post process the file to obtain an NC file containing the necessary code for the machine.

 This tutorial takes approximately thirty minutes to complete.

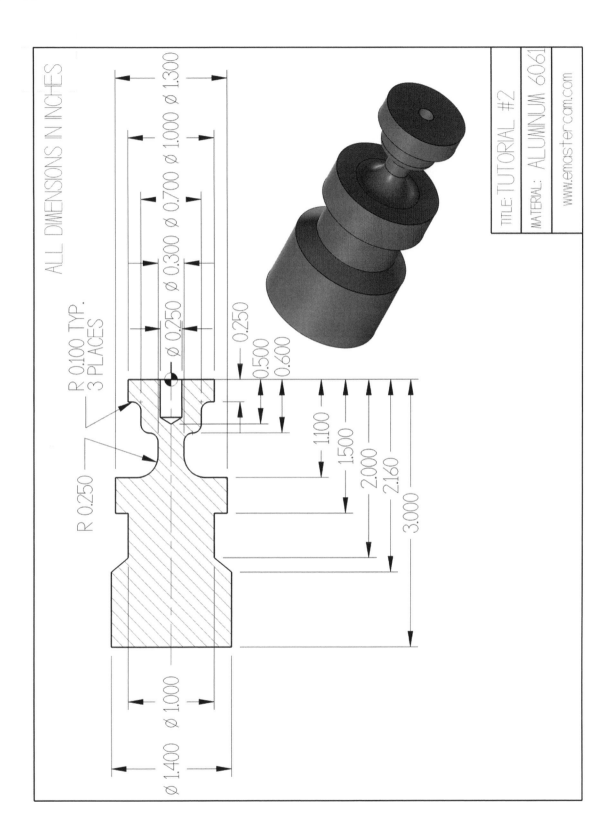

ALL DIMENSIONS IN INCHES

R 0.100 TYP.
3 PLACES

R 0.250

ø 0.250
ø 0.300
ø 0.700
ø 1.000
ø 1.300

0.250
0.500
0.600

1.100
1.500
2.000
2.160
3.000

ø 1.400
ø 1.000

TITLE: TUTORIAL #2
MATERIAL: ALUMINUM 6061
www.emastercam.com

GEOMETRY CREATION

STEP 1: SETTING UP THE GRAPHICAL USER INTERFACE

Please refer to the **Getting Started** section to set up the graphical user interface accordingly.

STEP 2: SELECT THE LATHE DEFAULT

In this step you will select the machine, in your case the **Lathe Default**. This allows you to set the plane to the Lathe +D +Z and to be able to enter the coordinates based on the lathe axes.

MACHINE

• From the **Machine Type** group, select the drop down arrow below the **Lathe** icon and select **Default** as shown.

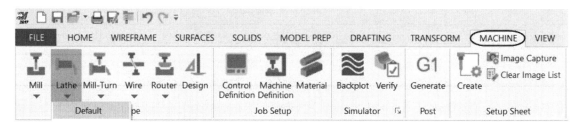

STEP 3: SET UP THE LATHE PLANE +D +Z

In this step you will learn how to set up the **Lathe Plane +D +Z** to be able to enter the coordinates using this plane.

• Select the **Planes** tab as shown. The **Planes Manager** panel will appear temporarily on the graphics window.

- In the **Planes** panel, select **+D +Z** and click in the **C** and **T** columns next to the **+D +Z** plane to set your **Construction plane** and **Tool plane** to the **+D +Z** plane as shown.

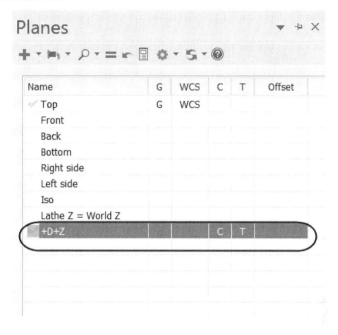

STEP 4: CREATE A RECTANGLE

In this step you will learn how to create a rectangle given the width, height, and anchor position.

Step Preview:

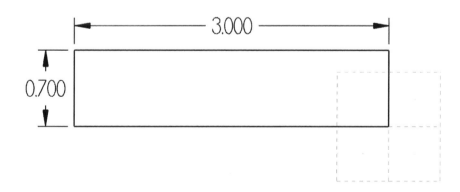

4.1 Create the 3.0" by 0.7" Rectangle

WIREFRAME

* From the **Shapes** group, select **Rectangle** as shown.

* Enter the **Width** and the **Height** as shown and press **Enter**.

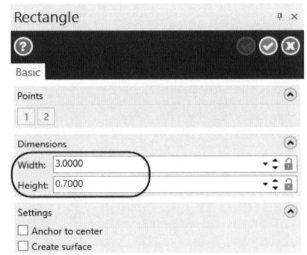

* [Select position of first corner]: Select the **AutoCursor Fast Point** icon from the **General Selection** toolbar and the field where you can type the coordinates will open at the upper left corner of the graphics window as shown.

* Type **0,-3** as shown and press **Enter**.

> **NOTE:** When working with the **+D +Z** plane, enter in the coordinates in this order (D,Z).

* Select the **OK** button to exit the command.
* Press **Alt + F1** to fit the geometry to the screen if necessary.

Lathe Training Tutorial   ***Mastercam*** 2018

◆ The geometry should look as shown in <u>Figure: 4.1.1</u>.

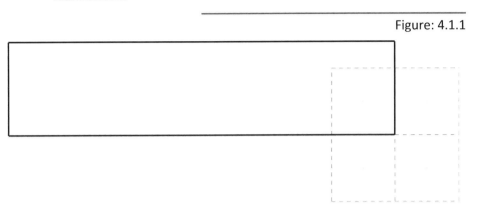

Figure: 4.1.1

NOTE: During the geometry creation of this tutorial, if you make a mistake you can undo the last step using the

Undo icon ⤺ or by pressing **Ctrl + Z**. You can undo as many steps as needed. If you delete or undo a step by

mistake, just use the **Redo** icon ⤻ or press **Ctrl + Y**. To delete unwanted geometry, select it first and then press **Delete** from the keyboard.

STEP 5: CREATE PARALLEL LINES

In this step you will create parallel lines from the rectangle we created in **Step #4**. The lines will be used as construction lines as well as part of the geometry.

Step Preview:

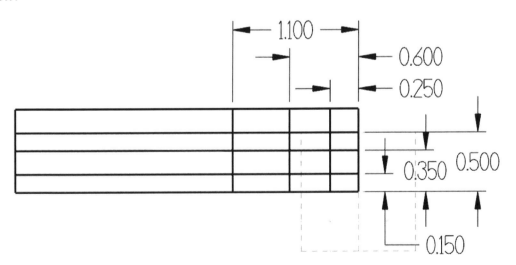

WIREFRAME

• From the **Lines** group, select **Line Parallel**.

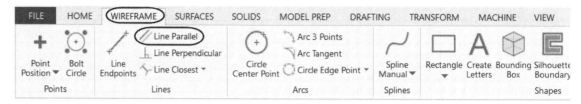

• [Select a line]: Select **Entity A** as shown.

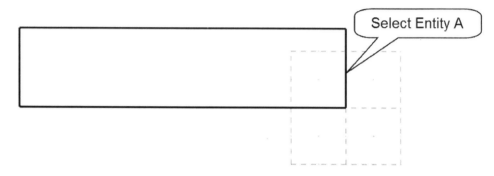

Select Entity A

• [Select the point to place a parallel line through]: Pick a point to the left of the selected line.

NOTE: The color of the geometry is cyan which means that the entity is "live" and you can still change the line parameters if needed.

• Enter the **Offset Distance 0.25**.

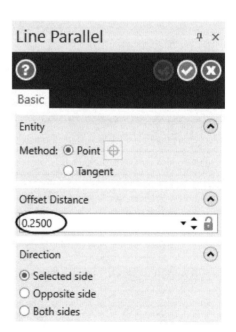

• Press **Enter** to position the line.
• Press **Enter** again to finish the line.

Mastercam 2018

♦ [Select a line]: Select **Entity A** again as shown.

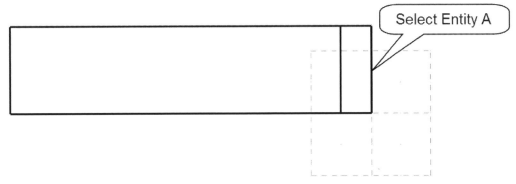

Select Entity A

♦ [Select the point to place a parallel line through]: Pick a point to the left of the selected line.
♦ Enter the **Offset Distance 0.6** and press **Enter** to position the line.

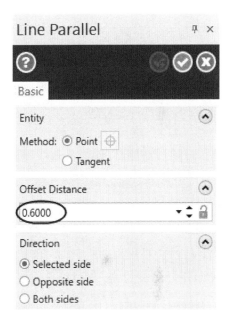

Line Parallel

Basic

Entity

Method: ◉ Point ⊕
        ○ Tangent

Offset Distance

0.6000

Direction

◉ Selected side
○ Opposite side
○ Both sides

♦ Press **Enter** to finish the line.
♦ [Select a line]: Select **Entity A** again as shown.

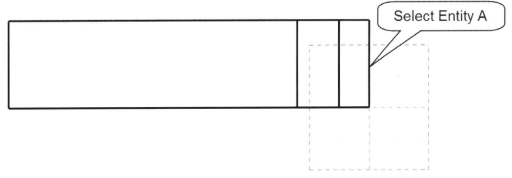

Select Entity A

♦ [Select the point to place a parallel line through]: Pick a point to the left of the selected line.

• Enter the **Offset Distance 1.1** and press **Enter** to position the line.

• Press **Enter** to finish the line.
• [Select a line]: Select **Entity B** as shown.

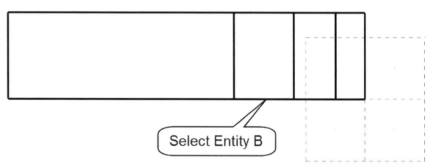

Select Entity B

• [Select the point to place a parallel line through]: Pick a point above the selected line.
• Enter the **Offset Distance 0.15** and press **Enter** to position the line.

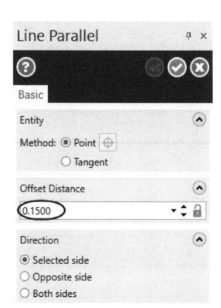

• Press **Enter** to finish the line.

• [Select a line]: Select **Entity B** again as shown.

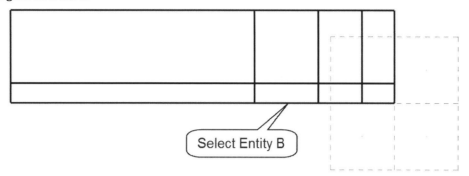

Select Entity B

• [Select the point to place a parallel line through]: Pick a point above the selected line.
• Enter the **Offset Distance 0.35** and press **Enter** to position the line.

• Press **Enter** to finish the line.
• [Select a line]: Select **Entity B** again as shown.

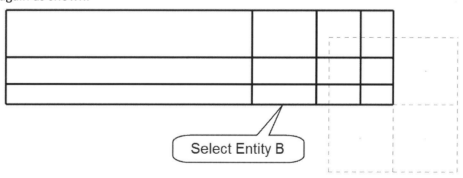

Select Entity B

• [Select the point to place a parallel line through]: Pick a point above the selected line.

* Enter the **Offset Distance 0.5** and press **Enter** to position the line.

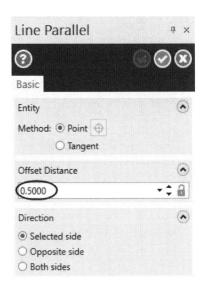

* Press **Enter** to finish the line.

* Select the **OK** button to exit the command.
* The geometry should look as shown in Figure: 5.0.1.

Figure: 5.0.1

STEP 6: CREATE THE FILLETS

In this step we will use the create fillet command to simultaneously create a fillet and trim two entities.

Step Preview:

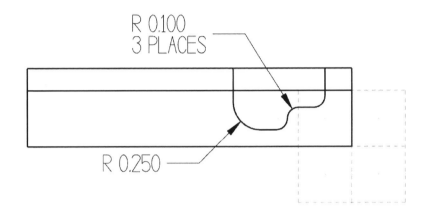

WIREFRAME
* From the **Modify** group, select **Fillet Entities**.

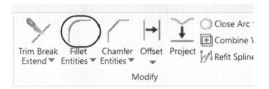

* Enter the **Radius 0.25** and make sure that the rest of the parameters are set as shown.

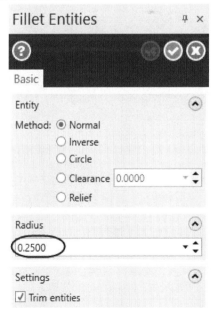

- [Fillet: Select an entity]: Select **Entity A** as shown in Figure: 6.0.1.
- [Fillet: Select another entity]: Select **Entity B** as shown in Figure: 6.0.1.

Figure: 6.0.1

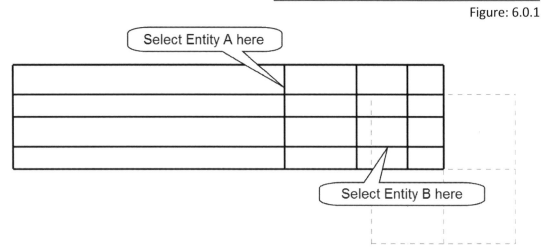

- Press **Enter** to continue.
- Change the **Radius** to **0.1**.

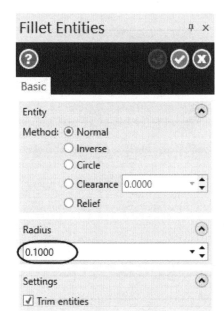

- [Fillet: Select an entity]: Select **Entity B** as shown in Figure: 6.0.2.
- [Fillet: Select another entity]: Select **Entity C** as shown in Figure: 6.0.2.
- [Fillet: Select an entity]: Select **Entity C** as shown in Figure: 6.0.2.
- [Fillet: Select another entity]: Select **Entity D** as shown in Figure: 6.0.2.
- [Fillet: Select an entity]: Select **Entity D** as shown in Figure: 6.0.2.
- [Fillet: Select another entity]: Select **Entity E** as shown in Figure: 6.0.2.

Figure: 6.0.2

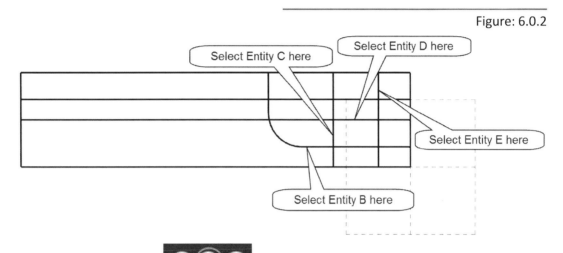

- Select the **OK** button to exit the command.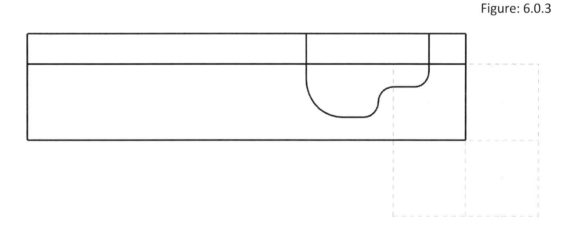
- The geometry should look as shown in Figure: 6.0.3

Figure: 6.0.3

STEP 7: TRIM THE GEOMETRY

This step shows you how to **Divide/delete** one entity using the **Trim Break Extend** command. When using **Divide/delete**, selecting a portion of a line will delete that portion up to its nearest intersection point or points.

Step Preview:

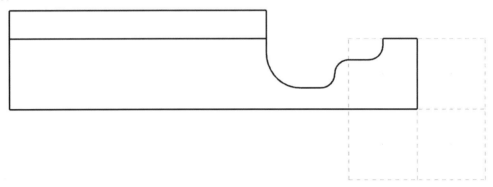

WIREFRAME
- From the **Modify** group, select **Trim Break Extend**.

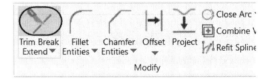

- Enable **Divide/delete**.

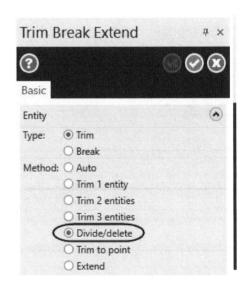

◆ [Select the curve to divide / delete]: Click on **Entity A** as shown in <u>Figure: 7.0.1</u>.
◆ [Select the curve to divide / delete]: Click on **Entity B** as shown in <u>Figure: 7.0.1</u>.
◆ [Select the curve`to divide / delete]: Click on **Entity C** as shown in <u>Figure: 7.0.1</u>.

Figure: 7.0.1

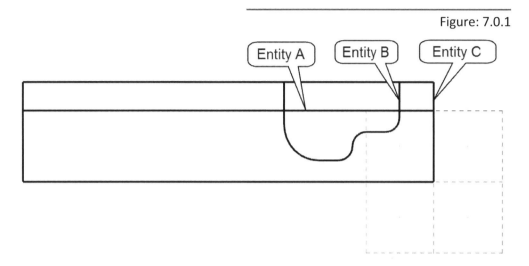

NOTE: Mastercam's auto-preview feature displays the results of the selected function as you move the mouse over the geometry. A dashed line represents entities that will be removed.

◆ [Select the curve to divide / delete]: Click on **Entity D** as shown in <u>Figure: 7.0.2</u>.

Figure: 7.0.2

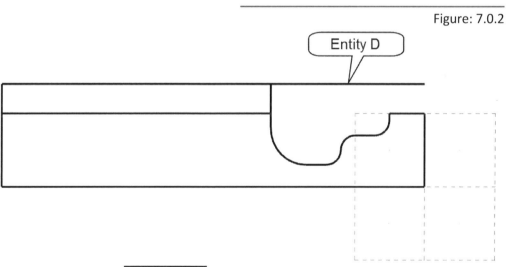

◆ Select the **OK** button to exit the command.

* The part should appear as shown in <u>Figure: 7.0.3</u> .

Figure: 7.0.3

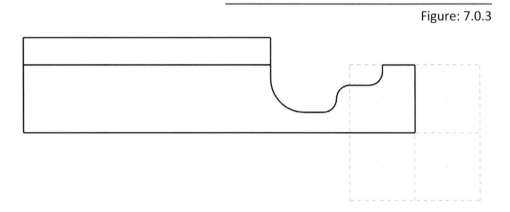

STEP 8: CREATE ADDITIONAL LINES

In this step we will create more parallel lines to be used as construction lines and as part of the geometry. We will also use the **Line Endpoints** command to create the angled line.

Step Preview:

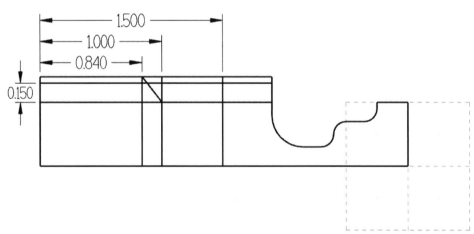

8.1 Create the parallel lines

WIREFRAME
* From the **Lines** group, select **Line Parallel**.

Lathe Training Tutorial
Mastercam 2018

◆ [Select a line]: Select **Entity A** as shown.

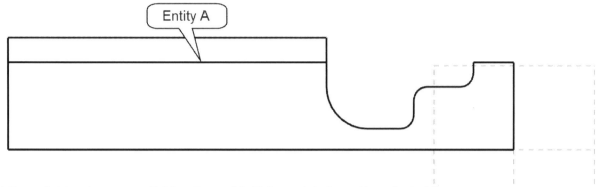

Entity A

◆ [Select the point to place a parallel line through]: Pick a point above the selected line.
◆ Enter the **Offset Distance 0.15** and press **Enter** to position the line.

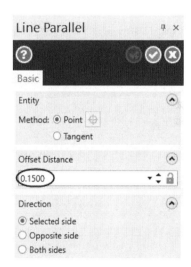

◆ Press **Enter** to finish the line.
◆ [Select a line]: Select **Entity B** as shown.

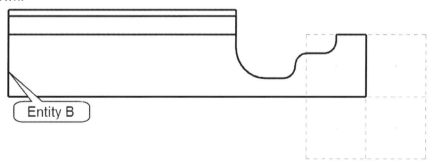

Entity B

◆ [Select the point to place a parallel line through]: Pick a point to the right of the selected line.

• Enter the **Offset Distance 0.84** and press **Enter** to position the line.

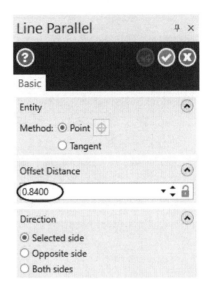

• Press **Enter** to finish the line.
• [Select a line]: Select **Entity B** again as shown.

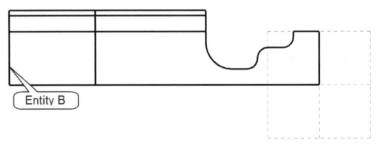

• [Select the point to place a parallel line through]: Pick a point to the right of the selected line.
• Enter the **Offset Distance 1.0** and press **Enter** to position the line.

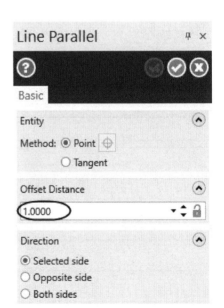

• Press **Enter** to finish the line.

◆ [Select a line]: Select **Entity B** again as shown.

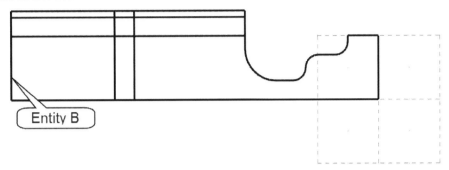

◆ [Select the point to place a parallel line through]: Pick a point to the right of the selected line.
◆ Enter the **Offset Distance 1.5** and press **Enter** to position the line.

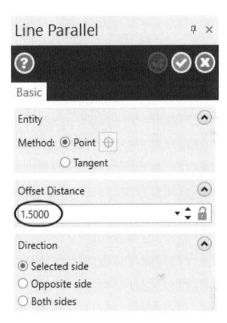

◆ Press **Enter** to finish the line.

◆ Select the **OK** button to exit the command.

8.2 Create the angled line

WIREFRAME
◆ From the **Lines** group, select **Line Endpoints**.

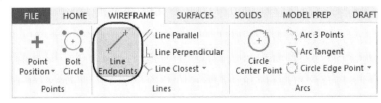

- [Specify the first endpoint]: Select **Endpoint A** as shown.
- [Specify the second endpoint]: Select **Endpoint B** as shown.

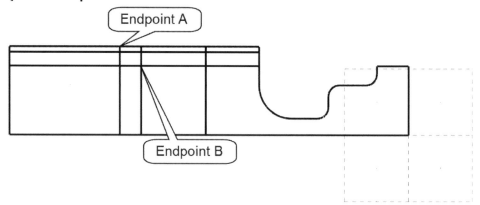

- Press **Enter** to finish the line.

- Select the **OK** button to exit the command.
- The geometry should look as shown in <u>Figure: 8.2.1</u>.

Figure: 8.2.1

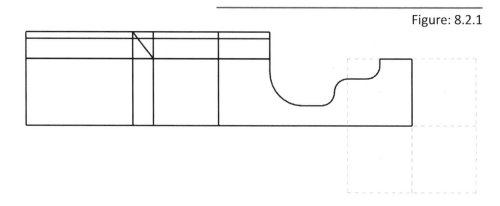

STEP 9: TRIM THE GEOMETRY

This step shows you how to trim one entity using the **Trim 2 entities** command and also how to use the **Divide/delete** command. When using the **Trim 2 entities** command, always select the portions of the lines you want to keep up to their intersection point.

Step Preview:

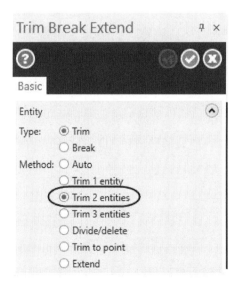

9.1 Use Trim 2 entities to clean up the geometry

WIREFRAME
◆ From the **Modify** group, select **Trim Break Extend**.

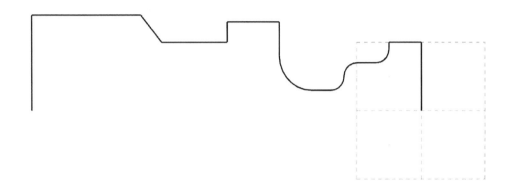

◆ Enable **Trim 2 entities**.

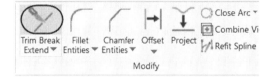

• [Select the entity to trim/extend]: Select **Entity A** as shown in <u>Figure: 9.1.1</u>.
• [Select the entity to trim/extend to]: Select **Entity B** as shown in <u>Figure: 9.1.1</u>.
• [Select the entity to trim/extend]: Select **Entity C** as shown in <u>Figure: 9.1.1</u>.
• [Select the entity to trim/extend to]: Select **Entity D** as shown in <u>Figure: 9.1.1</u>.
• [Select the entity to trim/extend]: Select **Entity D** as shown in <u>Figure: 9.1.1</u>.
• [Select the entity to trim/extend to]: Select **Entity E** as shown in <u>Figure: 9.1.1</u>.

Figure: 9.1.1

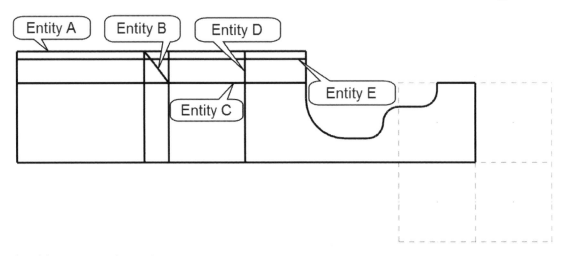

• The geometry should appear as shown in <u>Figure: 9.1.2</u>.

Figure: 9.1.2

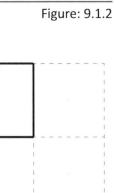

9.2 Use Divide/delete to clean up the geometry

• In the **Trim Break Extend** panel, select the **Divide/delete** button.

- [Select the curve to divide / delete]: Select **Entity A** as shown in Figure: 9.2.1.
- [Select the curve to divide / delete]: Select **Entity B** as shown in Figure: 9.2.1.

Figure: 9.2.1

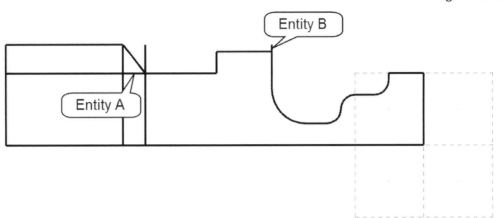

- Select the **OK** button to exit the command.

9.3 Delete the remaining construction lines

- Select the lines as shown in Figure: 9.3.1.

Figure: 9.3.1

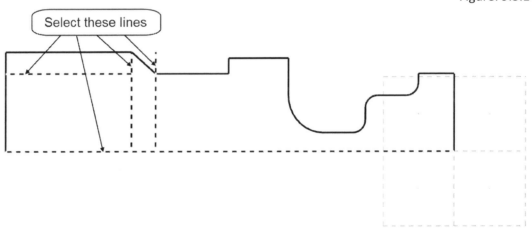

- Press the **Delete** key on your keyboard.

♦ The geometry should appear as shown in <u>Figure: 9.3.2</u>

Figure: 9.3.2

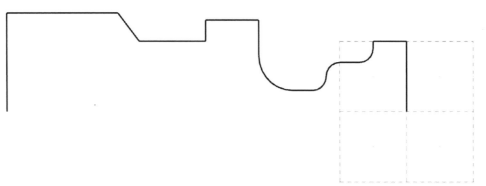

STEP 10: SAVE THE FILE

FILE
♦ **Save As**.

♦ Click on the **Browse** icon as shown.
♦ Find a location on the computer to save your file.
♦ File name: "Your Name_2".

PART SETUP:

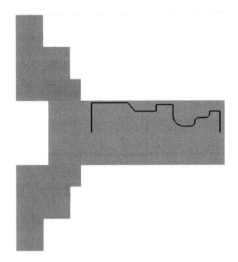

SETUP SHEET:

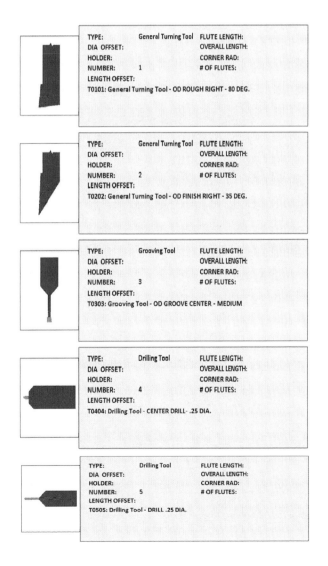

TYPE:	General Turning Tool	FLUTE LENGTH:
DIA OFFSET:		OVERALL LENGTH:
HOLDER:		CORNER RAD:
NUMBER:	1	# OF FLUTES:
LENGTH OFFSET:		

T0101: General Turning Tool - OD ROUGH RIGHT - 80 DEG.

TYPE:	General Turning Tool	FLUTE LENGTH:
DIA OFFSET:		OVERALL LENGTH:
HOLDER:		CORNER RAD:
NUMBER:	2	# OF FLUTES:
LENGTH OFFSET:		

T0202: General Turning Tool - OD FINISH RIGHT - 35 DEG.

TYPE:	Grooving Tool	FLUTE LENGTH:
DIA OFFSET:		OVERALL LENGTH:
HOLDER:		CORNER RAD:
NUMBER:	3	# OF FLUTES:
LENGTH OFFSET:		

T0303: Grooving Tool - OD GROOVE CENTER - MEDIUM

TYPE:	Drilling Tool	FLUTE LENGTH:
DIA OFFSET:		OVERALL LENGTH:
HOLDER:		CORNER RAD:
NUMBER:	4	# OF FLUTES:
LENGTH OFFSET:		

T0404: Drilling Tool - CENTER DRILL - .25 DIA.

TYPE:	Drilling Tool	FLUTE LENGTH:
DIA OFFSET:		OVERALL LENGTH:
HOLDER:		CORNER RAD:
NUMBER:	5	# OF FLUTES:
LENGTH OFFSET:		

T0505: Drilling Tool - DRILL .25 DIA.

STEP 11: SET UP THE TOOL SETTINGS AND THE STOCK

In this step you will learn how to assign tool numbers, tool offset numbers, and default values for feeds, speeds, and other toolpath parameters. You will also learn how to define the stock and chuck jaws using the lathe machine groups.

> **NOTE:** If the **Lathe Machine Group** is not displayed in the **Toolpaths Manager**, refer to **page 41** to select the **Lathe Default**. If another machine is already selected, from the **Machine** ribbon in the **Machine Type** group select **Design**. Then in the **Toolpaths Manager**, click on the **Delete all operations, groups and tools** icon to remove the existing **Machine Group**.

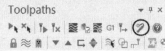

- Press **Alt** + **F1** to fit the drawing to the screen.
- The **Toolpaths Manage**r will be hidden to the left of the graphics window as shown.

- To lock it, click on the **Toolpaths** tab and then click on the **Auto Hide** icon a shown.

- Select the plus sign in front of **Properties** in the **Toolpaths Manager** to expand the **Toolpaths Group Properties**.

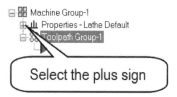

• Select **Tool settings** to set the tool parameters.

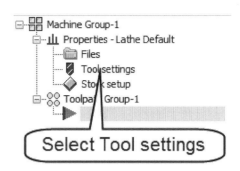

• Change the parameters to match the screenshot in Figure: 11.0.1.

Figure: 11.0.1

Default program number is used to enter a number if your machine requires a number for a program name.

Assign tool numbers sequentially allows you to overwrite the tool number from the library with the next available tool number.

Warn of duplicate tool numbers allows you to get a warning if you enter two tools with the same number.

Override defaults with modal values enables the system to keep the values that you enter.

Feed Calculation set to **From tool** uses the feed rate, plunge rate, retract rate and spindle speed from the tool definition.

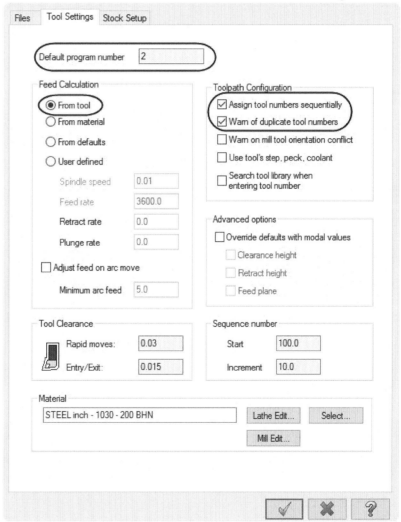

◆ Select the **Stock Setup** tab.

◆ Choose the **Properties** button to set up the stock for the **Left Spindle**.

◆ Define the stock by setting the stock geometry to **Cylinder** and entering the stock dimensions. Ensure you enable **Use Margins** and enter in the values as shown in Figure: 11.0.2.

Figure: 11.0.2

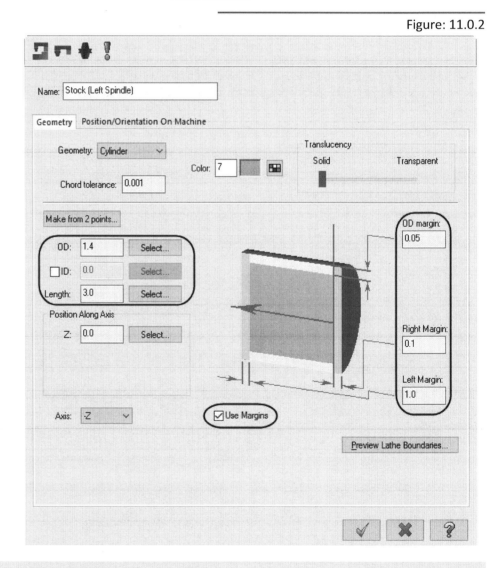

NOTE: The **stock** model that you create can be displayed with the part geometry when viewing the file or the toolpaths, during backplot, or while verifying toolpaths. You can create stock on the left or right spindle.

- Select the **OK** button to exit the **Machine Component Manager - Stock** dialog box.
- Ensure that **Left Spindle** is selected and then select the **Properties** button in the **Chuck Jaws** area as shown.

- Make the necessary changes to define the chuck size, the clamping method and the stock position. Ensure that you choose the clamping method **OD #1** as shown.

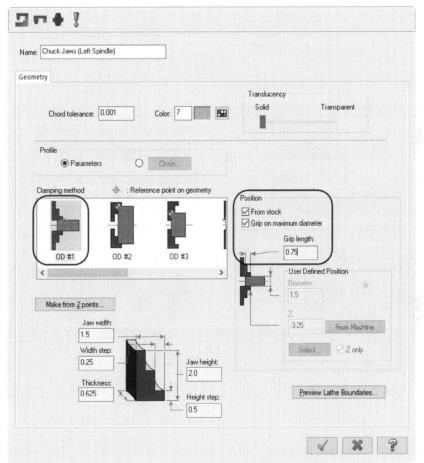

- Select the **OK** button to exit the **Machine Component Manager - Chuck Jaws** dialog box.

- Enable **Fit screen to boundaries** in the **Display Options** area.

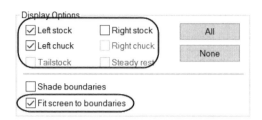

- Select the **OK** button to exit the **Machine Group Properties** dialog box.
- Press **Alt + F1** to fit the geometry to the screen.
- The stock should look as shown in <u>Figure: 11.0.3</u>.

Figure: 11.0.3

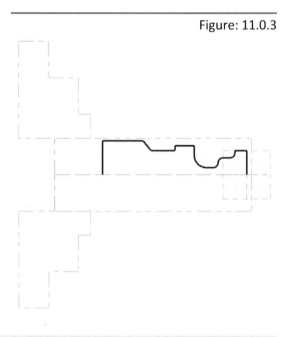

NOTE: The stock is not geometry and cannot be selected.

STEP 12: FACE THE PART

Face toolpaths allow the user to quickly clean the stock from one end of the part and create an even surface for future operations. Note that we do not have to chain any geometry to create the toolpath because of the extra material we specified on the right face in the stock setup. You can also select points to dictate where Mastercam will create the facing operation.

Toolpath Preview:

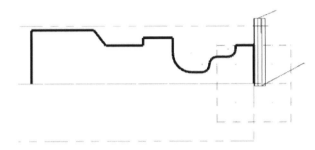

TURNING

• From the **General** group, select **Face**.

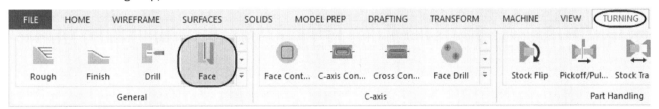

• Select the **OD Rough Right -80 Degree** tool and enter the comment as shown.

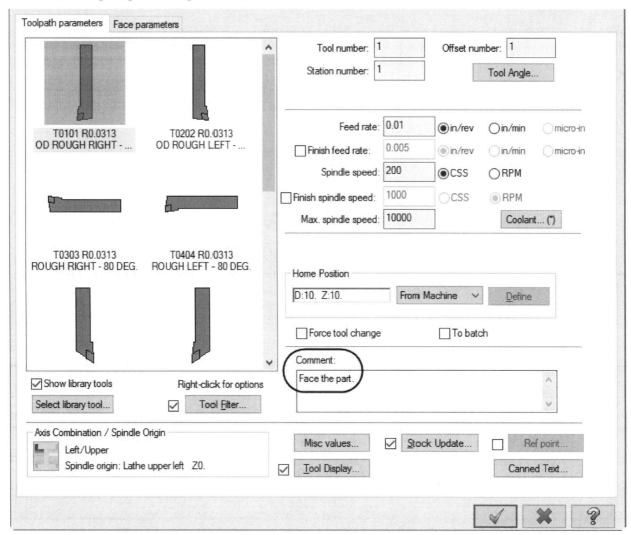

NOTE: The **Feed Rate** and the **Spindle Speeds** are based on the **Mastercam Tool Definitions.** They can be changed at any time, based on the material that you are going to machine.

• Select the **Face parameters** tab and make all of the necessary changes as shown.

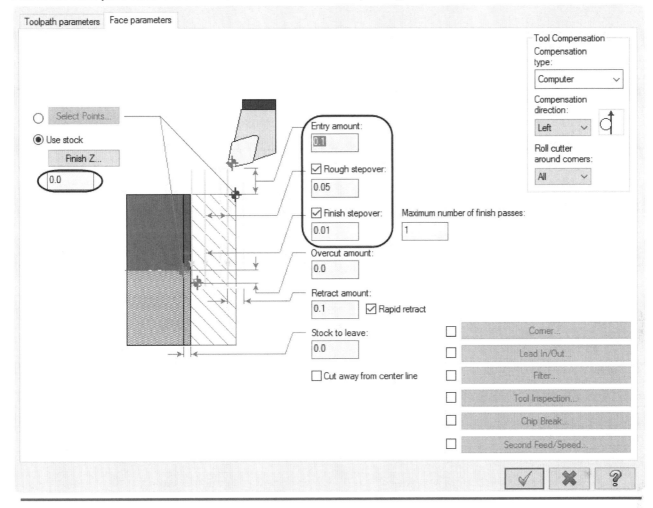

Entry amount sets the height at which the tool rapids to or from the part.

Rough stepover sets the roughing pass value.

Finish stepover sets the finish pass value.

Overcut amount determines how far past the center of the part the tool will cut.

Retract amount determines the distance the tool moves away from the face of the part before it moves to the start of the next cut.

Stock to leave sets the remaining stock after the tool completes all passes.

Cut away from center line sets the tool to start cutting closest to the center line and cut away from the center line at each pass.

• Once you have entered in all of the information select the **OK** button to exit the **Lathe Face** dialog box.

STEP 13: BACKPLOT THE TOOLPATH

Backplotting shows the path the tools take to cut the part. This display lets you spot errors in the program before you machine the part. As you backplot toolpaths, Mastercam displays additional information such as the X, Y, and Z coordinates, the path length, the minimum and maximum coordinates and the cycle time. It also shows any collisions between the workpiece and the tool.

* Make sure that the toolpath is selected (signified by the green check mark on the folder icon). If the operation is not selected choose the **Select all operations** icon.

* Select the **Backplot selected operations** icon.

* In the **Backplot** dialog box enable the **Display with color codes**, **Display tool, Display holder** and **Display rapid moves** icons as shown.

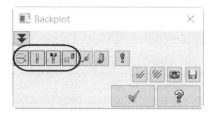

* To fit the workpiece to the screen, if needed, right mouse click in the graphics window and select the **Fit** icon or press **Alt + F1**.

* You can step through the **Backplot** by using the **Step forward** ▶▶ or **Step back** ◀◀ buttons.

* You can adjust the speed of the backplot with the **Run speed slider**.

* Select the **Play** button to run **Backplot**. ⊙ ■ ◀◀ ◀◀ ▶▶ ▶▶ ✎ ✎

• The toolpath should look as shown.

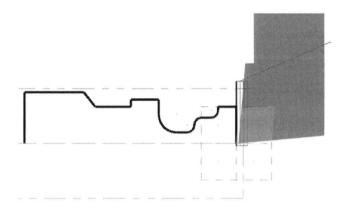

• Select the **OK** button to exit **Backplot**.
• Press **Alt + T** to remove the toolpath display.

STEP 14: SIMULATE THE TOOLPATH IN VERIFY

Verify shows the path the tools take to cut the part with material removal. This display lets you spot errors in the program before you machine the part. As you verify toolpaths, Mastercam displays additional information such as the X, Y, and Z coordinates, the path length, the minimum and maximum coordinates and the cycle time. It also shows any collisions between the workpiece and the tool.

• From the **Toolpaths Manager**, select the **Verify selected operations** icon as shown.

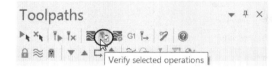

NOTE: Mastercam launches a new window that allows you to check the part using **Backplot** or **Verify.**

• In **Mastercam Simulator, Verify** should already be selected. Make any other necessary changes to match the settings as shown.

• Select the **Play** button to run **Verify**.

- To see the part from an **Isometric** view, right mouse click in the graphics window and select **Isometric** as shown.

- To fit the workpiece to the screen, right mouse click in the graphics window again and select **Fit**.

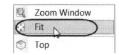

- The part should look as shown in Figure: 14.0.1.

Figure: 14.0.1

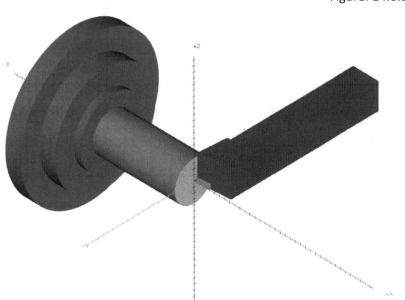

NOTE: To rotate the part, move the cursor to the center of the part and click and hold the mouse wheel and slowly move it in one direction.
To zoom in or out scroll up or down as needed.

- To go back to the Mastercam window, minimize the **Mastercam Simulator** window as shown.

STEP 15: ROUGH THE PART

Rough Toolpaths quickly remove large amounts of stock in preparation for a finish pass. Roughing passes are typically straight cuts parallel to the **Z axis**.

Toolpath Preview:

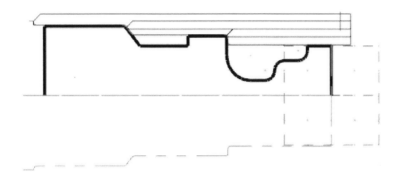

TURNING

• From the **General** group, select **Rough.**

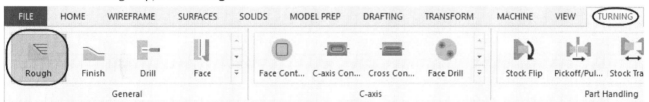

• Leave the default settings in the **Chaining** dialog box.

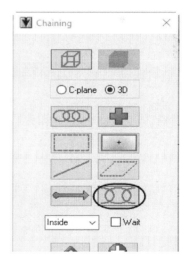

NOTE: The chaining mode is **Partial** by default. You will have to select the first entity and the last entity of the contour.

NOTE: To switch back to the Top view, right click in the graphics window and select **Top (WCS)**.

◆ [Select the entry point or chain the inner boundary]: Select **Entity A** as shown.

> **NOTE:** Make sure that the chaining direction is **CCW**. If necessary select the **Reverse** button in the **Chaining** dialog box.

◆ [Select the last entity]: Select **Entity B** as shown.

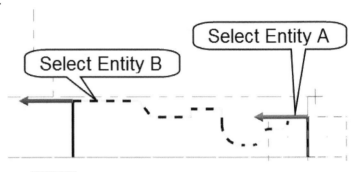

Select Entity B

Select Entity A

◆ Select the **OK** button to exit the **Chaining** dialog box.

◆ In the **Toolpath parameters** tab, select the same tool that we used in the facing operation and make all of the necessary changes as shown.

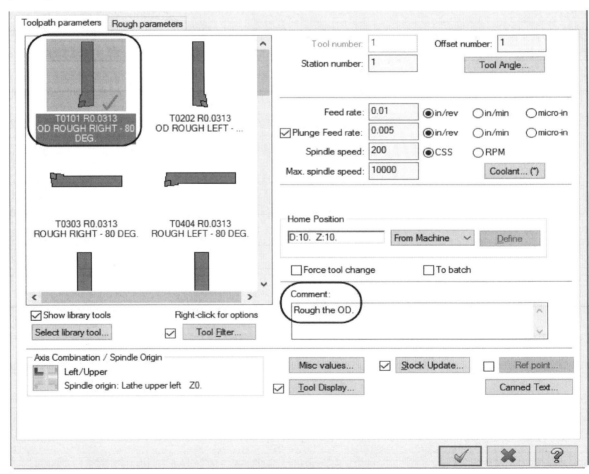

• Select the **Rough parameters** tab and make any necessary changes as shown.

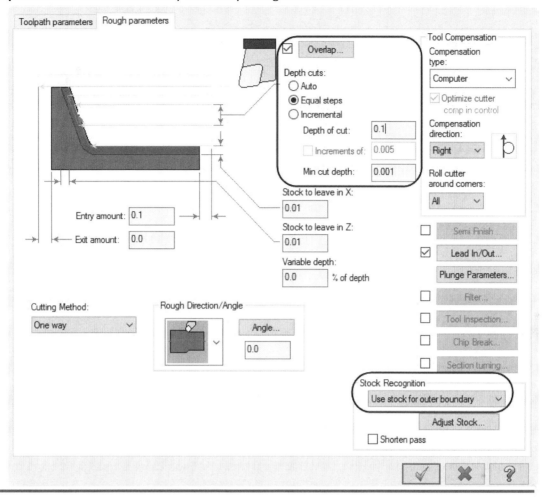

Depth of cut sets the amount of material to be removed during each pass.

Equal steps sets the **Depth of cut** value to the maximum amount of material that the tool can remove at each pass to ensure equal passes.

Min cut depth sets the minimum cut that can be taken per pass.

Stock to leave in X sets the remaining stock in the **X axis** after the tool completes all passes.

Stock to leave in Z sets the remaining stock in the **Z axis** after the tool completes all passes.

Entry amount sets the height at which the tool rapids to or from the part.

• Select the **Lead In/Out** button and choose the **Lead out** tab to extend the end of the contour as shown.

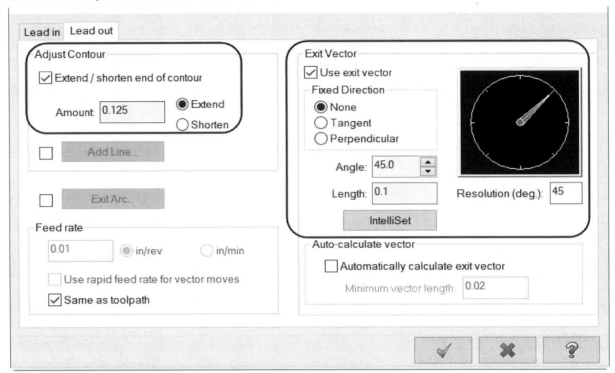

Adjust Contour allows you to extend or shorten the contour by an amount or by adding a line.

Feed rate allows you to specify a custom feed rate for the **Lead In/Out**.

Exit Vector allows you to create a tangent arc move or perpendicular move to start the toolpath. You can also manually define an entry/exit vector or let the system automatically calculate a vector for you.

• Select the **OK** button to exit the **Lead In/Out** dialog box.

• Select the **OK** button to exit the **Lathe Rough** dialog box.

15.1 Backplot the toolpath

- Once the operation has been regenerated, **Backplot** the toolpath.
- See **page 110** to review the procedure.

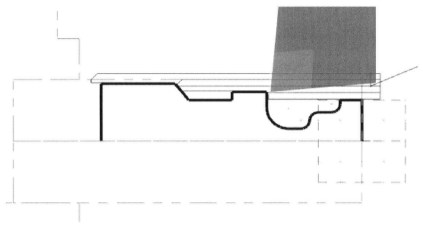

- Select the **OK** button to exit **Backplot**.

15.2 Verify the toolpaths

- To verify all toolpaths, from the **Toolpaths Manager**, choose the **Select all operations** icon.

- Select the **Verify selected operations** icon.

• See **page 111** to review the procedure.

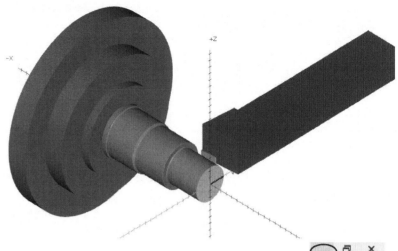

• To go back to the Mastercam window, minimize the **Mastercam Simulator** window as shown.

STEP 16: FINISH THE PART

Finish Toolpaths follow the contours of the chained geometry. Typically a finish toolpath follows a roughing toolpath.

Toolpath Preview:

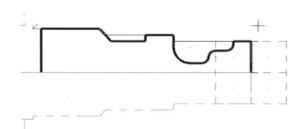

• Click on the **Select all operations** icon.

• Select the **Toggle display on selected operations** icon to turn the toolpath display off.

NOTE: You can also use **Alt + T** to toggle the toolpath display on or off.

TURNING

♦ From the **General** group, select **Finish**.

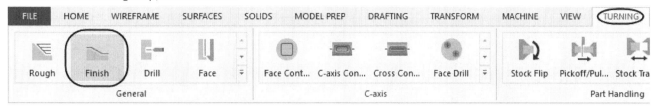

♦ Select the **Last** button in the **Chaining** dialog box as shown.

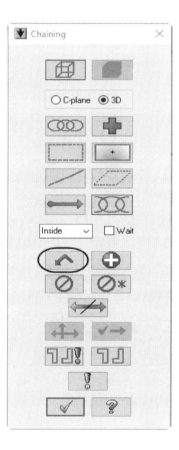

The **Last** button will automatically select the last chain that we used in the roughing toolpath.

♦ Select the **OK** button to exit the **Chaining** dialog box.

• Select the **OD Finish Right tool - 35 Degree** tool from the tool list and enter the comment as shown.

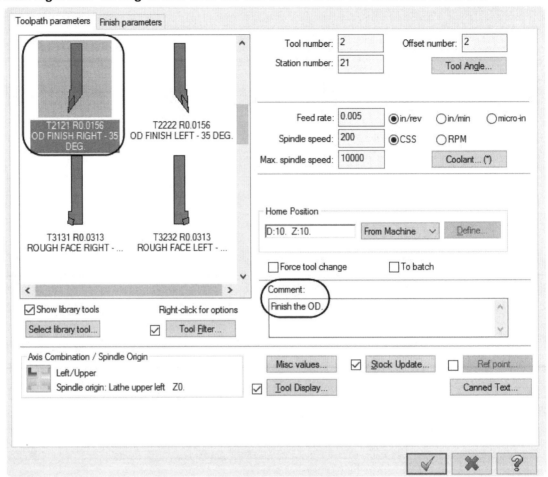

NOTE: The **Feed rate** and **Spindle speed** are based on the **Mastercam Tool Definition.**

• Select the **Finish parameters** tab and make all of the necessary changes as shown.

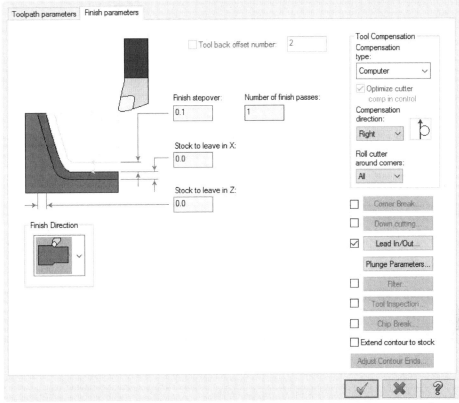

• Select the **Lead In/Out** button, choose the **Lead out** tab, and extend the end of the contour by **0.125** as shown.

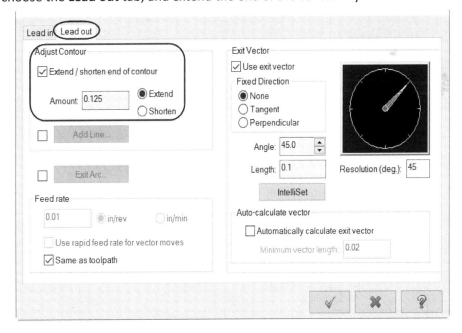

• Select the **OK** button to exit the **Lead In/Out** dialog box.

• Select the **OK** button to exit the **Finish Parameters** dialog box.

16.1 Backplot the toolpath

- Once the operation has been regenerated, **Backplot** the toolpath.
- See **page 110** to review the procedure.

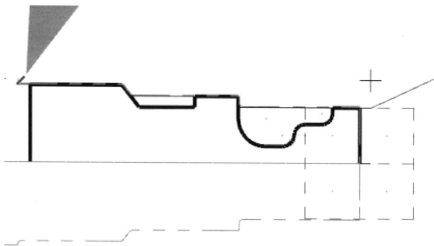

- Select the **OK** button to exit **Backplot**.

16.2 Verify the toolpaths

- To verify all toolpaths, from the **Toolpaths Manager**, choose the **Select all operations** icon.

- Select the **Verify selected operations** icon.

• See **page 111** to review the procedure.

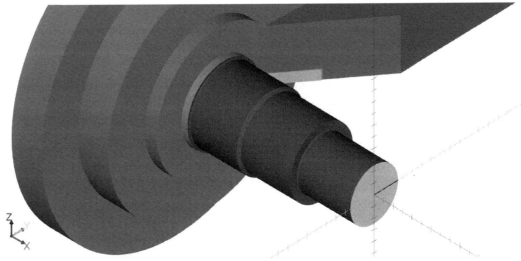

• To go back to the Mastercam window, minimize the **Mastercam Simulator** window as shown.

STEP 17: GROOVE THE PART USING THE MULTIPLE CHAINS METHOD

Groove toolpaths are used for machining indented or recessed areas that cannot be machined by roughing toolpaths or tools.

Toolpath Preview:

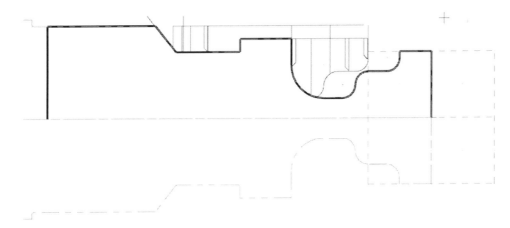

TURNING
• From the **General** group, click on the **Expand gallery** arrow key.

◆ Select **Groove**.

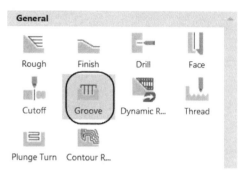

◆ Choose **Multiple chains** when the **Grooving Options** dialog box opens up as shown.

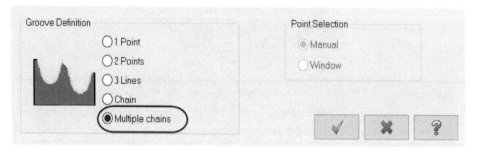

1 Point allows the user to select points from the graphics area to identify a groove.

2 Points allows you specify a groove by indicating the top corner of the groove and the point in the lower opposite corner.

3 Lines allows you to select three lines from the graphics screen to define the groove shape.

Chain allows you to chain a more complex shape to define a groove by chaining on-screen geometry.

Multiple chains allows you to chain multiple grooves by chaining on screen geometry.

Manual Point Selection allows you to manually select points from the graphics area.

Window Point Selection allows you to create a window in the graphics area and chains all of the points within the window.

◆ Select the **OK** button to exit the **Grooving Options** dialog box.

◆ The **Chaining method** should be set to **Partial** by default.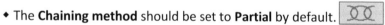

◆ [Select the entry point or chain the inner boundary]: Zoom in if needed and select **Entity A** as the first entity in the direction shown.

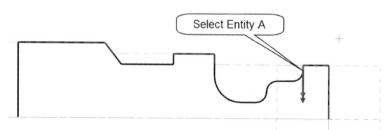

Select Entity A

• [Select the last entity]: Select **Entity B** as the last entity for the first groove as shown.

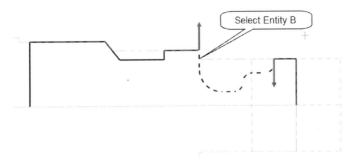

• [Select the inner boundary or select the retraction point or select done]: Select **Entity C** as the first entity as shown.

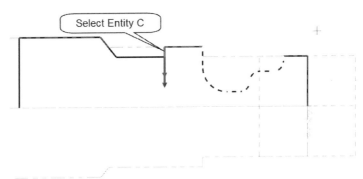

• [Select the last entity]: Select **Entity D** as the last entity for the second groove as shown.

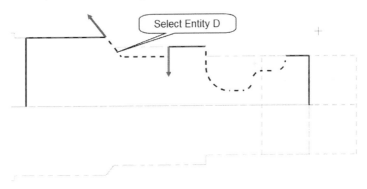

• Select the **OK** button to exit the **Chaining** dialog box.

♦ Select the **OD Groove Center - Medium** tool from the tool list and enter the comment as shown.

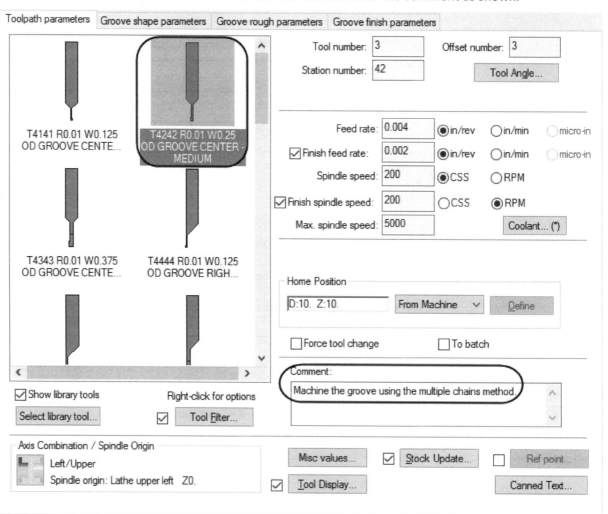

♦ Select the **Groove shape parameters** tab and enable **Use stock for outer boundary** as shown.

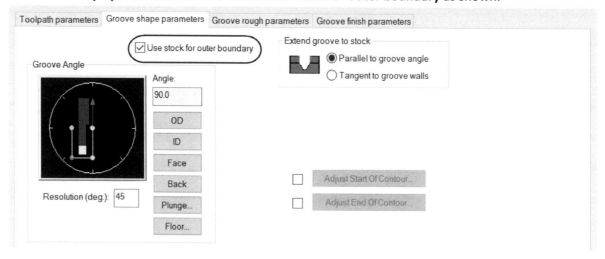

• Select the **Groove rough parameters** tab and make sure the parameters are set as shown.

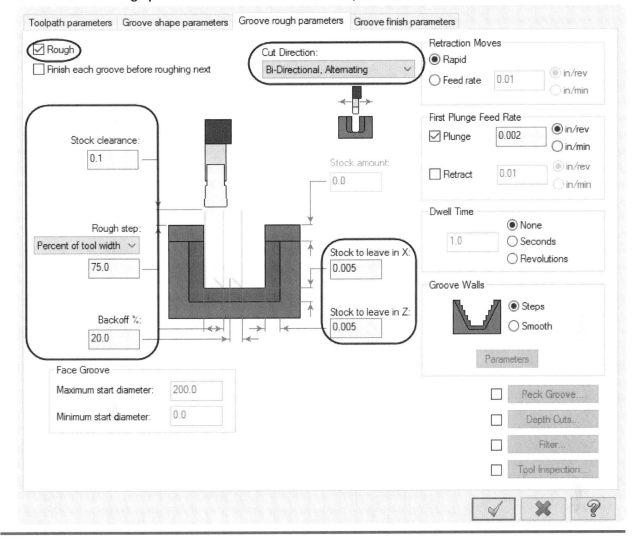

Cut Direction determines the direction that the tool will rough the groove (Positive, Negative, Bi-Directional, Alternating, Bi-Directional, Positive First, Bi-Directional, Negative First, or Chain Direction).

Stock clearance determines the point up to which the tool retracts after each pass.

Stock amount sets the remaining stock left by the previous operation.

Stock to leave in X sets the remaining stock in the **X axis** after the tool completes all rough passes.

Stock to leave in Z sets the remaining stock in the **Z axis** after the tool completes all rough passes.

Rough step sets the amount of material to be removed with each roughing pass. It can be set as a number of steps, a step amount or as a percentage of the tool width.

Backoff % sets how far the tool backs away from the wall of the groove before it retracts.

◆ Select the **Groove finish parameters** tab and make any necessary changes as shown.

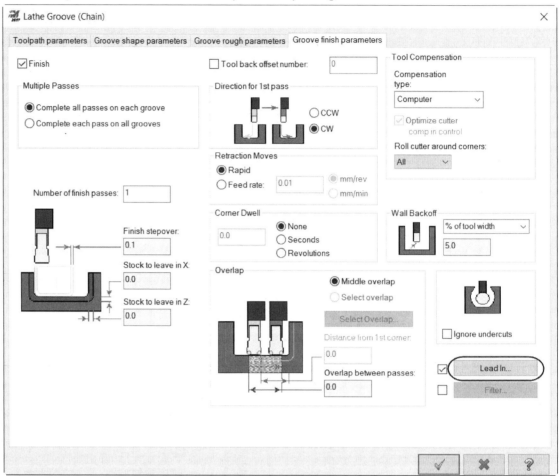

Direction for 1st pass determines the direction that the tool will finish the groove (**CCW** - Starting on the right wall or **CW** - starting with the left wall). With the first pass of a finish toolpath, the tool cuts down on one wall of the groove to the groove floor and then retracts out of the groove. On the second pass, the tool cuts down the opposite wall of the groove to the groove floor and moves across the groove floor to the point where the first pass ended.

Retraction Moves sets the retract moves to **Rapid** moves or with a specified **Feed rate.**

Finish stepover sets the maximum amount of material the tool will remove with the finish pass.

Stock to leave in X sets the remaining stock in the **X axis** after the tool completes all finish passes.

Stock to leave in Z sets the remaining stock in the **Z axis** after the tool completes all finish passes.

Overlap Distance from 1st corner sets the amount the tool cuts across the floor before retracting out of the groove.

Overlap between passes sets the amount the tool overlaps the first pass before it retracts.

Wall Backoff % sets how far the tool backs away from the wall of the groove after the first pass before it retracts.

• Select the **Lead In** button and change the **First pass lead in** entry vector to **Tangent** as shown.

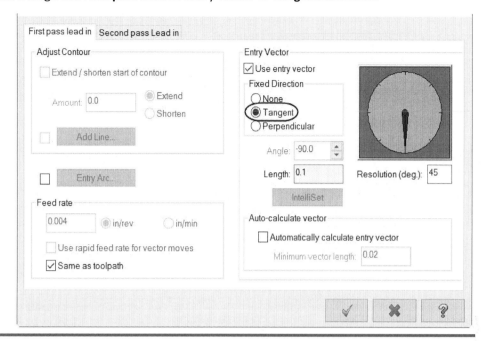

Tangent creates a tangent entry vector to the first move in the finish pass to allow the tool to smoothly engage into the groove.

• Select the **Second pass Lead in** tab and change the entry vector to **Tangent** as shown.

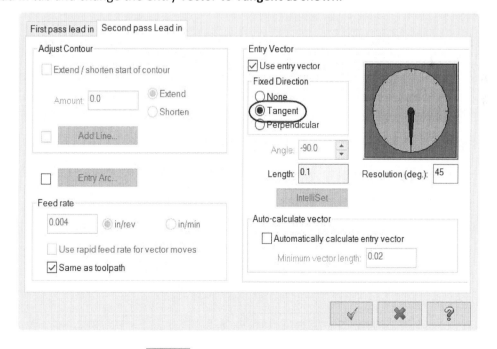

• Select the **OK** button to exit the **Lead In** dialog box.

• Select the **OK** button to exit the **Lathe Groove** dialog box and generate the toolpath.

17.1 Backplot the toolpath

• Once the operation has been regenerated, **Backplot** the toolpath.
• See **page 110** to review the procedure.

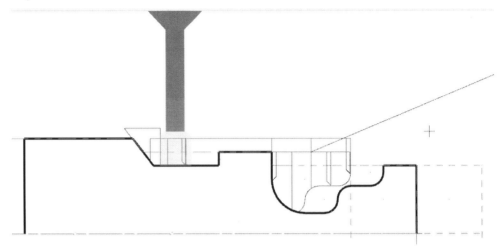

• Select the **OK** button to exit **Backplot**.

17.2 Verify the toolpaths

• To verify all toolpaths, from the **Toolpaths Manager**, choose the **Select all operations** icon.
• Select the **Verify selected operations** icon.

• See **page 111** to review the procedure.

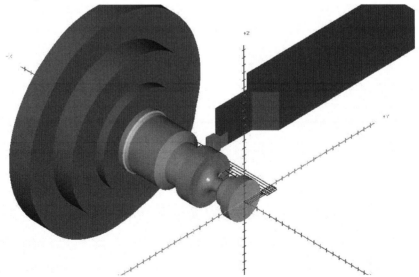

• To go back to the Mastercam window, minimize the **Mastercam Simulator** window as shown.

STEP 18: CENTER DRILL THE PART

Drill Toolpaths create a drilling toolpath on the face of the part along the center line. In this step, we will center drill the face before drilling the part to its finished size.

Toolpath Preview:

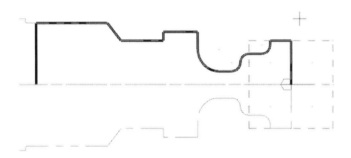

TURNING

♦ From the **General** group, select **Drill**.

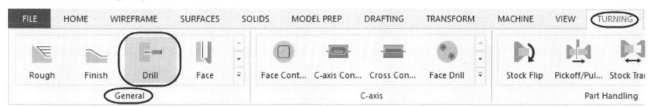

NOTE: You may need to scroll up within the **General** group by using the up arrow ⌃ to see the **Drill** icon.

NOTE: The **Lathe Drill Parameters** dialog box will automatically open. No chaining is required because Mastercam drills along the center line to create the toolpath. The drill depths are specified within the dialog box.

• Select the **0.25" Diameter Center Drill** from the tool list and enter the comment as shown.

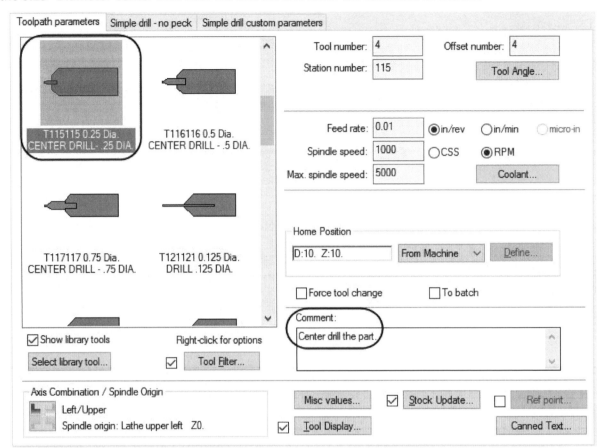

• Select the **Simple drill - no peck** tab and change the parameters to match the screenshot below.

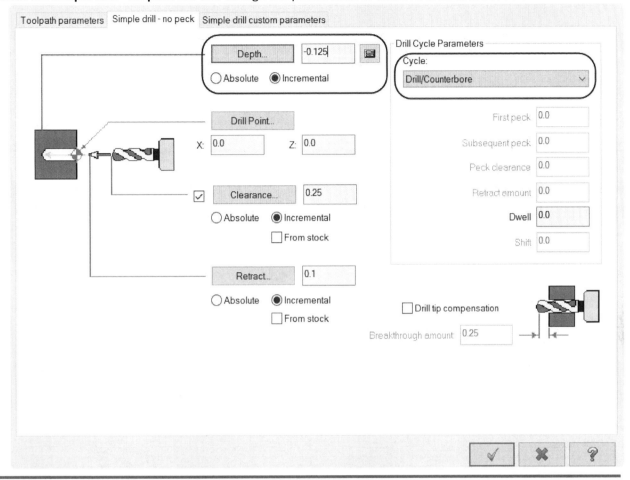

Depth sets the location of the bottom of the hole.

Drill Point X, Z allows you to choose the point location where you want to drill.

Clearance determines the point at which the tool starts to move at the feed rate towards the stock.

Drill tip compensation automatically adjusts the depth value by adding the tip of the drill to it.

Breakthrough amount allows you to add extra distance to the depth for through holes.

• Select the **OK** button to exit the **Lathe Drill** dialog box.

18.1 Backplot the toolpath

- Once the operation has been regenerated, **Backplot** the toolpath.
- See **page 110** to review the procedure.

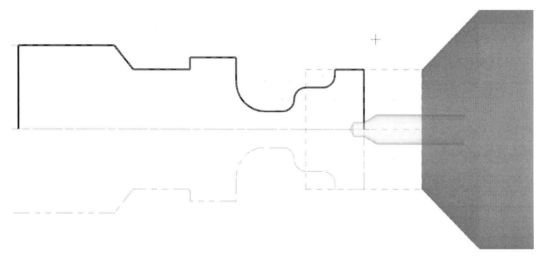

- Select the **OK** button to exit **Backplot**.

18.2 Verify the toolpaths

- To verify all toolpaths, from the **Toolpaths Manager**, choose the **Select all operations** icon.
- Select the **Verify selected operations** icon.

- See **page 111** to review the procedure.

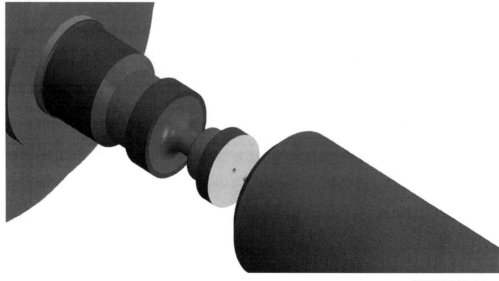

- To go back to the Mastercam window, minimize the **Mastercam Simulator** window as shown.

STEP 19: DRILL THE PART

In this step we will create another drilling operation to finish the part.

Toolpath Preview:

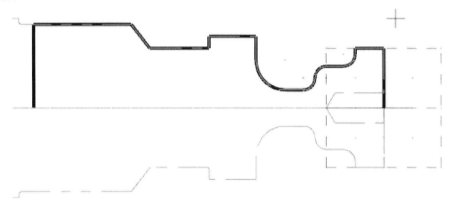

TURNING

• From the **General** group, select **Drill**.

♦ Select the **0.25" Drill** from the tool list and enter the comment as shown.

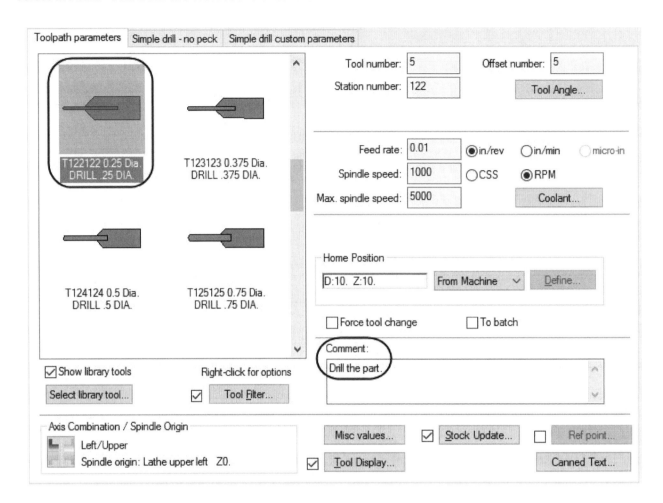

◆ Select the **Simple drill - no peck** tab and make the changes as shown.

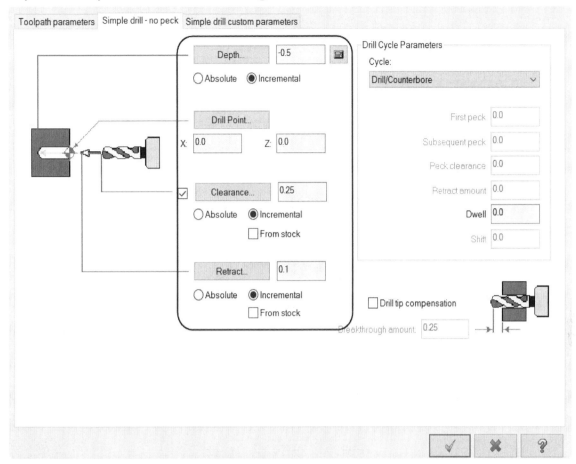

◆ Select the **OK** button to exit the **Lathe Drill** dialog box.

19.1 Backplot the toolpath

◆ Once the operation has been regenerated, **Backplot** the toolpath.
◆ See **page 110** to review the procedure.

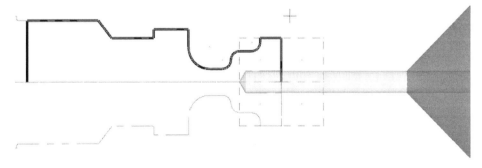

◆ Select the **OK** button to exit **Backplot**.

19.2 Verify the toolpaths

- To verify all toolpaths, from the **Toolpaths Manager**, choose the **Select all operations** icon.
- Select the **Verify selected operations** icon.

- See **page 111** to review the procedure.

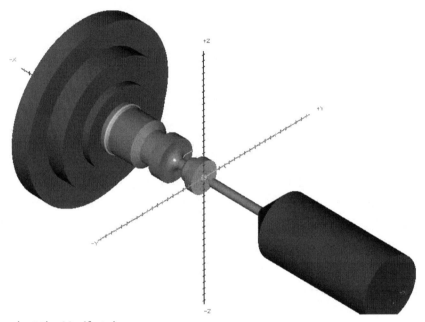

- To see a section through the part, select the **Verify** tab.
- Click on the **XY Clipping Plane** icon and select **Clip Top** as shown.

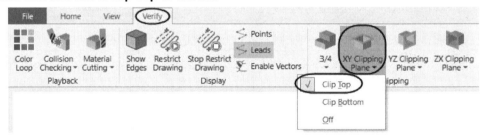

◆ The part should look as shown.

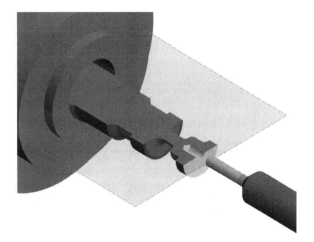

◆ To exit the section view, click on the **XY Clipping Plane** icon again and select **Off** as shown.

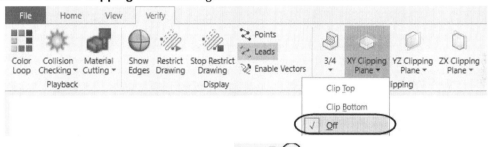

◆ To exit the **Mastercam Simulator** window click on the **Close** icon.

STEP 20: RUN THE POST PROCESSOR TO OBTAIN THE G-CODE FILE

Post Processing refers to the process by which the toolpaths in your Mastercam part files are converted to a format that can be understood by your machine tool's control. A special program reads your Mastercam file and writes the appropriate NC code.

◆ Make sure that all operations are selected, otherwise click on the **Select all operations** icon.

◆ Select the **Post selected operations** icon from the **Toolpaths Manager.**

• In the **Post processing** dialog box, make any necessary changes as shown below.

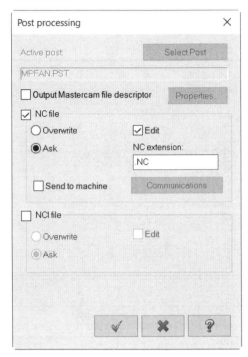

NC File enabled allows you to keep the NC file and to assign the same name as the MCAM file.

Edit enabled allows you to automatically launch the default editor.

• Select the **OK** button to continue.
• Save the NC file.

• The **Mastercam Code Expert** window will be launched and the NC program will appear as shown.

```
1    %
2    O0002
3    (PROGRAM NAME - TUTORIAL #2 TOOLPATH)
4    (DATE=DD-MM-YY - 10-01-17 TIME=HH:MM - 15:37)
5    (MCX FILE - C:\USERS\GONG.ZHANG\DOCUMENTS\MASTERCAM\LATHE\TUTORIAL #2 TOOLPATH.MCAM)
6    (NC FILE - C:\USERS\GONG.ZHANG\DOCUMENTS\MY MCAM2018\LATHE\NC\TUTORIAL #2 TOOLPATH.NC)
7    (MATERIAL - STEEL INCH - 1030 - 200 BHN)
8    G20
9    (TOOL - 1 OFFSET - 1)
10   (OD ROUGH RIGHT - 80 DEG.  INSERT - CNMG-432)
11   ( FACE THE PART. )
12   G0 T0101
13   G18
14   G97 S449 M03
15   G0 G54 X1.7 Z.055 M8
16   G50 S3600
17   G96 S200
18   G99 G1 X-.0625 F.01
19   G0 Z.155
20   X1.7
21   Z.01
22   G1 X-.0625
23   G0 Z.11
24   X1.7
25   Z0.
26   G1 X-.0625
27   G0 Z.1
28   ( ROUGH THE OD. )
29   X1.34
30   Z.21
31   G1 Z.11
32   Z-2.1394
```

• Select the **"X"** box in the upper right corner to exit the editor.

STEP 21: SAVE THE UPDATED MCAM FILE

REVIEW EXERCISE - STUDENT PRACTICE

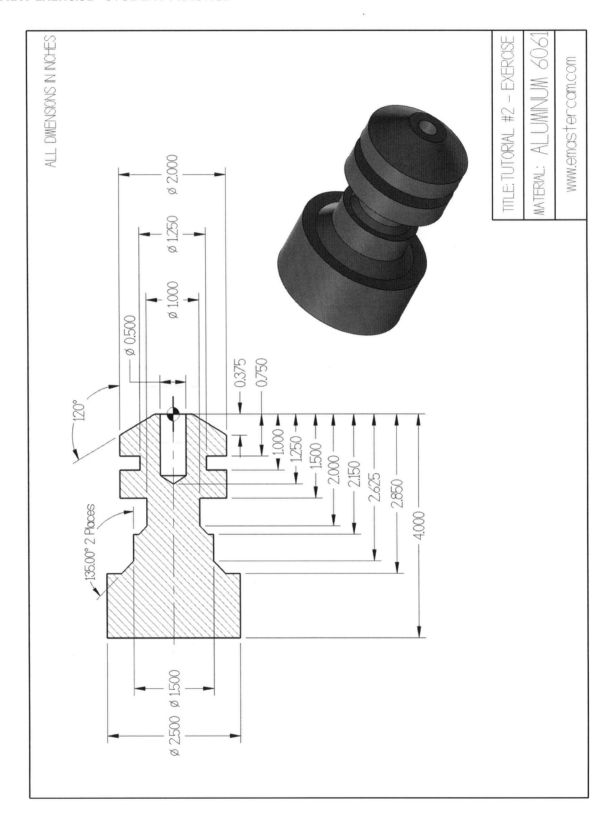

ALL DIMENSIONS IN INCHES

TITLE: TUTORIAL #2 – EXERCISE

MATERIAL: ALUMINUM 6061

www.emastercam.com

Ø 2.000
Ø 1.250
Ø 1.000
Ø 0.500

120°

135.00° 2 Places

0.375
0.750
1.000
1.250
1.500
2.000
2.150
2.625
2.850
4.000

Ø 1.500
Ø 2.500

CREATE THE GEOMETRY FOR TUTORIAL #2 EXERCISE

Use these commands to create the top half of the geometry.

- ◆ Line Endpoints.
- ◆ Line Parallel.
- ◆ Chamfer Entities.
- ◆ Trim Break Extend.
- ◆ Delete Entities.

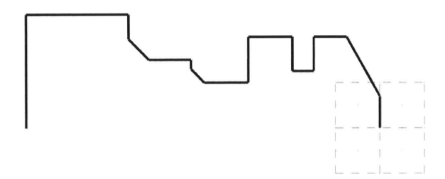

CREATE THE TOOLPATHS FOR TUTORIAL #2 EXERCISE

Create the Toolpaths for Tutorial #2 Exercise as per the instructions below.

Set the machine properties including the stock.
Rough, Face and Finish the OD.
* Use the stock setup to define the face operation.
* Use the OD Rough Right Tool for roughing and facing operations.
* Use an OD Finish Right tool for the finish operation.
* Extend the ends of the contour with Lead In/Lead Out so the tool machines beyond the end of the part.

Machine the groove.
* Chain the small groove using the Partial method.
* Use the OD Groove Center Medium Tool.
* Use stock for outer boundary.
* Rough and Finish the groove in the same toolpath.

Machine the last groove.
* Chain the final groove CCW.
* Use the same tool from the previous operation.
* Use stock for outer boundary.
* Rough and Finish the groove in the same toolpath.

Drill the Hole.
* Center Drill the Part.
* Use the **0.5"** Diameter Center Drill.
* Drill the Part.
* Use the **0.5"** Diameter Drill.

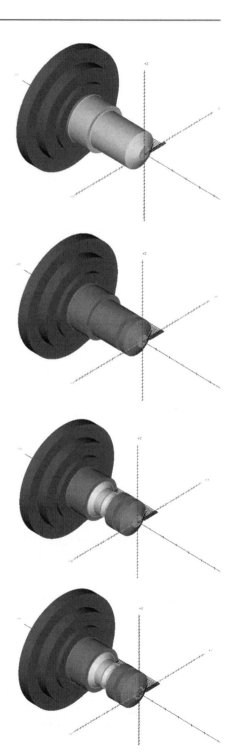

NOTES:

TUTORIAL #2 QUIZ

◆ What does a Drill Toolpath allow you to do and what is needed to create a drill toolpath?

◆ What is a groove toolpath intended for?

◆ How do you create a grooving toolpath using the width of the tool?

TUTORIAL #3

OVERVIEW OF STEPS TAKEN TO CREATE THE FINAL PART

From Parasolid file to CAD model:
* The student will open a Parasolid file in Mastercam.
* The student will need to create the geometry used to machine the part from the supplied solid model.

Create the 2D CAD Model used to generate toolpaths from:
* The student will create the upper profile of the part in the Top view on its own level.
* The profile of the part will be created using the Turn Profile command.

Create the necessary toolpaths to machine the part:
* The student will set up the stock size and the clamping method.
* The student will drill the part to remove the bulk of the material, then rough and finish the ID using the canned cycles.
* The OD of the part will be faced, roughed, and finished.
* Two grooving toolpaths will be created by modifying the tool setup to machine on an angle.
* A Cutoff toolpath will be created to finish the part.

Backplot and Verify the file:
* The Backplot will be used to simulate a step by step process of the tool's movements.
* The Verify will be used to watch a tool machine the part out of a solid model.

Post Process the file to generate the G-code:
* The student will then post process the file to obtain an NC file containing the necessary code for the machine.

 This tutorial takes approximately fifty minutes to complete.

GEOMETRY CREATION

STEP 1: SETTING UP THE GRAPHIC USER INTERFACE

Please refer to the **Getting Started** section to set up the graphical user interface accordingly.

STEP 2: DOWNLOAD THE FILE LATHE TRAINING TUTORIAL

You will require an internet connection to download this file.

RESOURCES: - Download the file from www.emastercam.com/trainingfiles.
◆ Save the file on the desktop.

STEP 3: REMOVING ANY MACHINE FROM THE TOOLPATHS MANAGER

In this step you have to clear any machine that might exist in the **Toolpaths Manager**. The only Mastercam product that does not require any machine is Design.

> **NOTE:** This tutorial covers machining a part in a VTL machine. We will bring in a Parasolid file and manipulate the geometry appropriately. It is important to make sure that in the **Toolpaths Manager** no machine is selected.

◆ To unhide and lock the manager panels, see **Tutorial 1 page 40**.

MACHINE
◆ If another machine is already selected, from the **Machine ribbon** in the **Machine Type** group select **Design**.
◆ From the **Toolpaths Manager**, click on the **Delete all operations, groups and tools** icon as shown.

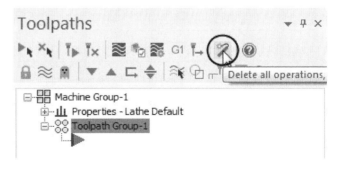

• This warning message will appear on the screen.

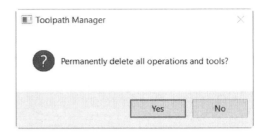

• Select the **Yes** button to continue.
• In the **Toolpaths Manager** you should have no **Machine Group** as shown.

STEP 4: OPEN THE PARASOLID FILE IN MASTERCAM

In this step we will open the Parasolid file in Mastercam.

• From the **Quick Access Toolbar** located at the upper left corner of the screen, select the **Open** icon as shown.

• Ensure the **Files type** is set to **Parasolid Files (*.x_t; *.x_b, *.xmt)**. This will show all the SolidWorks files you have on your desktop.

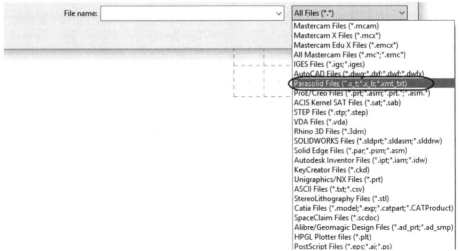

• Locate the file in the location it was saved i.e. the desktop.

• Select the file **TUTORIAL #3.X_T** as shown in <u>Figure: 4.0.1</u>.

Figure: 4.0.1

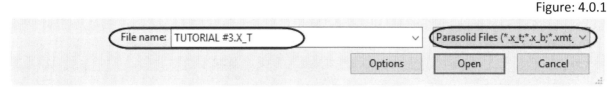

• Click on **Options** button and make sure **Import Solids** is enabled.

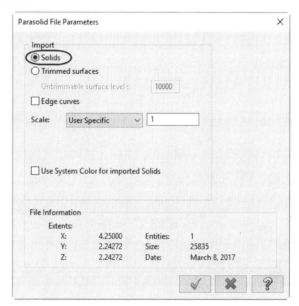

• Select **OK** button to exit the **Parasolid File Parameters** dialog box and **Open** the file.
• Right mouse click in the graphics window and select the **Isometric** view.

• Press **Alt + F1** to fit the geometry into the graphics window.
• Press **Alt + S** to see the part in the shaded mode.

NOTE: Currently you have a solid. Unlike wireframe models, which are a collection of curves, and surface models, which are a collection of surfaces, a solid model is a single entity.
Any time you want to see the solid in a shaded or unshaded mode press **Alt + S**.

• The part should appear as shown in <u>Figure: 4.0.2</u>.

Figure: 4.0.2

STEP 5: CHANGE THE MAIN LEVEL TO 2

In this step we will change the main level to 2 to differentiate the geometry that will be created from the solid model.

• From the bottom of the **Toolpaths Manager**, select the **Levels** tab as shown.

• Click in the **Name** area in the **Levels Manager** and highlight the existing name and enter **"Solid"** as shown.

◆ Press **Enter** once complete.

• Click in the **Number** area and enter in the level number **2** and type in the name **"Turn Profile Geometry"** as shown.

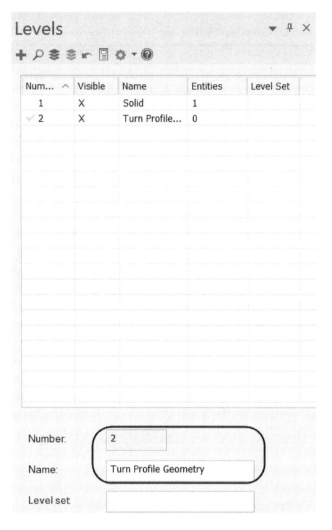

• Press **Enter** once complete.

STEP 6: CREATE A TURN PROFILE OF THE PART

In this step we will use the solid we imported as a Parasolid file and create geometry from it. **Turn Profile** will create a 2D profile from an existing solid, solid face or surface. The profile will be created in the top view of the active WCS by either spinning the solid about the **X axis** or creating a cross section (slice) through the selected solid in the XY plane.

Step Preview:

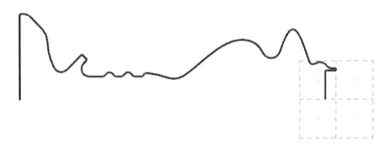

WIREFRAME

♦ From the **Shapes** group, select **Turn Profile** as shown.

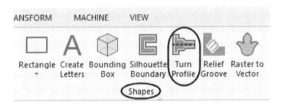

♦ To select the **Top** view, right mouse click in the graphics window and select **Top (WCS)** as shown

▢	Zoom Window
℗	Unzoom 80%
⟲	Dynamic Rotation
⊞	Fit
	Top (WCS)
	Front (WCS)
	Right (WCS) / Top (WCS)
	Isometric (WCS)
	GView

♦ Scroll down on the mouse wheel to unzoom the geometry.

* [Select solid bodies, solid faces or surfaces]: Select the solid on the graphic user interface.

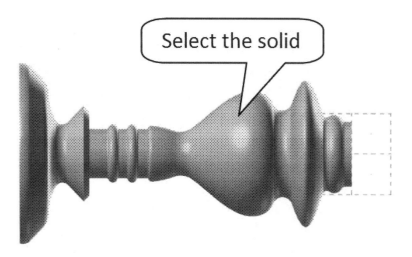

* Click on the **End Selection** button or press **Enter** to finish the selection.
* The **Turn Profile** panel will appear. Set the **Method** to **Spin** and the **Profile** to **Upper Profile** as shown.

Spin is used to create a profile by spinning the solid about the WCS **X axis**.

Slice is used to create the profile from a slice through the middle of the solid in the WCS XY plane.

Tessellation Tolerance sets the maximum allowed deviation of a given triangular facet from the selected surfaces.

Profile controls whether the upper, lower or both halves of the profile (Full Profile) are created.

• Select the **OK** button to generate the geometry.

NOTE: This may take a minute depending on the processing speed of your computer.

• In the **Levels** panel, click in the **Visible** column next to **Level 1** to remove the **X** and make it invisible as shown.

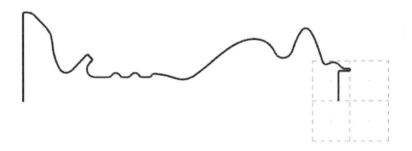

• The geometry should appear as shown in <u>Figure: 6.0.1</u>.

Figure: 6.0.1

STEP 7: SAVE THE FILE

FILE
• **Save As.**

• Click on the **Browse** icon as shown.
• Find a location on the computer to save your file.
• File name: "Your Name_3".

TOOLPATH CREATION

PART SETUP:

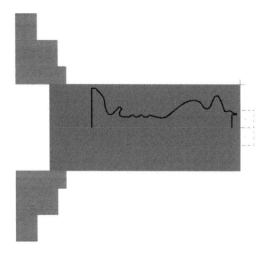

SETUP SHEET:

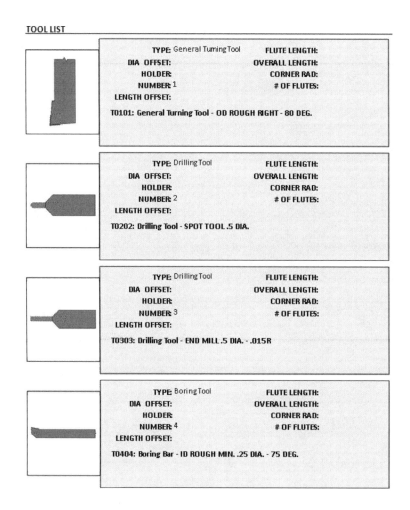

TOOL LIST

TYPE: General Turning Tool	FLUTE LENGTH:
DIA OFFSET:	OVERALL LENGTH:
HOLDER:	CORNER RAD:
NUMBER: 1	# OF FLUTES:
LENGTH OFFSET:	

T0101: General Turning Tool - OD ROUGH RIGHT - 80 DEG.

TYPE: Drilling Tool	FLUTE LENGTH:
DIA OFFSET:	OVERALL LENGTH:
HOLDER:	CORNER RAD:
NUMBER: 2	# OF FLUTES:
LENGTH OFFSET:	

T0202: Drilling Tool - SPOT TOOL .5 DIA.

TYPE: Drilling Tool	FLUTE LENGTH:
DIA OFFSET:	OVERALL LENGTH:
HOLDER:	CORNER RAD:
NUMBER: 3	# OF FLUTES:
LENGTH OFFSET:	

T0303: Drilling Tool - END MILL .5 DIA. - .015R

TYPE: Boring Tool	FLUTE LENGTH:
DIA OFFSET:	OVERALL LENGTH:
HOLDER:	CORNER RAD:
NUMBER: 4	# OF FLUTES:
LENGTH OFFSET:	

T0404: Boring Bar - ID ROUGH MIN. .25 DIA. - 75 DEG.

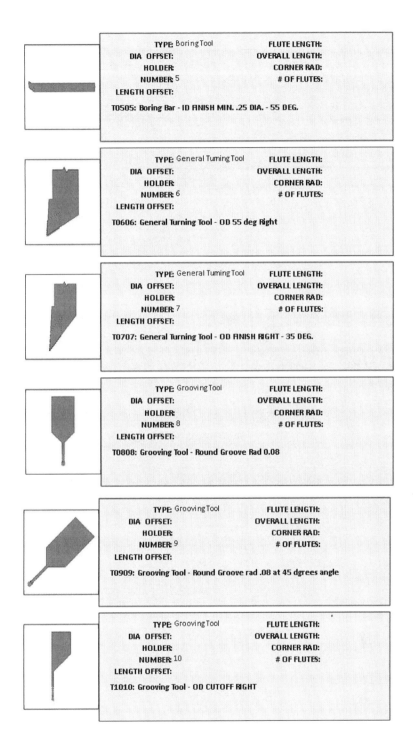

TYPE: Boring Tool
DIA OFFSET:
HOLDER:
NUMBER: 5
LENGTH OFFSET:
FLUTE LENGTH:
OVERALL LENGTH:
CORNER RAD:
OF FLUTES:

T0505: Boring Bar - ID FINISH MIN. .25 DIA. - 55 DEG.

TYPE: General Turning Tool
DIA OFFSET:
HOLDER:
NUMBER: 6
LENGTH OFFSET:
FLUTE LENGTH:
OVERALL LENGTH:
CORNER RAD:
OF FLUTES:

T0606: General Turning Tool - OD 55 deg Right

TYPE: General Turning Tool
DIA OFFSET:
HOLDER:
NUMBER: 7
LENGTH OFFSET:
FLUTE LENGTH:
OVERALL LENGTH:
CORNER RAD:
OF FLUTES:

T0707: General Turning Tool - OD FINISH RIGHT - 35 DEG.

TYPE: Grooving Tool
DIA OFFSET:
HOLDER:
NUMBER: 8
LENGTH OFFSET:
FLUTE LENGTH:
OVERALL LENGTH:
CORNER RAD:
OF FLUTES:

T0808: Grooving Tool - Round Groove Rad 0.08

TYPE: Grooving Tool
DIA OFFSET:
HOLDER:
NUMBER: 9
LENGTH OFFSET:
FLUTE LENGTH:
OVERALL LENGTH:
CORNER RAD:
OF FLUTES:

T0909: Grooving Tool - Round Groove rad .08 at 45 dgrees angle

TYPE: Grooving Tool
DIA OFFSET:
HOLDER:
NUMBER: 10
LENGTH OFFSET:
FLUTE LENGTH:
OVERALL LENGTH:
CORNER RAD:
OF FLUTES:

T1010: Grooving Tool - OD CUTOFF RIGHT

STEP 8: SELECT THE LATHE DEFAULT

In this step you will select the machine, in your case the Lathe default. This allows you to set the plane to the Lathe +D +Z and to be able to enter the coordinates based on the lathe axes.

MACHINE
- From the Machine Type group, select the drop down arrow below Lathe and select **Default** as shown.

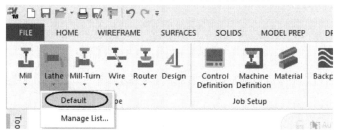

STEP 9: SET UP THE LATHE PLANE +D +Z

In this step you will learn how to set up the **Lathe Plane +D +Z** to be able to enter the coordinates using this plane.

- Select the **Planes** tab from the bottom of the screen as shown.

> **NOTE:** The **Planes** tab may be on the left side of the screen as shown.

- In the **Planes** panel, select **+D +Z** and click in the **C** and **T** columns next to the **+D +Z** plane to set your **Construction plane** and **Tool plane** to the **+D +Z** plane as shown.

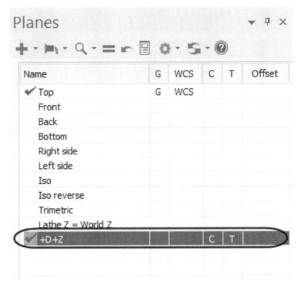

STEP 10: SET UP THE TOOL SETTINGS AND THE STOCK

In this step you will learn how to assign tool numbers, tool offset numbers, and default values for feeds, speeds, and other toolpath parameters. You will also learn how to define the stock and chuck jaws using the lathe machine groups.

- Select the **Toolpaths** tab as shown.

- Select the plus sign in front of **Properties** in the **Toolpaths Manager** to expand the **Toolpaths Group Properties.**

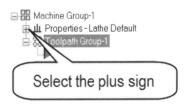

- Select **Tool settings** to set the tool parameters.

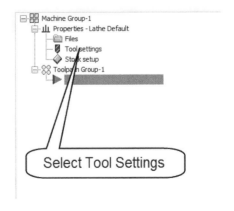

• Change the parameters to match the screenshot in Figure: 10.0.1.

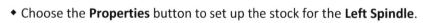

Default program number is used to enter a number if your machine requires a number for a program name.

Assign tool numbers sequentially allows you to overwrite the tool number from the library with the next available tool number.

Warn of duplicate tool numbers allows you to get a warning if you enter two tools with the same number.

Override defaults with modal values enables the system to keep the values that you enter.

Feed Calculation set to **From tool** uses the feed rate, plunge rate, retract rate and spindle speed from the tool definition.

• Select the **Stock Setup** tab.

• Choose the **Properties** button to set up the stock for the **Left Spindle**.

◆ Define the stock by setting the stock geometry to **Cylinder** and entering the stock dimensions. Ensure you enable **Use Margins** and enter the values as shown in <u>Figure: 10.0.2</u>.

Figure: 10.0.2

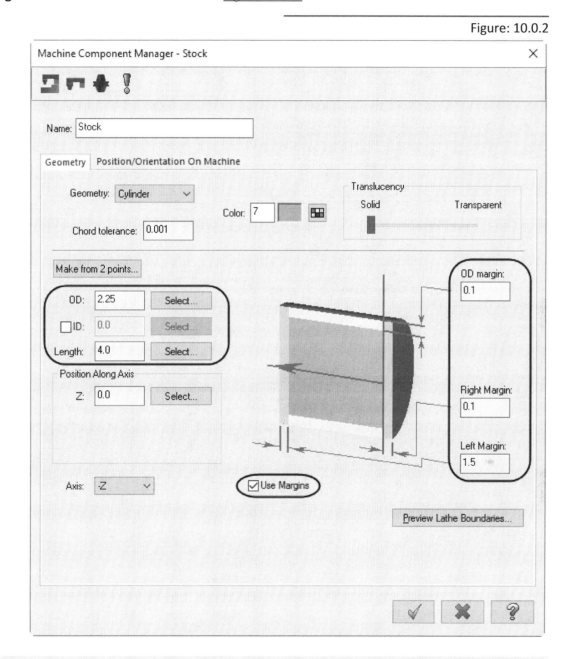

NOTE: The **stock** model that you create can be displayed with the part geometry when viewing the file or the toolpaths, during backplot, or while verifying toolpaths. You can create stock on the left or right spindle.

◆ Select the **OK** button to exit the **Machine Component Manager - Stock** dialog box.

• Ensure that **Left Spindle** is selected and then select the **Properties** button in the **Chuck Jaws** area as shown.

• Make the necessary changes to define the chuck size, the clamping method and the stock position. Ensure that you choose the clamping method **OD #1** as shown in the graphic below.

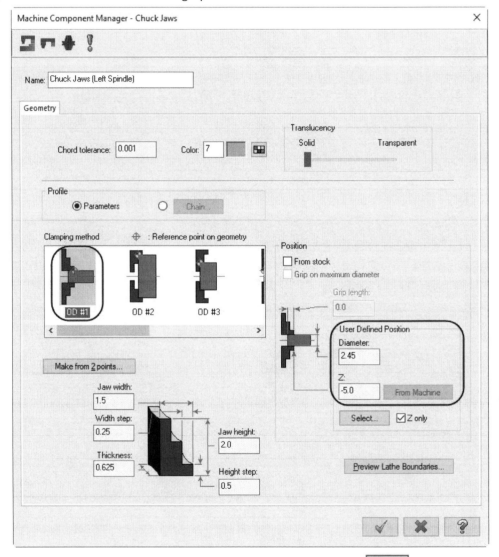

• Select the **OK** button to exit the **Machine Component Manager - Chuck Jaws** dialog box.

- Enable **Fit screen to boundaries** in the **Display Options** area.

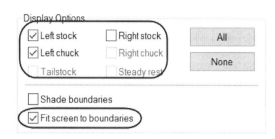

- Select the **OK** button to exit the **Machine Group Properties** dialog box.
- Press **Alt + F1** to fit the geometry to the screen.
- The stock should look as shown in <u>Figure: 10.0.3</u>.

Figure: 10.0.3

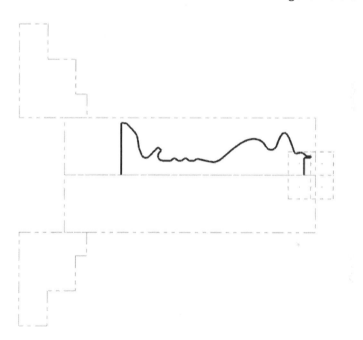

NOTE: The stock is not geometry and cannot be selected.

STEP 11: FACE THE PART

Face toolpaths allow the user to quickly clean the stock from one end of the part and create an even surface for future operations. Note that we do not have to chain any geometry to create the toolpath because of the extra material we specified on the right face in the stock setup. You can also select points to dictate where Mastercam will create the facing operation.

Toolpath Preview:

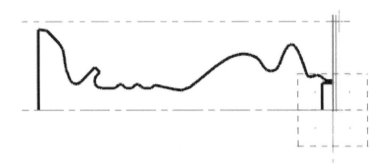

TURNING

• From the **General** group, click on the **Face** icon.

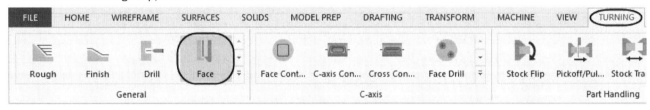

♦ Select the **OD Rough Right -80 Degree** tool and enter the comment.

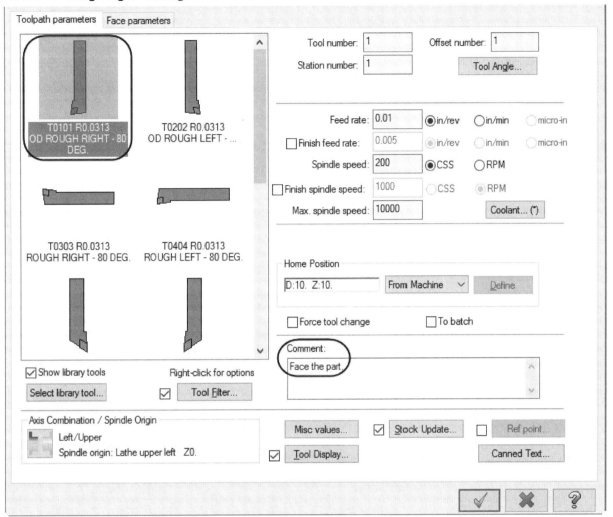

NOTE: The **Feed rate** and the **Spindle speeds** are based on the **Mastercam Tool Definitions**. They can be changed at any time, based on the material that you are going to machine.

● Select the **Face parameters** tab and make all of the necessary changes as shown in the screenshot below.

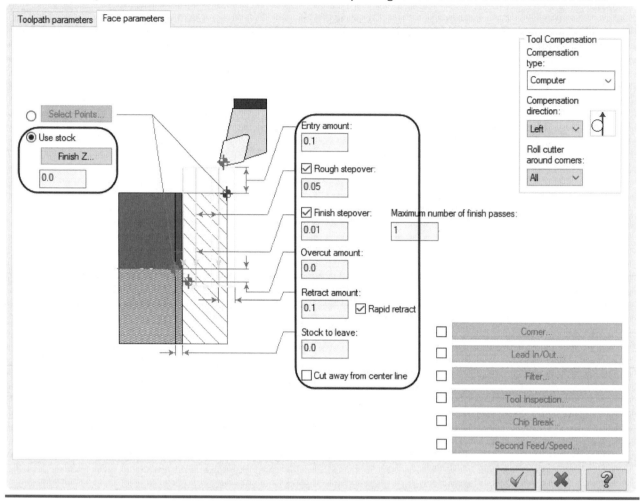

Entry amount sets the height at which the tool rapids to or from the part.

Rough stepover sets the roughing pass value.

Finish stepover sets the finish pass value.

Overcut amount determines how far past the center of the part the tool will cut.

Retract amount determines the distance the tool moves away from the face of the part before it moves to the start of the next cut.

Stock to leave sets the remaining stock after the tool completes all passes.

Cut away from the center line sets the tool to start cutting closest to the center line and cut away from the center line at each pass.

● Select the **OK** button to exit the **Lathe Face** dialog box.

STEP 12: BACKPLOT THE TOOLPATHS

Backplotting shows the path the tools take to cut the part. This display lets you spot errors in the program before you machine the part. As you backplot toolpaths, Mastercam displays additional information such as the X, Y, and Z coordinates, the path length, the minimum and maximum coordinates and the cycle time.

♦ Make sure that the toolpath is selected (signified by the green check mark on the folder icon). If the operation is not selected choose the **Select all operations** icon.

♦ Select the **Backplot selected operations** icon.

♦ In the **Backplot** dialog box, enable the **Display with color codes**, **Display tool**, **Display holder** and **Display rapid moves** icons as shown.

♦ To fit the workpiece to the screen, if needed, right mouse click in the graphics window again and select the **Fit** icon or press **Alt + F1**.

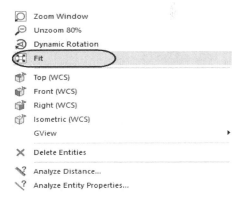

♦ You can step through the **Backplot** by using the **Step forward** or **Step back** buttons.

♦ You can adjust the speed of the backplot with the **Run speed slider**.

♦ Select the **Play** button to run **Backplot**.

- The toolpath should look as shown.

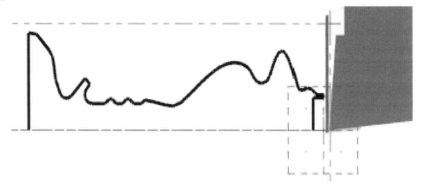

- Select the **OK** button to exit **Backplot**.

STEP 13: SIMULATE THE TOOLPATH IN VERIFY

Verify shows the path the tools take to cut the part with material removal. This display lets you spot errors in the program before you machine the part. As you verify toolpaths, Mastercam displays additional information such as the X, Y, and Z coordinates, the path length, the minimum and maximum coordinates and the cycle time. It also shows any collisions between the workpiece and the tool.

- To verify all toolpaths, from the **Toolpaths Manager**, choose the **Select all operations** icon.

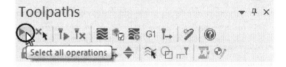

- Select the **Verify selected operation**s icon.

- Select the **Play Simulation** button to run **Verify**.

• The part should look as shown in Figure: 13.0.1.

Figure: 13.0.1

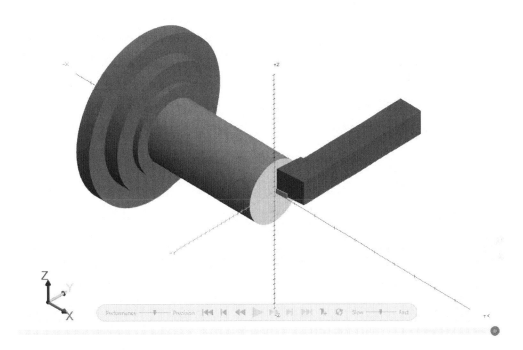

NOTE: To rotate the part, move the cursor to the center of the part and click and hold the mouse wheel and slowly move it in one direction.
To zoom in or out hold down the mouse wheel and scroll up or down as needed.

• To go back to the Mastercam window, minimize the **Mastercam Simulator** window as shown.
• Hover the cursor over the **Toolpaths Manager** and press **T** or press **Alt** + **T** to remove the toolpath display.

STEP 14: CENTER DRILL THE PART

Drill Toolpaths create a drilling toolpath on the face of the part along the center line. In this step, we will center drill the face before drilling the part to remove the bulk of the material on the ID.

Toolpath Preview:

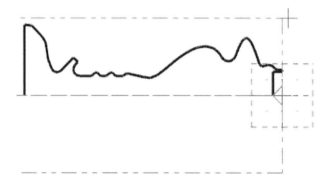

TURNING

• From the **General** group, select the **Drill** icon.

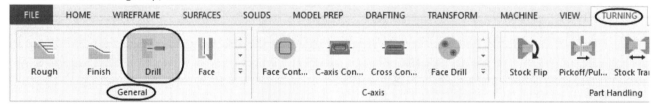

NOTE: The **Lathe Drill** dialog box will automatically open. No chaining is needed because Mastercam drills along the center line to create the toolpath. Drill depths are specified within the dialog box.

♦ Select the **0.5" Diameter Spot Drill** from the tool list and enter the comment as shown.

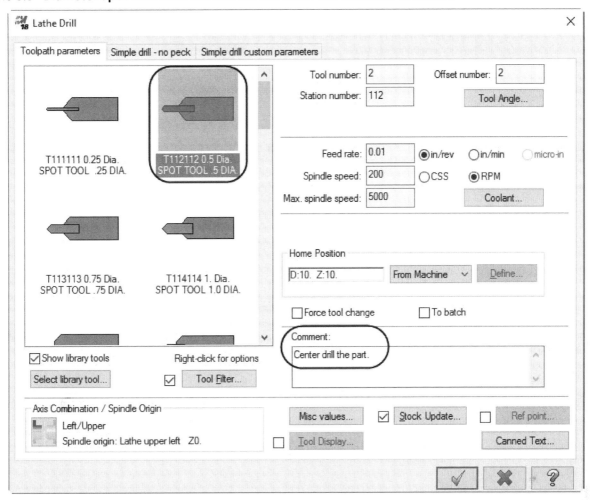

◆ Select the **Simple drill - no peck** tab and change the parameters to match the screenshot below.

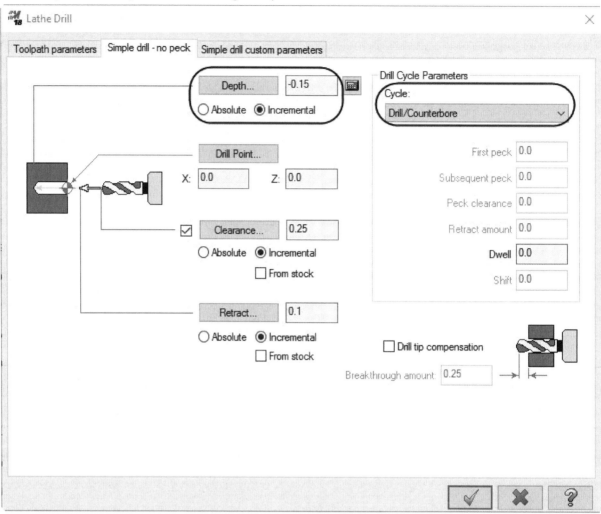

◆ Select the **OK** button to exit the **Lathe Drill** dialog box.

14.1 Backplot the toolpath

- Once the operation has been regenerated **Backplot** the toolpath.
- See **page 169** to review the procedure.

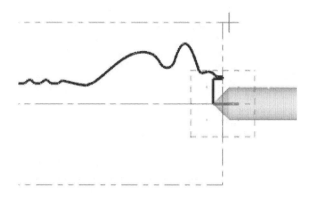

- Select the **OK** button to exit **Backplot**.

14.2 Verify the toolpaths

- To verify all toolpaths, from the **Toolpaths Manager**, choose the **Select all operations** icon.
- See **page 170** to review the procedure.

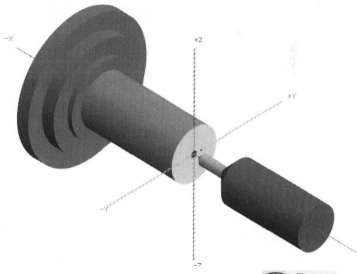

- To go back to the Mastercam window, minimize the **Mastercam Simulator** window as shown.

STEP 15: DRILL THE PART

In this step we will create another drilling operation to remove the bulk of the material on the ID in preparation for an ID roughing operation.

Toolpath Preview:

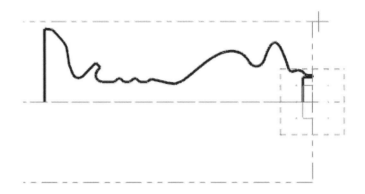

TURNING

♦ From the **General** group, select the **Drill** icon.

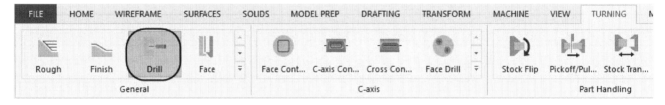

◆ Select the **0.5 Dia. End Mill** from the tool list and enter the comment as shown.

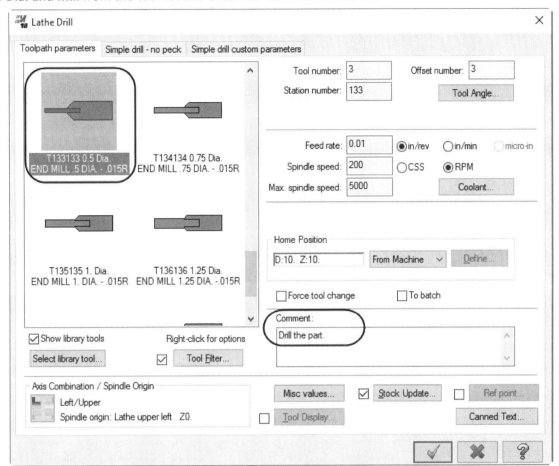

• Select the **Simple drill - no peck** tab and make the changes as shown in the graphic below.

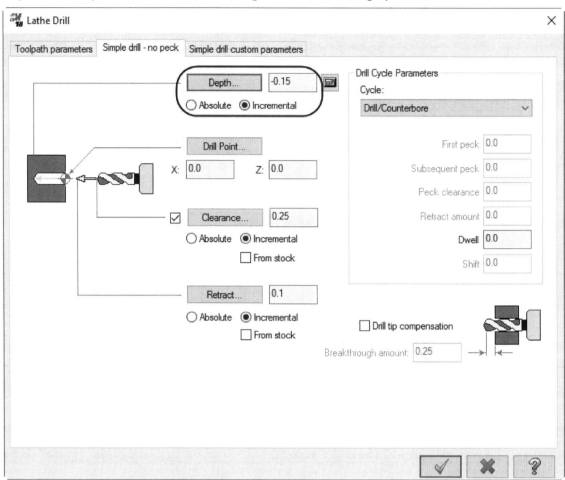

• Select the **OK** button to exit the **Lathe Drill** dialog box.

15.1 Backplot the toolpath

◆ Once the operation has been regenerated **Backplot** the toolpath.
◆ See **page 169** to review the procedure.

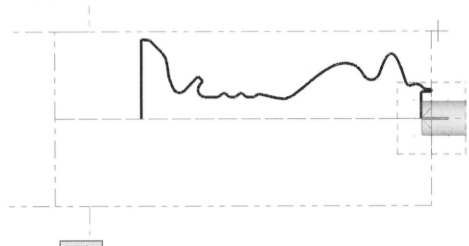

◆ Select the **OK** button to exit **Backplot**.

15.2 Verify the toolpaths

◆ To verify all toolpaths, from the **Toolpaths Manager**, choose the **Select all operations** icon.
◆ See **page 170** to review the procedure.

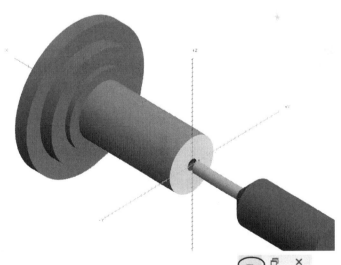

◆ To go back to the Mastercam window, minimize the **Mastercam Simulator** window as shown.

STEP 16: ROUGH THE ID USING A CANNED ROUGH TOOLPATH

Canned Rough Toolpaths allow you to enter parameters that define how the toolpath is cut in preparation for a finish operation. The dialog box displays only those parameters that are supported by your machine controller's roughing canned cycle program.

Toolpath Preview:

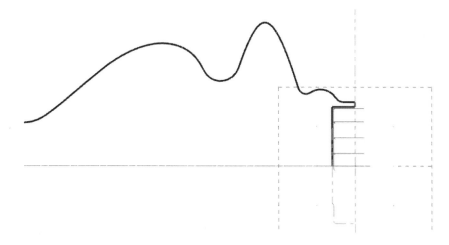

TURNING

♦ From the **General** group, click on the **Expand gallery** arrow key.

♦ From the **Canned** group, select **Rough.**

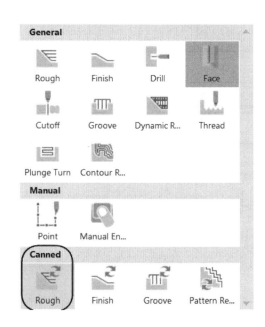

◆ Leave the default settings in the **Chaining** dialog box.

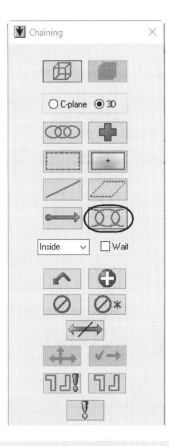

NOTE: The chaining mode is **Partial** by default. You will have to select the first entity and the last entity of the contour.

◆ Select **Entity A.**

> **NOTE:** Make sure that the chaining direction is **CCW**, otherwise select the **Reverse** button in the **Chaining** dialog box.

◆ Select **Entity B.**

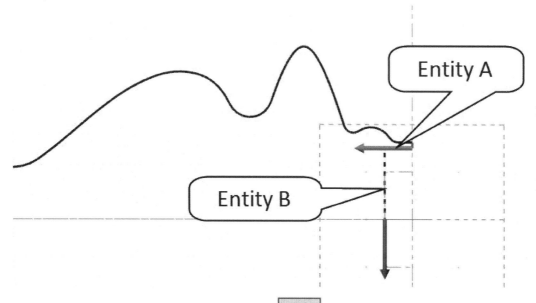

◆ Select the **OK** button to exit the **Chaining** dialog box.

◆ In the **Toolpath parameters** tab, select the **ID Rough Min. 0.25" Dia. - 75 Deg.** tool and enter the comment as shown.

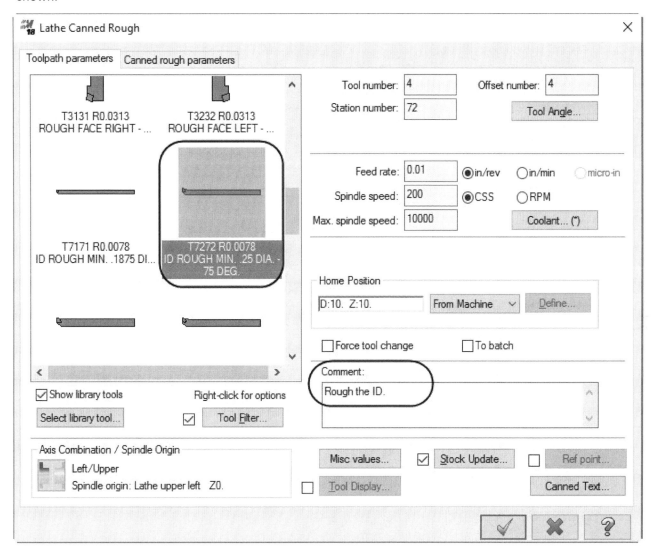

♦ Select the **Canned rough parameters** tab and make any necessary changes as shown.

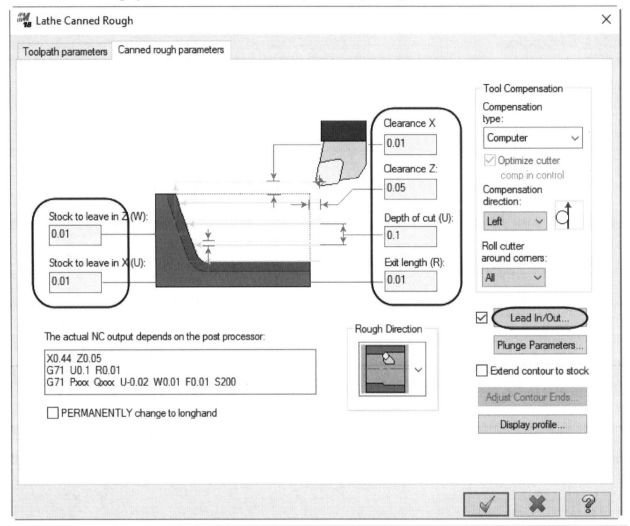

Stock to leave in Z (W) sets the remaining stock in the **Z axis** after the tool completes all passes.

Stock to leave in X (U) sets the remaining stock in the **X axis** after the tool completes all passes.

Clearance X sets the extension at the start or end of the chain in the **X** direction.

Clearance Z sets the extension at the start or end of the chain in the **Z** direction.

Depth of cut (U) sets the amount of material to be removed during each cutting pass.

Exit Length (R) sets the height of the 45 degree retract move at the end of the pass.

♦ Select the **Lead In/Out** button. In the **Lead in** tab, disable **Extend / shorten start of contour**.

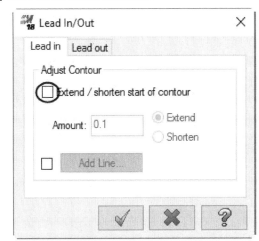

♦ Select the **Lead out** tab. Enable **Extend / shorten end of contour** and select **Shorten**. Then specify an amount of **0.23**.

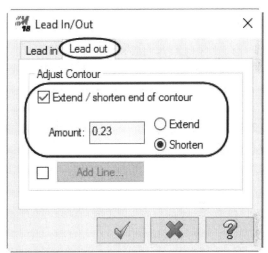

> **NOTE:** We need to shorten the contour for the lead out to make sure that the tool will not crash into the part on the next finish canned operation that uses the rough settings.

♦ Select the **OK** button to exit the **Lead In/Out** dialog box.

• Select the **Plunge Parameters** button and make sure that the parameters are set as shown.

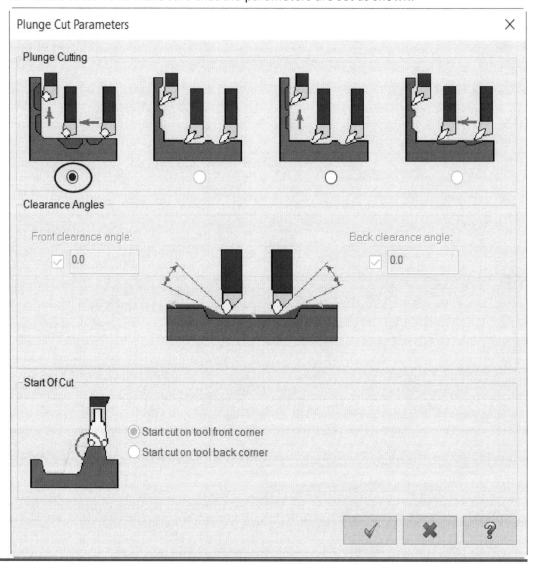

Plunge Cut Parameters sets the way the tool handles undercuts along the toolpath. The tool can plunge into undercuts in either **X**, **Z**, or both axes.

No Plunging Allowed - The tool skips over any undercuts in the chained path.

___

• Select the **OK** button to exit the **Plunge Cut Parameters** dialog box.

• Select the **OK** button to exit the **Lathe Canned Rough** dialog box.

16.1 Backplot the toolpath

• Once the operation has been regenerated, **Backplot** the toolpath.
• See **page 169** to review the procedure.

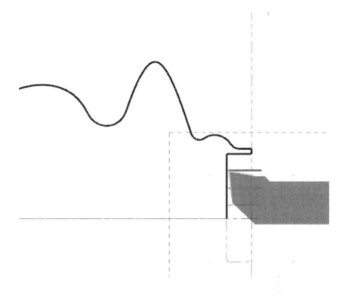

• Select the **OK** button to exit **Backplot**.

16.2 Verify the toolpaths

• To verify all toolpaths, from the **Toolpaths Manager**, choose the **Select all operations** icon.
• Select the **Verify selected operations** icon.

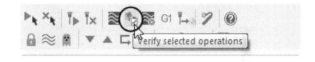

• See **page 170** to review the procedure.

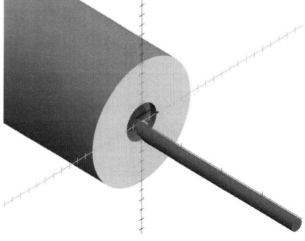

• To go back to the Mastercam window, minimize the **Mastercam Simulator** window as shown.

STEP 17: FINISH THE ID USING A CANNED FINISH TOOLPATH

Finish Toolpaths cut parallel to the part geometry, making one final cut on the part and refining the canned roughing or pattern repeat toolpath. You must have an existing canned rough or canned pattern repeat operation in order to create a canned finish toolpath.

Toolpath Preview:

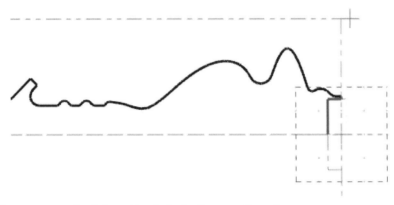

- In the **Toolpaths Manager** panel, click on the **Select all operations** icon.

- Select **Toggle display on selected operations** to turn the toolpath display off.

> **NOTE:** You can also use **Alt + T** or **T** to toggle the toolpath display on or off.

TURNING

♦ From the **General** group, select **Canned Finish**.

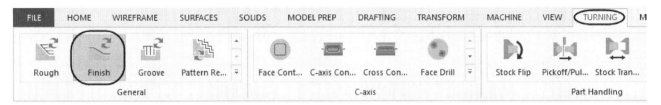

> **NOTE:** The chaining dialog box does not appear because a **Canned Finish** toolpath uses the information from the **Canned Rough** toolpath.

♦ Select the **ID Finish Min. 0.25" Dia. - 55 Degree** tool from the tool list and enter the comment as shown.

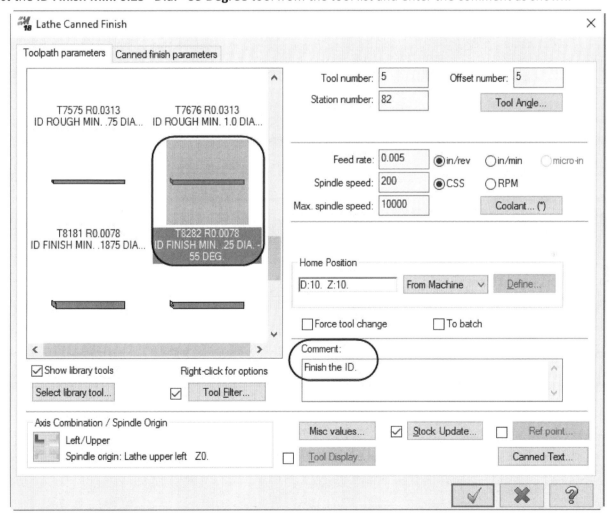

> **NOTE:** The **Feed rate** and **Spindle speed** are based on the **Mastercam Tool Definition**.

◆ Select the **Canned finish parameters** tab and make all of the necessary changes as shown.

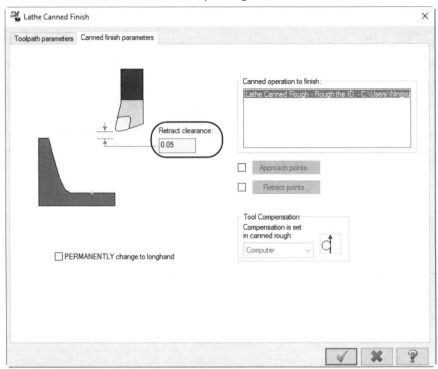

◆ Select the **OK** Button to exit the **Lathe Canned Finish** dialog box.

17.1 Backplot the toolpath

◆ Once the operation has been regenerated, **Backplot** the toolpath. See **page 169** to review the procedure.

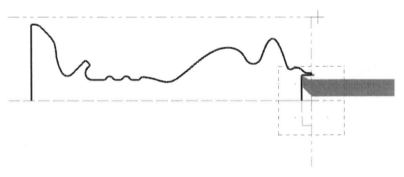

◆ Select the **OK** button to exit **Backplot**.

17.2 Verify the toolpaths

- To verify all toolpaths, from the **Toolpaths Manager**, choose the **Select all operations** icon.
- Select the **Verify selected operations** icon.

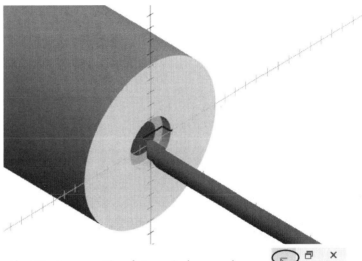

- See **page 170** to review the procedure.

- To go back to the Mastercam window, minimize the **Mastercam Simulator** window as shown.

STEP 18: ROUGH THE OD USING A ROUGH TOOLPATH

Rough Toolpaths quickly remove large amounts of stock in preparation for a finish pass. Roughing passes are typically straight cuts parallel to the **Z axis**.

Toolpath Preview:

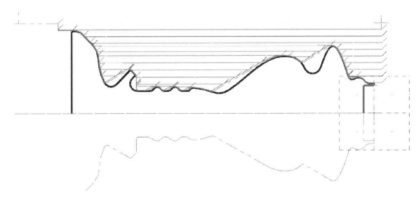

TURNING

♦ From the **General** group, select **Rough.**

♦ Leave the default settings in the **Chaining** dialog box.

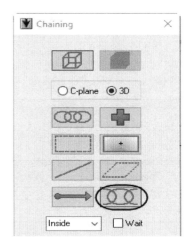

> **NOTE:** The chaining mode is **Partial** by default. You will have to select the first entity and the last entity of the contour.

> **NOTE:** To switch back to the Top view, right click in the graphics window and select **Top (WCS).**

♦ [Select the entry point or chain the inner boundary]: Select **Entity A** as shown.

> **NOTE:** Make sure that the chaining direction is **CCW**. If necessary select the **Reverse** button in the **Chaining** dialog box. ⟷

♦ [Select the last entity]: Select **Entity B** as shown.

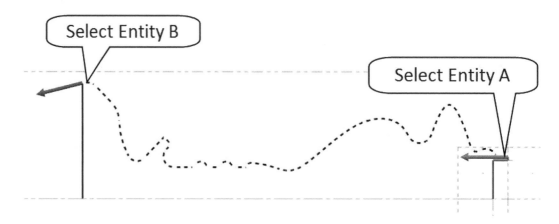

ROUGH THE OD USING A ROUGH TOOLPATH

TUTORIAL #3

- Select the **OK** button to exit the **Chaining** dialog box. ✔
- In the **Toolpath parameters** tab, select the **OD 55 Degree Right** tool and make all of the necessary changes as shown.

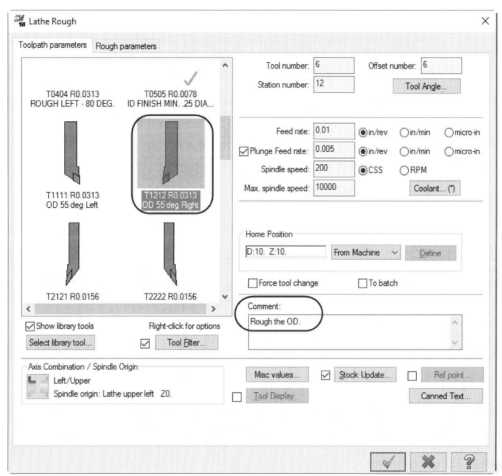

Mastercam 2018 **Lathe Training Tutorial** Page | 193

• Select the **Rough parameters** tab and make any necessary changes as shown.

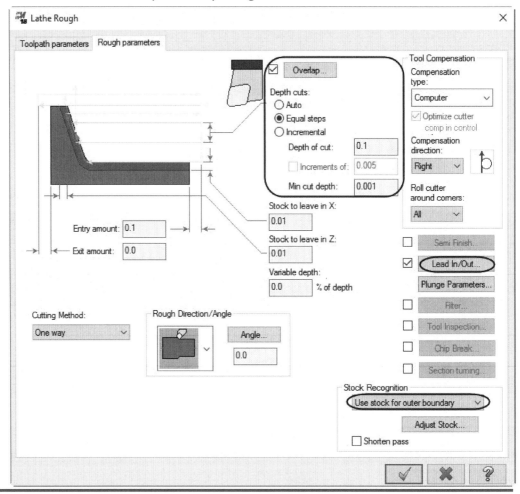

Depth of cut sets the amount of material to be removed during each cutting pass.

Equal steps sets the **Depth of cut** value to the maximum amount of material that the tool can remove at each pass to ensure equal passes.

Min cut depth sets the minimum cut that can be taken per pass.

Stock to leave in X sets the remaining stock in the **X axis** after the tool completes all passes.

Stock to leave in Z sets the remaining stock in the **Z axis** after the tool completes all passes.

Entry amount sets the height at which the tool rapids to or from the part.

Stock recognition adjusts the area of stock to be removed by the roughing operation.

Use stock for outer boundary uses a section of the stock boundary as the outer boundary.

♦ Select the **Lead In/Out** button. In the **Lead in** tab, set the **Entry Vector Angle** to **-135** degree as shown.

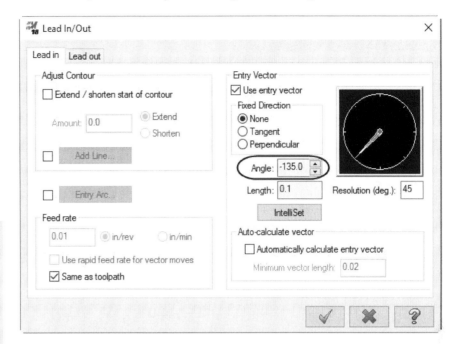

NOTE: Entry Vector allows you to create a tangent arc move or perpendicular move to start the toolpath. You can also manually define an entry/exit vector or let the system automatically calculate a vector for you.

♦ Select the **Lead out** tab and make sure the parameters are set as shown.

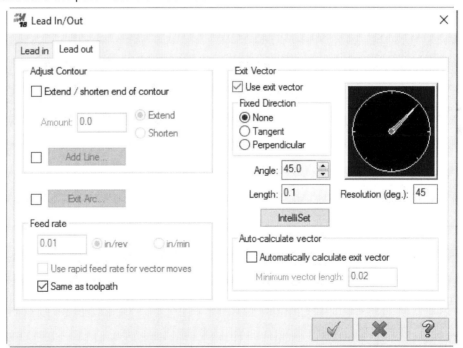

♦ Select the **OK** button to exit the **Lead In/Out** dialog box.

♦ Select the **OK** button to exit the **Lathe Rough** dialog box.

18.1 Backplot the toolpath

- Once the operation has been regenerated, **Backplot** the toolpath.
- See **page 169** to review the procedure.

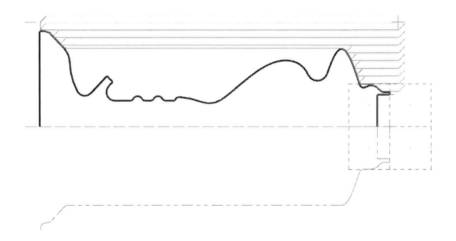

> **NOTE:** In the roughing toolpath, the tool does not plunge into undercuts along the toolpath and there is still a lot of stock left in the part. Therefore we need to go back to the **Rough Parameters** page and change the **Plunge Parameters**. Also, notice that end of the contour is not cut properly, the tool stops at certain point before reach the end point of the contour and go back to the start point agian. In order to have a better cut at the end of the chain, we need to add a line to extend the end of contour.

- Select the **OK** button to exit **Backplot**.

18.2 Change the Plunge Cutting Method

- In the **Toolpaths Manager**, click on the **Parameters** of **Lathe Rough** toolpath as shown.

- In the **Rough Parameters** page, select the **Plunge Parameters** button.

◆ Change the **Plunge Cutting** and make any necessary changes as shown.

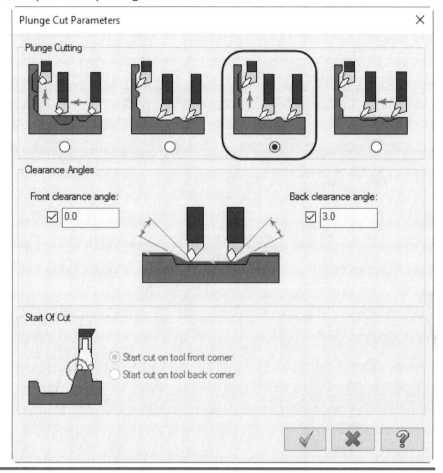

Allow plunging in relief - The tool cuts into undercuts on the side cutting edge of the insert.

Back clearance angle prevents the tool back from cutting with the entire length of the insert's back as the tool plunges to the next cut depth.

◆ Select the **OK** button to exit the **Plunge Cut Parameters** dialog box.

18.3 Add a Contour Line

◆ In the **Rough Parameters** page, select the **Lead In/Out** button.

- Selece **Lead out** tab, enable **Add Line** and click on the **Add Line** button.

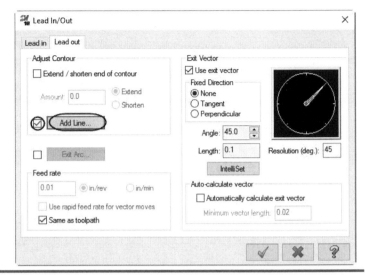

Adjust Contour allows you to extend or shorten the contour by an amount or by adding a line.

Add Line create a lead in/out move by adding a line to the chained geometry.

- The **New Contour Line** dialog box will appear. Set the **Length** to **0.2"** and the **Angle** to **180** degree.

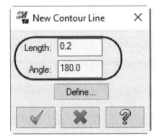

- Select the **OK** button to exit the **New Contour Line** dialog box.

- Select the **OK** button to exit the **Lead In/Out** dialog box.

- Select the **OK** button to exit the **Lathe Rough** dialog box.

18.4 Backplot the toolpath

- To update the toolpath, from the **Toolpaths Manager**, select **Regenerate all selected operations**.

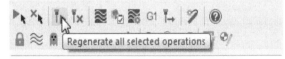

- Once the operation has been regenerated, **Backplot** the toolpath.

◆ See **page 169** to review the procedure.

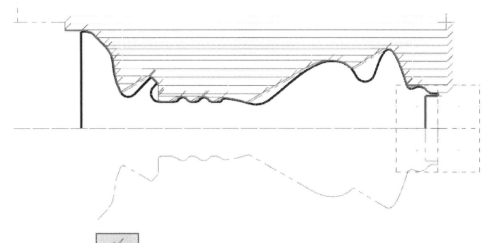

◆ Select the **OK** button to exit **Backplot**.

18.5 Verify the toolpaths

◆ To verify all toolpaths, from the **Toolpaths Manager**, choose the **Select all operations** icon.

◆ Select the **Verify selected operations** icon.

- See **page 170** to review the procedure.

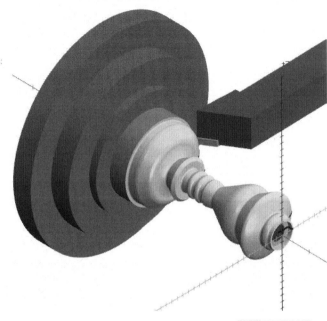

- To go back to the Mastercam window, minimize the **Mastercam Simulator** window as shown.

STEP 19: FINISH THE OD

Finish Toolpaths follow the contours of the chained geometry. Typically a finish toolpath follows a roughing toolpath.

Toolpath Preview:

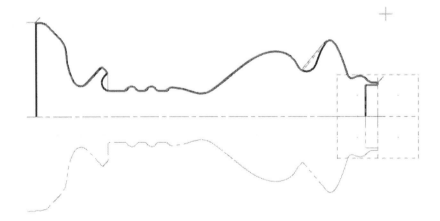

- Click on the **Select all operations** icon.

• Select the **Toggle display on selected operations** icon to turn the toolpath display off.

> **NOTE:** You can also use **Alt + T** to toggle the toolpath display on or off.

TURNING

• From the **General** group, select **Finish**.

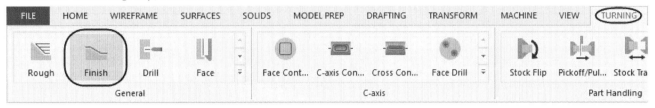

• Select the **Last** button in the **Chaining** dialog box as shown.

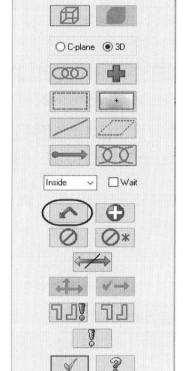

The **Last** button will automatically select the last chain that we used in the roughing toolpath.

• Select the **OK** button to exit the **Chaining** dialog box.

◆ Select the **OD Finish Right tool - 35 Degree** tool from the tool list and enter the comment as shown.

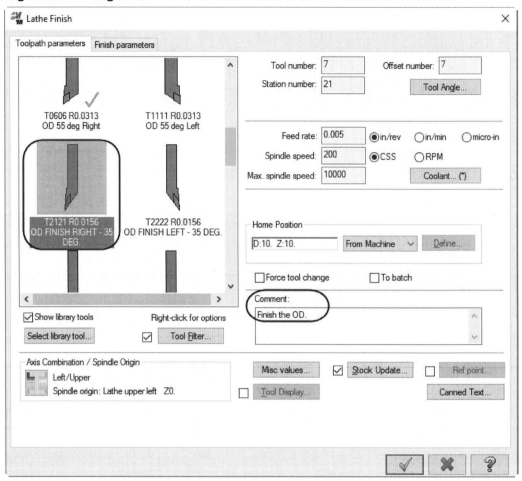

NOTE: The **Feed rate** and **Spindle speed** are based on the **Mastercam Tool Definition.**

• Select the **Finish parameters** tab and make all of the necessary changes as shown.

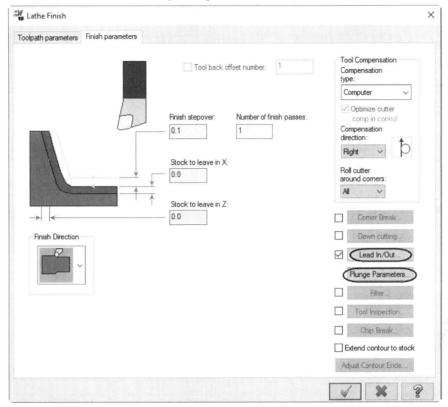

• Select the **Lead In/Out** button. In the **Lead in** page, set the **Entry Vector Angle** to **-135** degree.

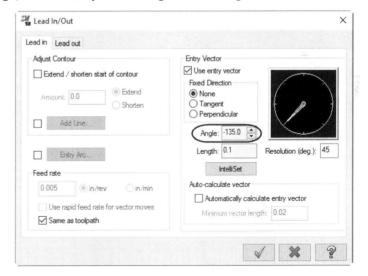

- ◆ Choose the **Lead out** tab and make any necessary changes as shown.

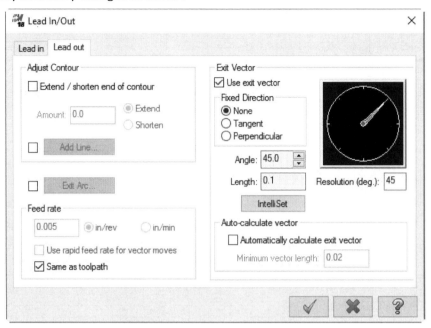

- ◆ Select the **OK** button to exit the **Lead In/Out** dialog box.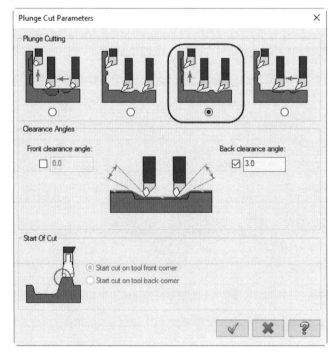
- ◆ Select the **Plunge Parameters** button and change **Plunge Cutting** as shown.

- ◆ Select the **OK** button to exit the **Plunge Cut Parameters** dialog box.

- ◆ Select the **OK** button to exit the **Finish Parameters** dialog box.

19.1 Backplot the toolpath

- Once the operation has been regenerated, **Backplot** the toolpath.
- See **page 169** to review the procedure.

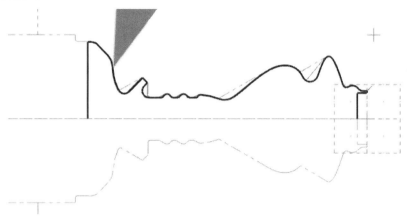

- Select the **OK** button to exit **Backplot**.

19.2 Verify the toolpaths

- To verify all toolpaths, from the **Toolpaths Manager**, choose the **Select all operations** icon.

- Select the **Verify selected operations** icon.

* See **page 170** to review the procedure.

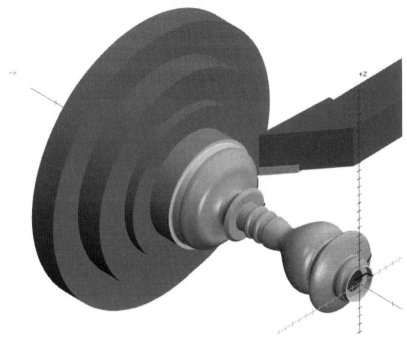

* To go back to the Mastercam window, minimize the **Mastercam Simulator** window as shown.

STEP 20: MACHINE THE GROOVE

Groove toolpaths are used for machining indented or recessed areas that cannot be machined by roughing toolpaths or tools.

Toolpath Preview:

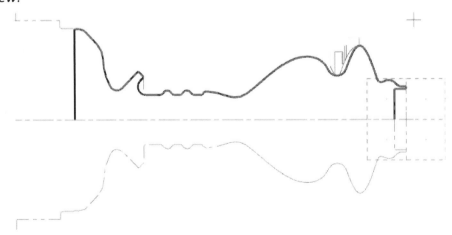

TURNING

◆ From the **General** area, click on the **Expand gallery** arrow key.

◆ Select **Groove.**

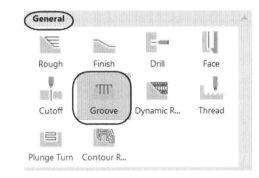

◆ Choose **Chain** when the **Grooving Options** dialog box appears.

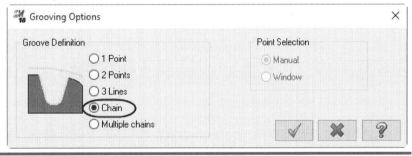

---

1 Point allows the user to select points from the graphics area to identify a groove.

2 Points allows you to specify a groove by indicating the top corner of the groove and the point in the lower opposite corner.

3 Lines allows you to select three lines from the graphics screen to define the groove shape.

Chain allows you to chain a more complex shape to define a groove by chaining on-screen geometry.

Multiple Chains allows you to chain multiple grooves by chaining on screen geometry.

Manual Point Selection allows you to manually select points from the graphics area.

Window Point Selection allows you to create a window in the graphics area and chains all of the points within the window.

◆ Select the **OK** button to exit the **Grooving Options** dialog box.

• The **Chaining** dialog box will open, leave **Partial** as the chaining method.

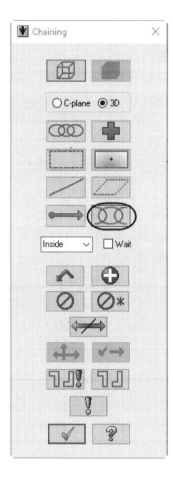

• [Select the entry point or chain the inner boundary]: Select **Entity A** as shown.
• [Select the last entity]: Select **Entity B** as your last entity of the chain for the groove as shown.

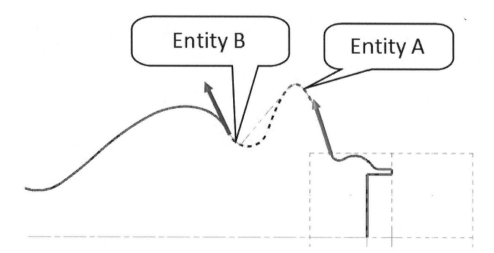

- Click on the **Expand dialog** icon to expand **Chaining** dialog box.

- The **Chaining** dialog box will be as shown. Select the **Dynamic** button to change the start point of the contour.

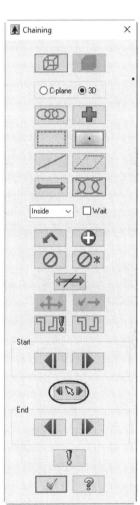

NOTE: Dynamic move allows you to move the start or end of a selected chain to any position along an entity, without restricting the start/end to an entity endpoint.

- ◆ [Select a chain arrow to move]: Select the green(start) arrow and move it to the point as shown.

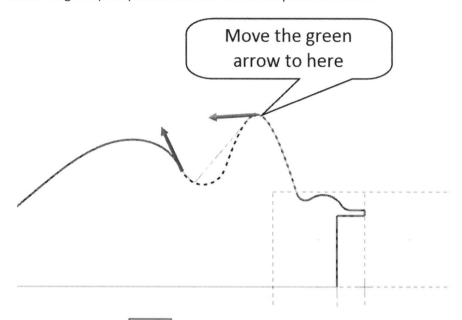

Move the green arrow to here

- ◆ Select the **OK** button to exit the **Chaining** dialog box.
- ◆ Select the **OD Groove Center Medium** tool from the tool list. Right click on the tool and select **Edit tool**.

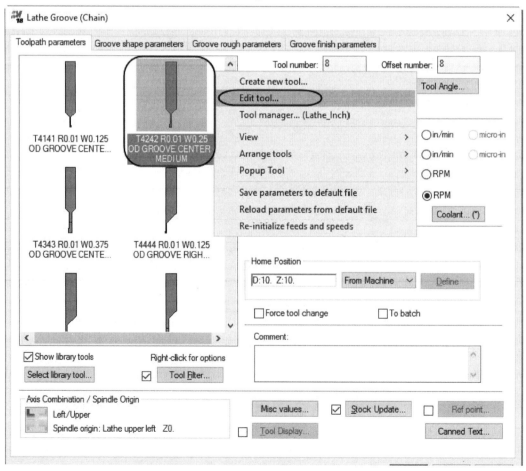

• In the **Inserts** page, change the **Style** to **Single End (radius)** and **Insert Thickness** to **0.188**. In the **Insert Geometry** section, set **B** value to **0.08** and **A** value to **0.1** .

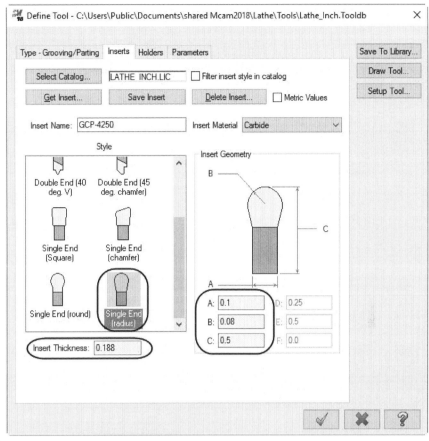

NOTE: In **Insert Geometry** area, **B** value should be entered first, because **A** value should always be less than twice of **B** value.

• Select the **Holders** page and change the **Shank Cross Section** to **0.188** and change values in **Holder Geometry.**

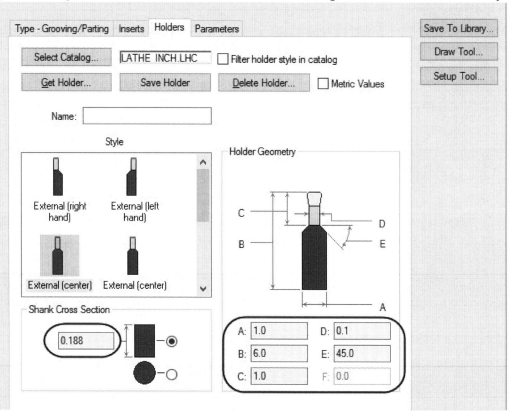

• Select the **Parameters** page, name the tool **Round Groove Rad 0.08** and change the **Compensation** type.

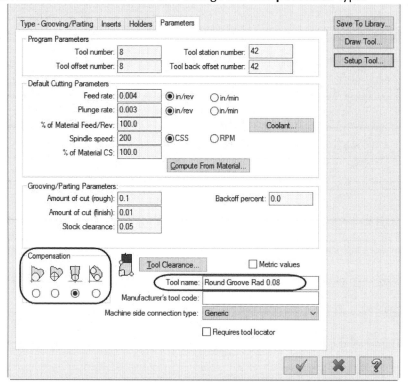

• Select the **OK** button to exit the **Define Tool** dialog box.
• The **Toolpath parameters** page should look as shown.

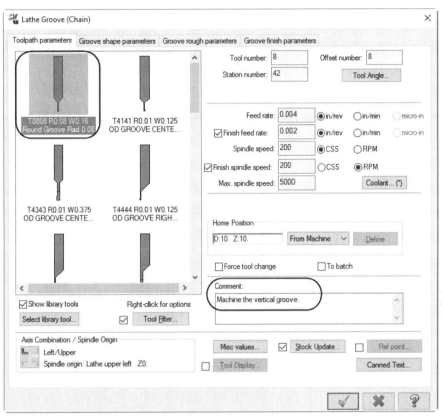

• Select the **Groove shape parameters** tab and enable **Use stock for outer boundary** as shown.

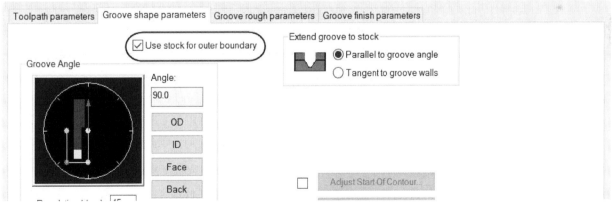

◆ Select the **Groove rough parameters** tab and make any changes as shown.

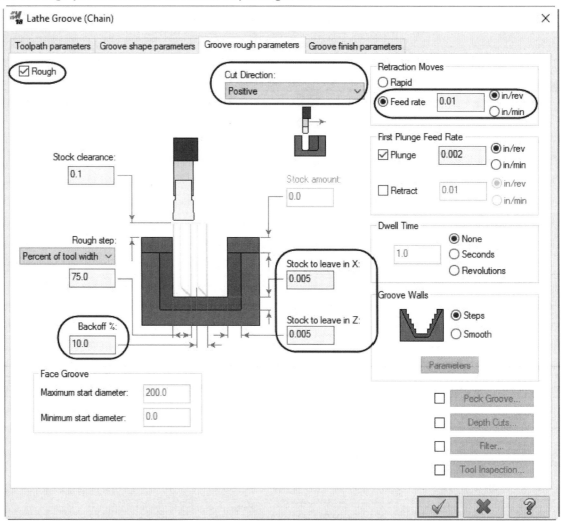

Cut Direction determines the direction that the tool will rough the groove (Positive, Negative, Bi-Directional, Alternating, Bi-Directional, Positive First, Bi-Directional, Negative First or Chain Direction).

Stock clearance determines the point up to which the tool retracts after each pass.

Stock amount sets the remaining stock left by the previous operation.

Stock to leave in X sets the remaining stock in the **X axis** after the tool completes all rough passes.

Stock to leave in Z sets the remaining stock in the **Z axis** after the tool completes all rough passes.

Rough step sets the amount of material to be removed with each roughing pass. It can be set as a number of steps, a step amount or as a percentage of the tool width.

Backoff % sets how far the tool backs away from the wall of the groove before it retracts.

• Select the **Groove finish parameters** tab and make any necessary changes as shown.

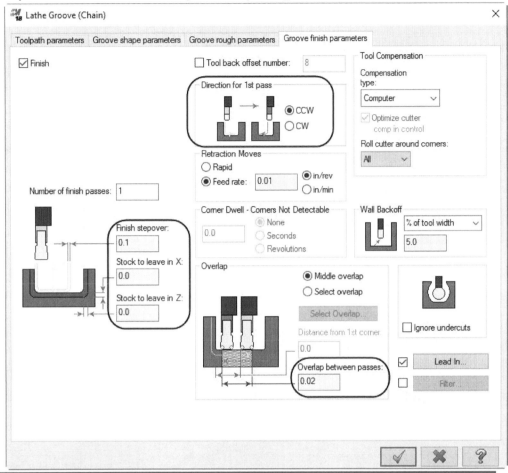

Direction for 1st pass determines the direction that the tool will finish the groove (**CCW** - starting on the right wall or **CW** - starting with the left wall.) With the first pass of a finish toolpath; the tool cuts down on one wall of the groove to the groove floor and then retracts out of the groove. On the second pass, the tool cuts down the opposite wall of the groove to the groove floor, moves across the groove floor to the point where the first pass ended.

Retraction Moves sets the retract moves to **Rapid** moves or with the **Feed rate.**

Finish stepover sets the maximum amount of material the tool will remove with the finish pass. It allows you to get a warning if you enter two tools with the same number.

Stock to leave in X sets the remaining stock in the **X axis** after the tool completes all finish passes.

Stock to leave in Z sets the remaining stock in the **Z axis** after the tool completes all finish passes.

Overlap Distance from 1st corner sets the amount the tool cuts across the floor before retracting out of the groove.

Overlap between passes sets the amount the tool overlaps the first pass before it retracts.

Wall Backoff % sets how far the tool backs away from the wall of the groove after the first pass before it retracts.

- Select the **Lead In** button and change the **First pass lead in** to **Tangent** as shown.

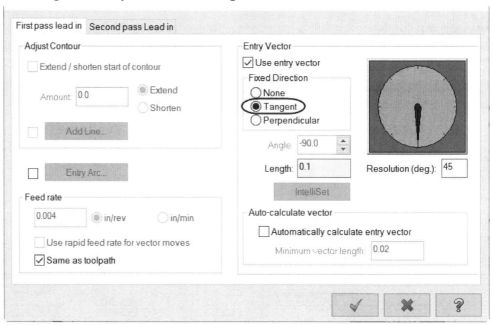

- Select the **Second pass Lead in** tab and change the entry vector to **-90°** as shown.

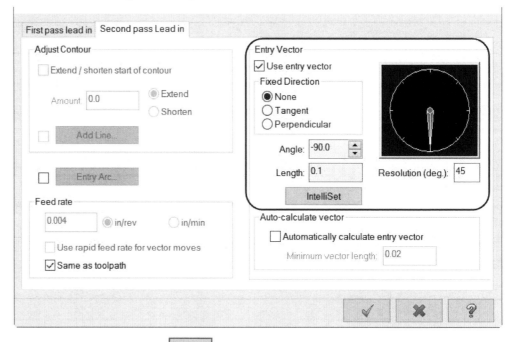

- Select the **OK** button to exit the **Lead In** dialog box.

- Select the **OK** button to exit the **Lathe Groove (Chain)** dialog box and generate the toolpath.

20.1 Backplot the toolpath

- Once the operation has been regenerated, **Backplot** the toolpath.
- See **page 169** to review the procedure.

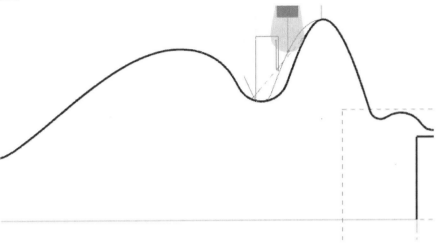

- Select the **OK** button to exit **Backplot**.

20.2 Verify the toolpaths

- To verify all toolpaths, from the **Toolpaths Manager**, choose the **Select all operations** icon.
- Select the **Verify selected operations** icon.

- See **page 170** to review the procedure.

- To go back to the Mastercam window, minimize the **Mastercam Simulator** window as shown.

STEP 21: MACHINE THE ANGLED GROOVE

Groove toolpaths are used for machining indented or recessed areas that cannot be machined by roughing toolpaths or tools.

Toolpath Preview:

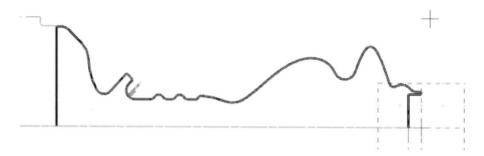

TURNING

* From the **General** group, select **Groove**.

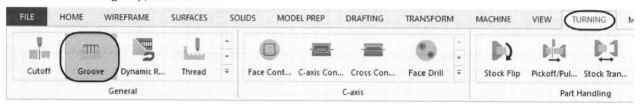

* Choose **Multiple chains** when the **Grooving Options** dialog box appears.

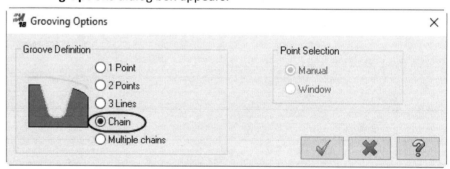

* Select the **OK** button to exit the **Grooving Options** dialog box.

• The **Chaining** dialog box will open, leave **Partial** as the chaining method.

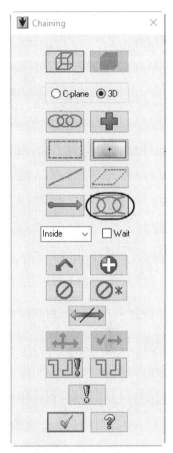

• [Select the entry point or chain the inner boundary]: Select **Entity A** as the first entity of the chain as shown.
• [Select the last entity]: Select **Entity B** as the last entity of the chain for the groove as shown.

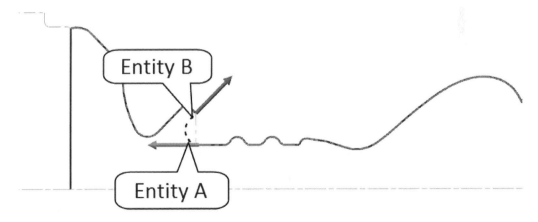

• Select the **OK** button to exit the **Chaining** dialog box.

◆ Enter a comment in the **Comment** field and right click in the tool list and select **Create new tool** as shown.

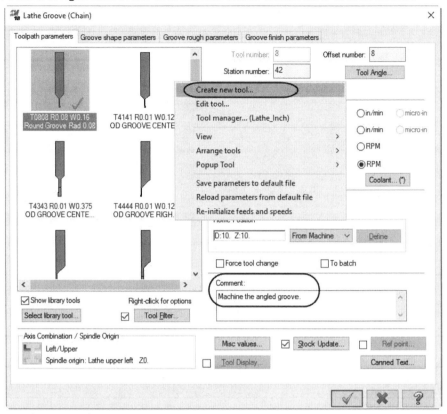

◆ Select the **Grooving/Parting** as the tool type as shown.

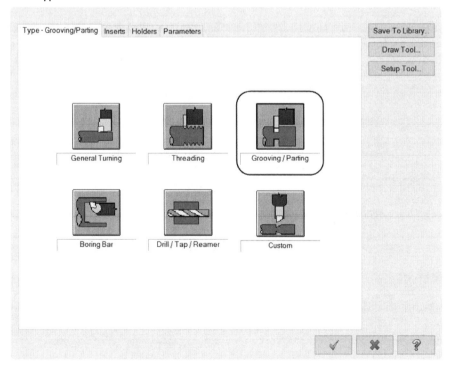

◆ The **Inserts** tab will automatically be selected. Select the **Single End (Radius)** insert and make any changes as shown in the screenshot below.

NOTE: The value for **B** in **Insert Geometry** must be entered first.

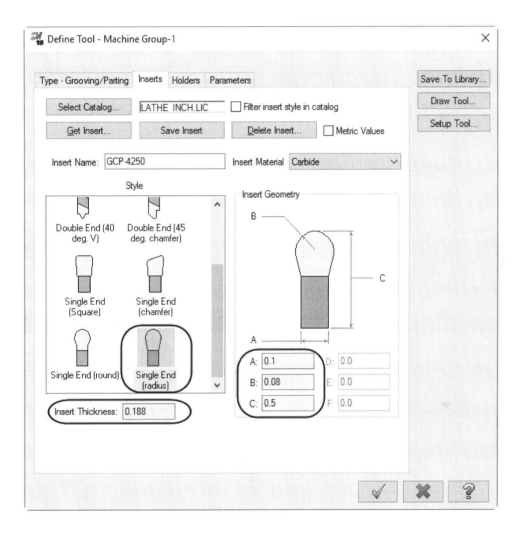

◆ Select the **Holders** tab and make all the changes as shown.

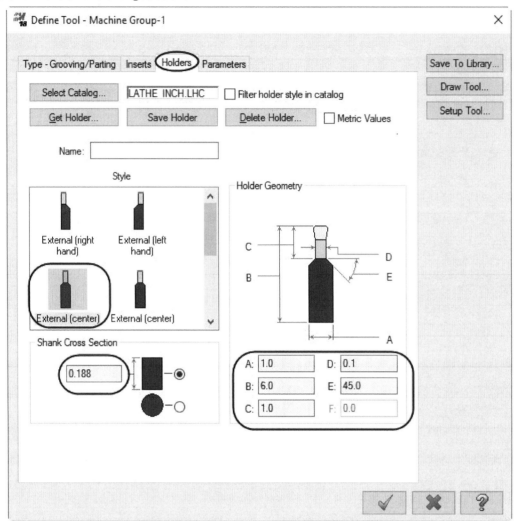

• Select the **Parameters** tab, name the tool **Round Groove Rad. 0.08 at 45 degree angle** and make the changes to the tool as shown.

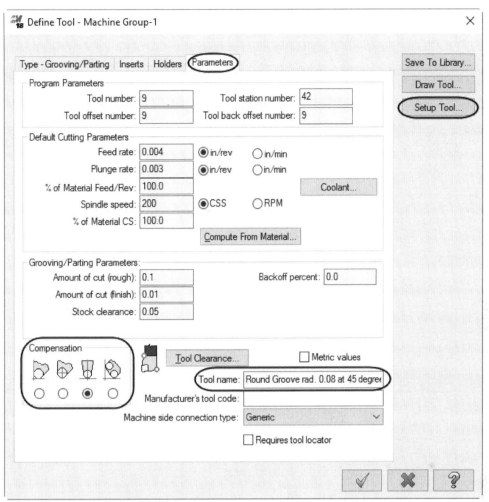

• Select the **Setup Tool** button as shown on the previous page select the **Plunge Direction** button. This will tell Mastercam at what angle the tool should machine.

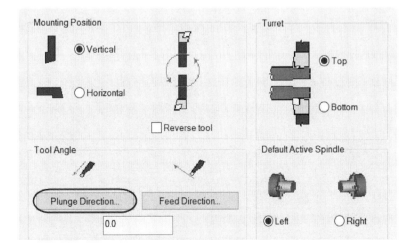

- [Select a line parallel to the plunge direction]: Select **Entity A** as shown.

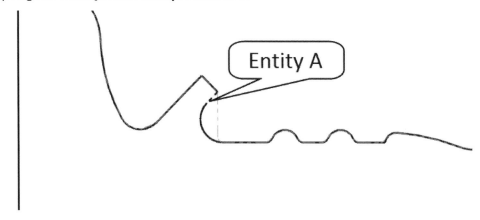

- The **Plunge Direction** should read **-45°** as shown.

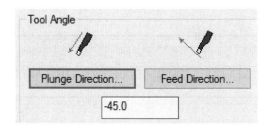

- Select the **OK** button to exit the **Lathe Tool Setup** dialog box.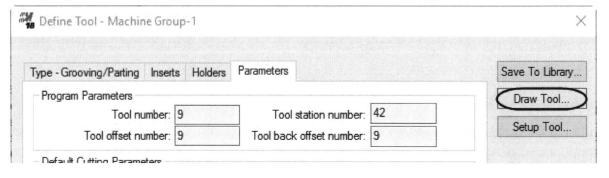
- To see a preview of how the tool looks, select the **Draw Tool** button.

◆ The preview of the tool should appear as shown.

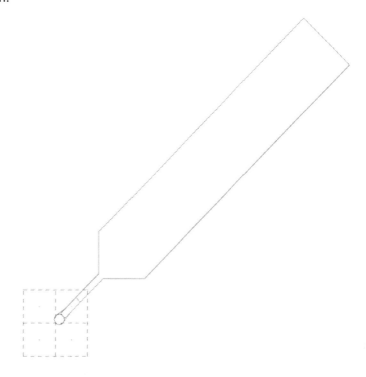

> **NOTE:** To save the tool to the library you can select the **Save to Library** button. Otherwise, the tool will be available only for this job.

◆ Press **Enter** once complete.

◆ Select the **OK** button to exit the **Define Tool** dialog box.

- Select the **Groove shape parameters** tab and enable **Use stock for outer boundary**. Note that the groove angle has been changed to **45°**.

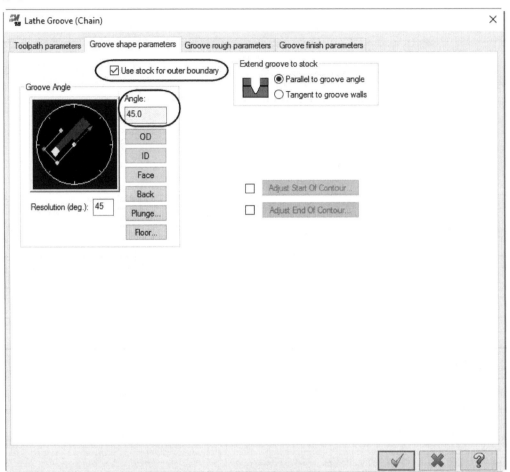

♦ Select the **Groove rough parameters** tab and make any changes as shown.

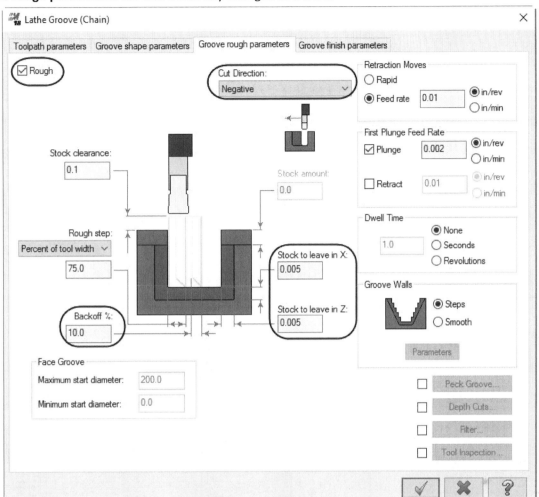

◆ Select the **Groove finish parameters** tab and make all necessary changes as shown.

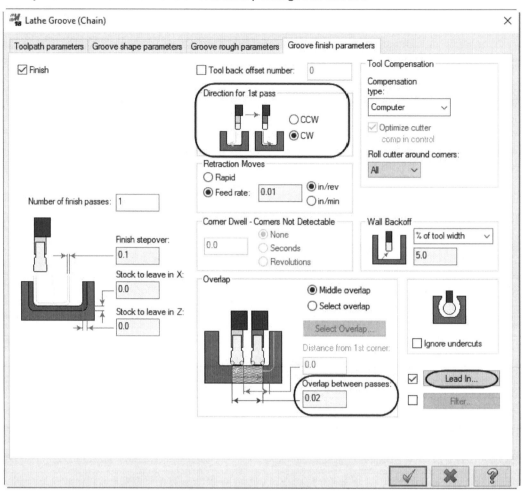

◆ Select the **Lead In** button. In the **First pass Lead in** page, make sure the parameters are set as shown.

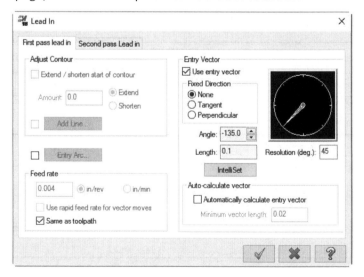

◆ Select the **Second pass Lead in** tab, change the **Angle** to **-135** degree as shown.

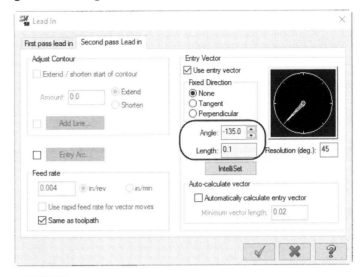

◆ Select the **OK** button to exit the **Lead In** dialog box.

◆ Select the **OK** button to exit the **Lathe Groove (Chain)** dialog box and generate the toolpath.

21.1 Backplot the toolpath

◆ Once the operation has been regenerated, **Backplot** the toolpath. See **page 169** to review the relevant procedure.

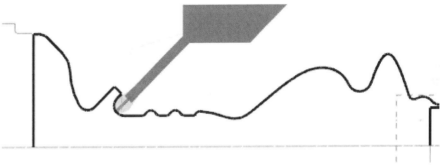

◆ Select the **OK** button to exit **Backplot**.

21.2 Verify the toolpaths

• To verify all toolpaths, from the **Toolpaths Manager**, choose the **Select all operations** icon. See **page 170** to review the relevant procedure.

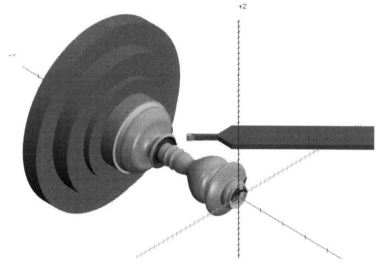

• To go back to the Mastercam window, minimize the **Mastercam Simulator** window as shown.

STEP 22: CUTOFF THE PART

Lathe Cutoff Toolpaths vertically cut off pieces of the part such as sections of bar stock.

Toolpath Preview:

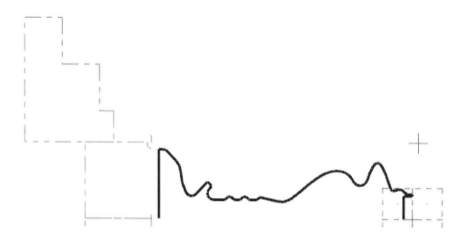

TURNING

♦ From the **General** group, select the **Cutoff** icon.

♦ [Select cutoff boundary point]: Select **Endpoint A** as shown.

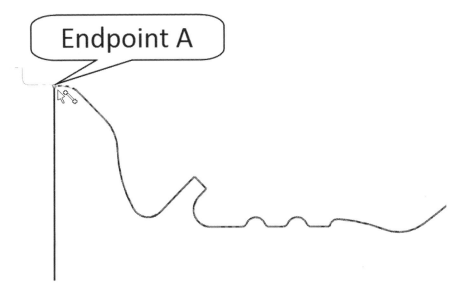

• Scroll to the bottom of the tool list and choose the **OD Cutoff Right** tool and enter the comment as shown.

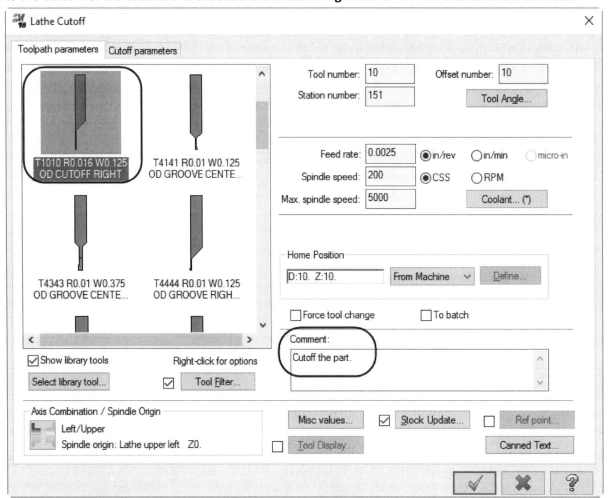

● Select the **Cutoff parameters** tab and make any necessary changes to match the screenshot below.

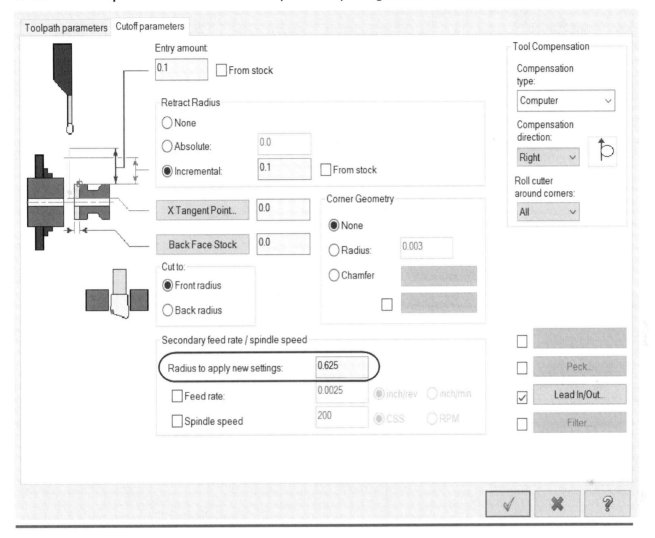

Retract Radius sets the distance from the stock where the tool starts with the feed rate.

X Tangent Point sets the distance as a radius value up to which the tool cuts to.

Cut to: determines if the center of the **Front Radius** or **Back Radius** is going to reach the final depth.

Corner Geometry parameters allow you to create a chamfer or radius on the corner of the part.

● Select the **OK** button to exit the **Lathe Cutoff** dialog box.

22.1 Backplot the toolpath

- Once the operation has been regenerated, **Backplot** the toolpath.
- See **page 169** to review the relevant procedure.

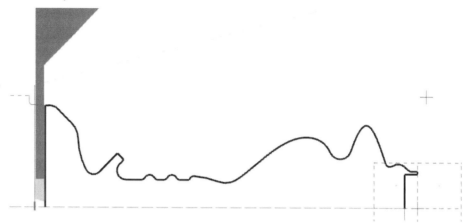

- Select the **OK** button to exit **Backplot**.

22.2 Verify the toolpaths

- To verify all toolpaths, from the **Toolpaths Manager**, choose the **Select all operations** icon.
- Select the **Verify selected operations** icon.

- See **page 170** to review the procedure.

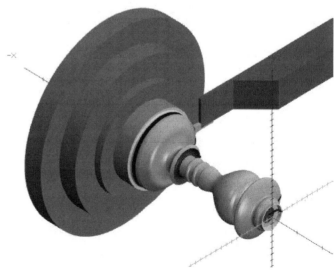

- To exit the **Mastercam Simulator** click on the **Close** icon.

STEP 23: RUN THE POST PROCESSOR TO OBTAIN THE G-CODE FILE

Post Processing refers to the process by which the toolpaths in your Mastercam part files are converted to a format that can be understood by your machine tool's control. A special program reads your Mastercam file and writes the appropriate NC code.

* Make sure that all operations are selected, otherwise click on the **Select all operations** icon.
* Select the **Post selected operations** icon from the **Toolpaths Manager.**

* In the **Post processing** dialog box, make any necessary changes as shown below.

NC File enabled allows you to keep the NC file and to assign the same name as the MCAM file.

Edit enabled allows you to automatically launch the default editor.

* Select the **OK** button to continue.
* Save the NC file.

• The **Mastercam Code Expert** window will be launched and the NC program will appear as shown.

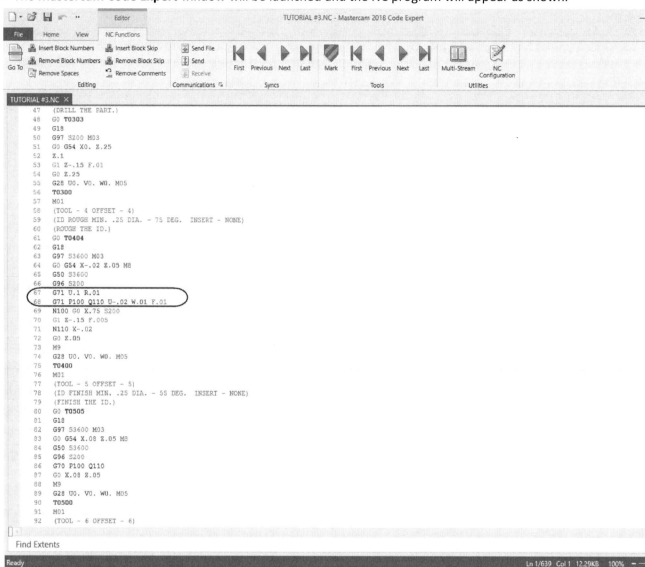

• You can see the canned cycle **G71** in the **G-code**.
• Select the **"X"** box at the upper right corner to exit the editor.

STEP 24: SAVE THE UPDATED MCAM FILE

REVIEW EXERCISE - STUDENT PRACTICE

IMPORT THE GEOMETRY FOR TUTORIAL #3 EXERCISE

Import the Parasolid file.
* Use **File Open** and make sure that you change the file extension to Parasolid files.

Create the turn profile geometry.
* In the **Plane Manager** change the **WCS** to the **Top** plane.
* Use the **Levels Manager** to create a new level and make the new level the **Main Level.**
* **Turn Profile**.

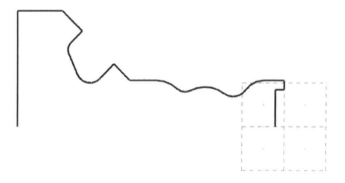

CREATE THE TOOLPATHS FOR TUTORIAL #3 EXERCISE

Create the Toolpaths for the Tutorial #3 Exercise as per the instructions below.

Set the machine properties including the stock.

Face and Drill the part

* Use the stock setup to define the face operation.
* Use the **OD Rough Right** Tool for facing operations.
* Use **0.75 Diameter Spot Drill** Tool to center drill the part.
* Use **0.75 Diameter End Mill** Tool to drill the part to a depth of 0.1.

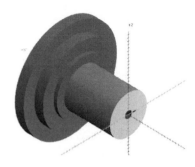

Rough and Finish the ID using a canned rough toolpath

* Use the **ID Rough Min. 0.375 Diameter** Tool for the canned rough operation.
* Set **Clearance X** and **Clearance Z** to **0.01**.
* Change the **Rough Direction**.
* Set the **Lead In/Out** page.
* Use the **ID Finish 0.5 Diameter** Tool for the canned finish operation.
* Set **Retract Clearance** to **0.05**.

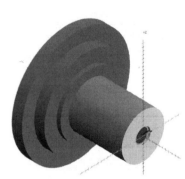

Rough and Finish the OD

* Use the **OD Right 55 Degree** Tool for the roughing operation.
* Use the **OD Finish Right 35 Degree** Tool for the finish operation.
* Change the **Plunge Cut Parameters**.
* Set the **Lead In/Out** page.
* Extend the ends of the contour with **Lead In/Lead Out** so the tool machines beyond the end of the part.

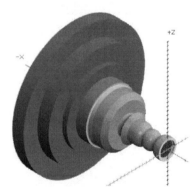

Machine the groove on an angle.

* Chain the groove.
* Set up the roughing tool so that it machines the groove on the correct angle.
* Create a custom round tool with the tool radius equal to the smaller fillet size to finish the groove.
* **Use stock for outer boundary**.

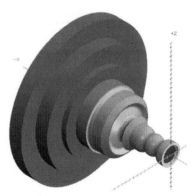

Cutoff the part.

• Choose the top left hand corner of the part as the cutoff boundary.
• Select the **OD Cutoff Right** tool.
• Select an appropriate depth to machine to.

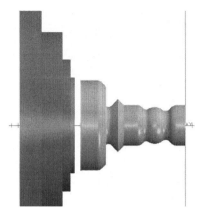

NOTES:

TUTORIAL #3 QUIZ

◆ Why would you use a canned rough cycle?

◆ What type of toolpath must precede a canned finish cycle?

◆ Where can you modify the groove angle?

TUTORIAL #4

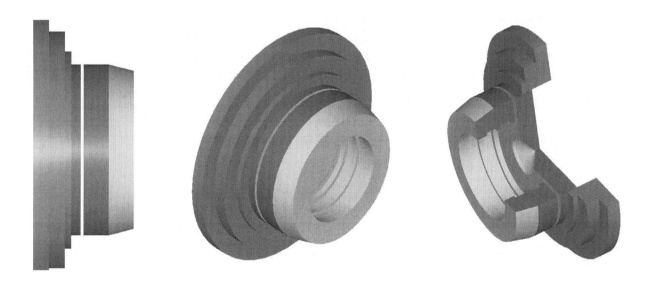

OVERVIEW OF STEPS TAKEN TO CREATE THE FINAL PART:

From drawing to CAD model:
* From the drawing we can gain an idea of how to create the geometry in Mastercam.
* The student will need to create geometry that will be used to machine the ID and OD of the part.
* The drawing should be created the specified distance away from the origin.

Create the 2D CAD Model used to generate toolpaths from:
* The student will create the upper profile of the part. Only half of the geometry is needed to create the necessary toolpaths to machine the part.
* Simple geometry commands will be used to create the profile.
* The student will break some geometry to help create a groove toolpath.

Create the necessary toolpaths to machine the part:
* The student will face the part, then rough and finish the OD.
* The student will drill the part to remove the bulk of the material, then rough, finish, and groove the ID.
* A Cutoff toolpath will complete the toolpaths.

Backplot and Verify the file:
* The Backplot will be used to simulate a step by step process of the tool's movements.
* The Verify will be used to watch a tool machine the part out of a solid model.

Post Process the file to generate the G-code:
* The student will then post process the file to obtain an NC file containing the necessary code for the machine.

 This tutorial takes approximately thirty minutes to complete.

TITLE: TUTORIAL #4

MATERIAL: ALUMINUM 6061

www.emastercam.com

ALL DIMENSIONS IN INCHES

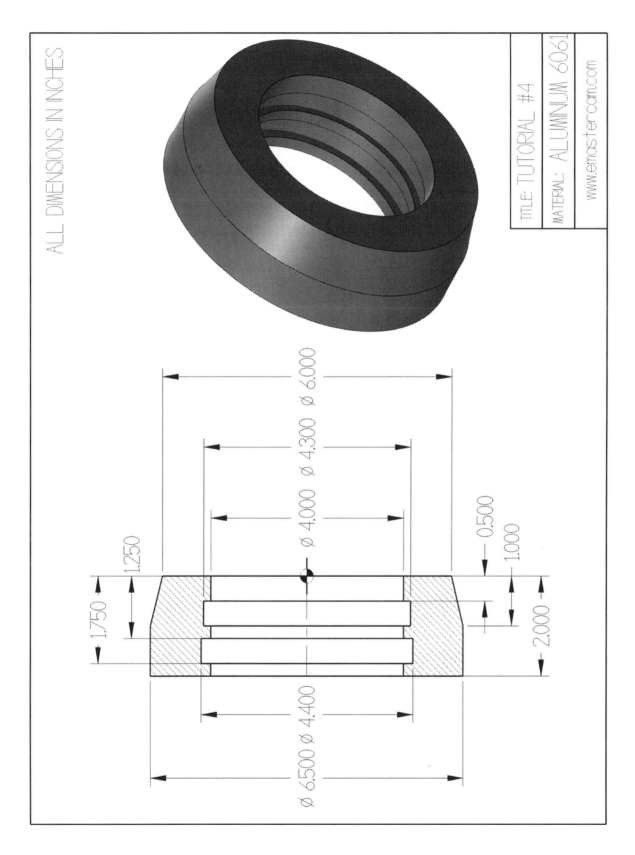

Ø 6.000

Ø 4.300

Ø 4.000

0.500

1.000

2.000

1.250

1.750

Ø 6.500 Ø 4.400

GEOMETRY CREATION

STEP 1: SETTING UP THE GRAPHIC USER INTERFACE

Please refer to the **Getting Started** section to set up the graphical user interface accordingly.

STEP 2: CREATE A RECTANGLE TO REPRESENT THE OUTSIDE PROFILE

In this step you will create a rectangle to represent the profile of the part. In later steps we will create lines parallel to the rectangle and trim them together.

Step Preview:

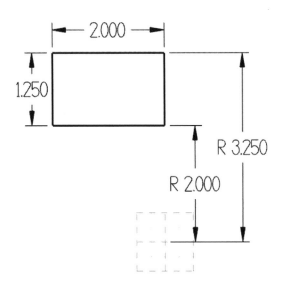

2.1 Set the Construction plane and Tool plane to +D +Z

* To set the **Construction plane** and **Tool plane** to **+D +Z** see **page 78**.

2.2 Create a 2.0" by 1.25" rectangle

WIREFRAME

• From the **Shape** group, select **Rectangle**.

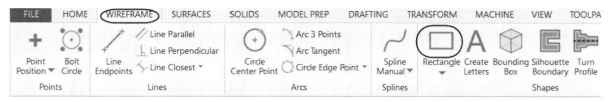

• Enter the **Width** then press tab on your keyboard and enter the **Height** as shown (**Enter**).

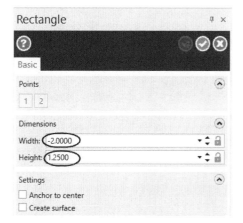

• [Specify the first endpoint]: Press the **Space bar** from the keyboard or select the **AutoCursor Fast Point** icon from the **General Selection** toolbar and the field where you can type the coordinates will open at the upper left corner of the graphics window as shown.

• Enter in the coordinates **4, 0** (**Enter**).

> **NOTE:** When working with the **+D +Z** plane, enter in the coordinates in this order (D,Z).

• Select the **OK** button to exit the command.
• Press **Alt + F1** to fit the geometry to the graphics window.

* Scroll down on the mouse wheel to see the **Origin** as shown.

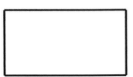

* Press **Alt + F1** to fit the geometry to the graphics window.

> **NOTE:** While creating the geometry for this tutorial, if you make a mistake, you can undo the last step using the **Undo** icon.   You can undo as many steps as needed. If you delete or undo a step by mistake, just use the **Redo** icon.
>
> To delete unwanted geometry, select the geometry first and then press **Delete** from the keyboard.

STEP 3: CREATE PARALLEL LINES

In this step we will create parallel lines to be used as construction lines.

Step Preview:

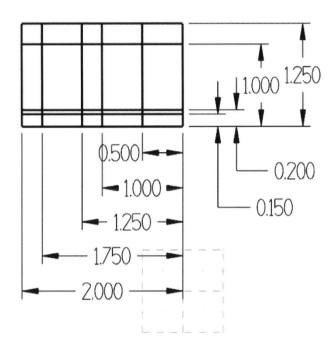

3.1 Create the horizontal lines

WIREFRAME

• From the **Lines** group, select **Line Parallel**.

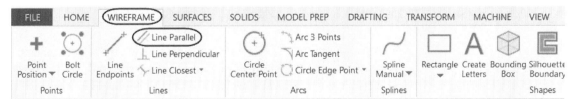

* [Select a line]: Select **Entity A** as shown in <u>Figure: 3.1.1</u>.

Figure: 3.1.1

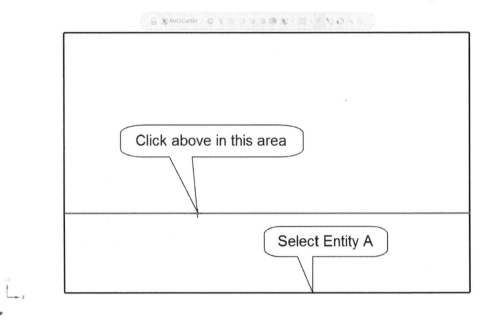

* [Select the point to place a parallel line through]: Pick a point above the line we just selected as shown in <u>Figure: 3.1.1</u>.
* Enter the **Offset Distance 0.15**.
* Press **Enter** to position the line.

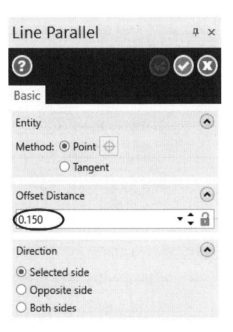

- [Select a line]: Select the same **Entity A** as shown in Figure: 3.1.1.
- [Select the point to place a parallel line through]: Pick a point above the line we just selected as shown in Figure: 3.1.1.
- Enter the **Offset Distance 0.2**.

- Press **Enter** to position the line.
- [Select a line]: Select **Entity A** as shown in Figure: 3.1.1.
- [Select the point to place a parallel line through]: Pick a point above the line we just selected as shown in Figure: 3.1.1.
- Enter the **Offset Distance 1.0**.

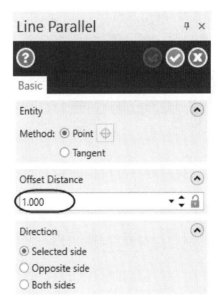

- Press **Enter** to position the line.
- Press **Enter** to stay within the command.

• The part should appear as shown in <u>Figure: 3.1.2</u>.

Figure: 3.1.2

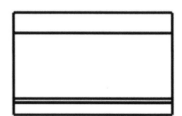

3.2 Create the vertical lines

• [Select a line]: Select **Entity B** as shown in <u>Figure: 3.2.1</u>.

Figure: 3.2.1

Click to the left

Select Entity B

- [Select the point to place a parallel line through]: Pick a point to the left of **Entity B** as shown in <u>Figure: 3.2.1</u>.
- Enter the **Distance 0.5**.

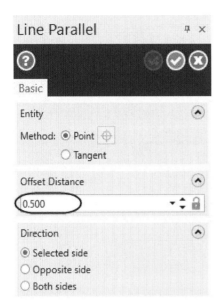

- Press **Enter** to position the line.
- [Select a line]: Select **Entity B** as shown in <u>Figure: 3.2.1</u>.
- [Select the point to place a parallel line through]: Pick a point to the left of **Entity B** as shown in <u>Figure: 3.2.1</u>.
- Enter the **Distance 1.0 (Enter)**.

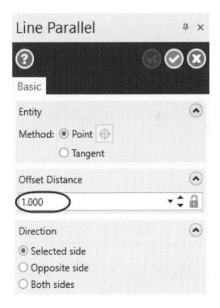

- Press **Enter** to position the line.
- [Select a line]: Select **Entity B** as shown in <u>Figure: 3.2.1</u>.
- [Select the point to place a parallel line through]: Pick a point to the left of **Entity B** as shown in <u>Figure: 3.2.1</u>.

• Enter the **Distance 1.25**.

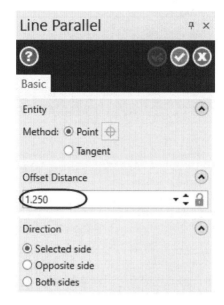

• Press **Enter** to position the line.
• [Select a line]: Select **Entity B** as shown in <u>Figure: 3.2.1</u>.
• [Select the point to place a parallel line through]: Pick a point to the left of **Entity B** as shown in <u>Figure: 3.2.1</u>.
• Enter the **Distance 1.75**.

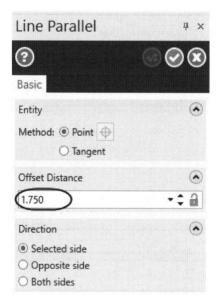

• Press **Enter** to position the line.

• Select the **OK** button to exit the command.

◆ The part should appear as shown in <u>Figure: 3.2.2</u>.

Figure: 3.2.2

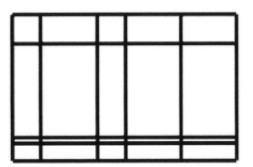

STEP 4: CREATE A LINE GIVEN THE ENDPOINTS

In this step we will create an angled line given the endpoints.

Step Preview:

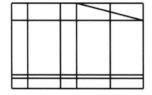

WIREFRAME

* From the **Lines** group, select **Line Endpoints**.

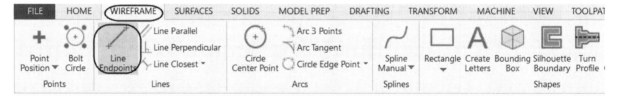

* [Specify the first endpoint]: Select **Endpoint A** as shown.
* [Specify the second endpoint]: Select **Endpoint B** as shown.

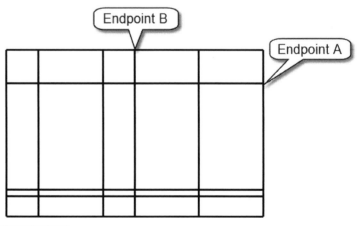

* Select the **OK** button to exit the command.

STEP 5: DELETE THE CONSTRUCTION LINE

In this step we will delete the construction line that was used in step 4. This will reduce the amount of unnecessary geometry on the screen.

Step Preview:

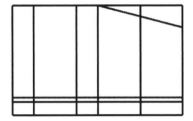

• Select **Entity A** as shown below.

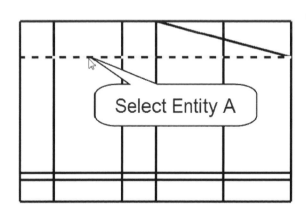

• Press the **Delete** key from the keyboard.

STEP 6: TRIM THE GEOMETRY

In this step we will use the **Trim Break Extend** command to trim the geometry.

Step Preview:

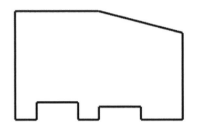

6.1 Use the Divide/delete command

WIREFRAME

• From the **Modify** group, select **Trim Break Extend**.

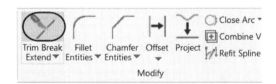

♦ Enable the **Divide/delete** button.

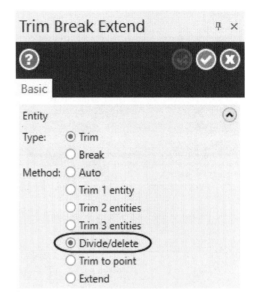

NOTE: When using the **Divide/delete** command, ensure you select the portion of the line you wish to delete. The entity will be trimmed up to an intersection point.

♦ [Select the curve to divide / delete]: Click on the line at the point shown below to delete the line up to its intersection points as shown.

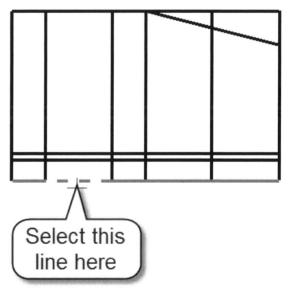

Select this line here

♦ [Select the curve to divide / delete]: Click on the line at the point shown below to delete the line up to its intersection points as shown.

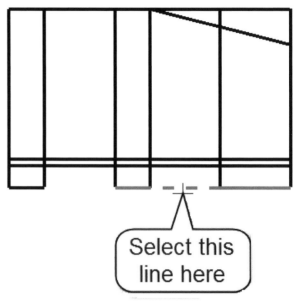

Select this line here

♦ The part should appear as shown in Figure: 6.1.1.

Figure: 6.1.1

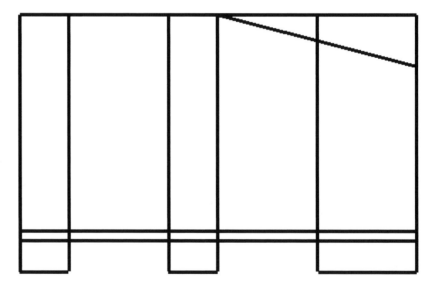

♦ Enable the **Trim 2 entities** button.

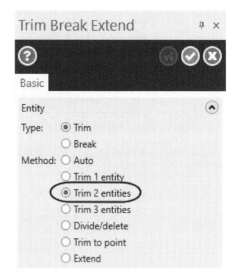

NOTE: Ensure you select the lines on or close to the points shown below to achieve the proper result.

♦ [Select the entity to trim/extend]: Select **Entity A** as shown in Figure: 6.1.2.
♦ [Select the entity to trim/extend to]: Select **Entity B** as shown in Figure: 6.1.2.
♦ [Select the entity to trim/extend]: Select **Entity B** as shown in Figure: 6.1.2.
♦ [Select the entity to trim/extend to]: Select **Entity C** as shown in Figure: 6.1.2.

Figure: 6.1.2

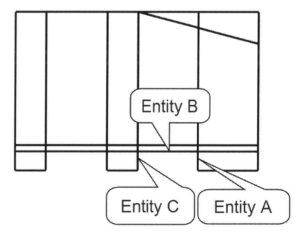

- [Select the entity to trim/extend]: Select **Entity D** as shown in <u>Figure: 6.1.3</u>.
- [Select the entity to trim/extend to]: Select **Entity E** as shown in <u>Figure: 6.1.3</u>.
- [Select the entity to trim/extend]: Select **Entity E** as shown in <u>Figure: 6.1.3</u>.
- [Select the entity to trim/extend to]: Select **Entity F** as shown in <u>Figure: 6.1.3</u>.

Figure: 6.1.3

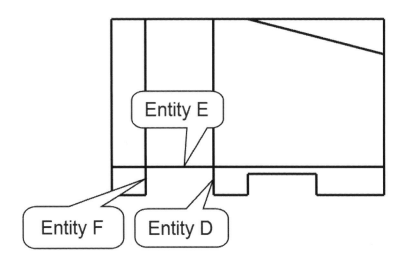

- [Select the entity to trim/extend]: Select **Entity G** as shown in <u>Figure: 6.1.4</u>.
- [Select the entity to trim/extend to]: Select **Entity H** as shown in <u>Figure: 6.1.4</u>.
- [Select the entity to trim/extend]: Select **Entity H** as shown in <u>Figure: 6.1.4</u>.
- [Select the entity to trim/extend to]: Select **Entity I** as shown in <u>Figure: 6.1.4</u>.

Figure: 6.1.4

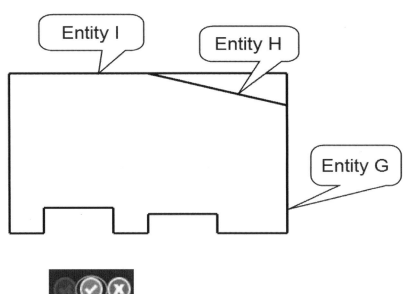

- Select the **OK** button to exit the command.

• The part should appear as shown in Figure: 6.1.5.

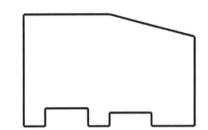

Figure: 6.1.5

STEP 7: SAVE THE FILE

FILE
• **Save As.**

• Click on the **Browse** icon as shown.
• Find a location on the computer to save your file.
• File name: "Your Name_4".

TOOLPATH CREATION

PART SETUP:

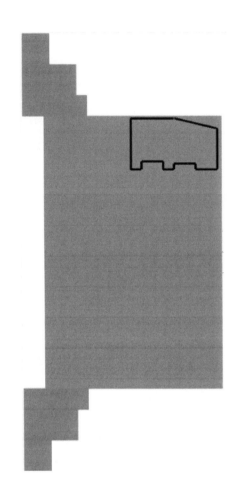

Mastercam. 2018

SETUP SHEET:

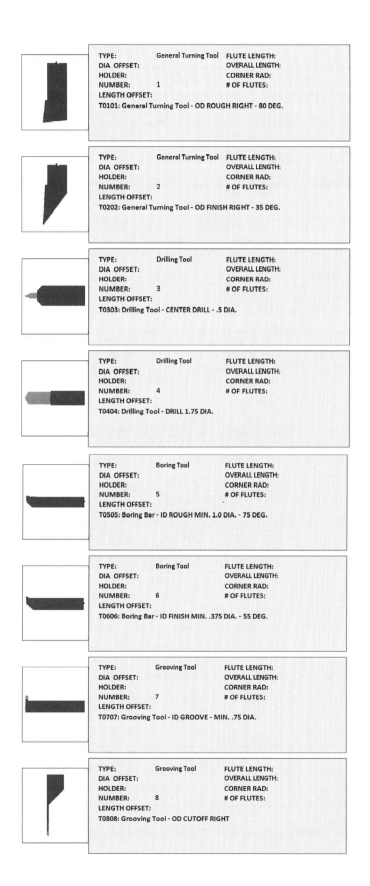

TYPE: General Turning Tool   FLUTE LENGTH:
DIA OFFSET: OVERALL LENGTH:
HOLDER: CORNER RAD:
NUMBER: 1   # OF FLUTES:
LENGTH OFFSET:
T0101: General Turning Tool - OD ROUGH RIGHT - 80 DEG.

TYPE: General Turning Tool   FLUTE LENGTH:
DIA OFFSET: OVERALL LENGTH:
HOLDER: CORNER RAD:
NUMBER: 2   # OF FLUTES:
LENGTH OFFSET:
T0202: General Turning Tool - OD FINISH RIGHT - 35 DEG.

TYPE: Drilling Tool   FLUTE LENGTH:
DIA OFFSET: OVERALL LENGTH:
HOLDER: CORNER RAD:
NUMBER: 3   # OF FLUTES:
LENGTH OFFSET:
T0303: Drilling Tool - CENTER DRILL - .5 DIA.

TYPE: Drilling Tool   FLUTE LENGTH:
DIA OFFSET: OVERALL LENGTH:
HOLDER: CORNER RAD:
NUMBER: 4   # OF FLUTES:
LENGTH OFFSET:
T0404: Drilling Tool - DRILL 1.75 DIA.

TYPE: Boring Tool   FLUTE LENGTH:
DIA OFFSET: OVERALL LENGTH:
HOLDER: CORNER RAD:
NUMBER: 5   # OF FLUTES:
LENGTH OFFSET:
T0505: Boring Bar - ID ROUGH MIN. 1.0 DIA. - 75 DEG.

TYPE: Boring Tool   FLUTE LENGTH:
DIA OFFSET: OVERALL LENGTH:
HOLDER: CORNER RAD:
NUMBER: 6   # OF FLUTES:
LENGTH OFFSET:
T0606: Boring Bar - ID FINISH MIN. .375 DIA. - 55 DEG.

TYPE: Grooving Tool   FLUTE LENGTH:
DIA OFFSET: OVERALL LENGTH:
HOLDER: CORNER RAD:
NUMBER: 7   # OF FLUTES:
LENGTH OFFSET:
T0707: Grooving Tool - ID GROOVE - MIN. .75 DIA.

TYPE: Grooving Tool   FLUTE LENGTH:
DIA OFFSET: OVERALL LENGTH:
HOLDER: CORNER RAD:
NUMBER: 8   # OF FLUTES:
LENGTH OFFSET:
T0808: Grooving Tool - OD CUTOFF RIGHT

STEP 8: SET UP THE TOOL SETTINGS AND THE STOCK

In this step you will learn how to assign tool numbers, tool offset numbers, and default values for feeds, speeds, and other toolpath parameters. You will also learn how to define the stock and chuck jaws using the lathe machine groups.

- Press **Alt** + **F1** to fit the drawing to the screen.
- To display the **Toolpaths Manager** panel select the **Toolpaths** tab as shown.

Toolpaths Solids Planes Levels Recent Functions

> **NOTE:** If the **Lathe Machine Group** is not displayed in the **Toolpaths Manager,** see **Tutorial 2 page 78.** If another machine is already selected, to remove it see **Tutorial 2 page 102.**

- Select the plus sign (**+**) in front of **Properties** in the **Toolpaths Manager** to expand the **Toolpaths Group Properties.**

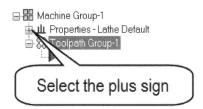

- Select **Tool settings** to set the tool parameters.

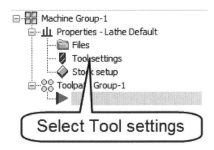

◆ Change the parameters to match the screenshot in Figure: 8.0.1.

Figure: 8.0.1

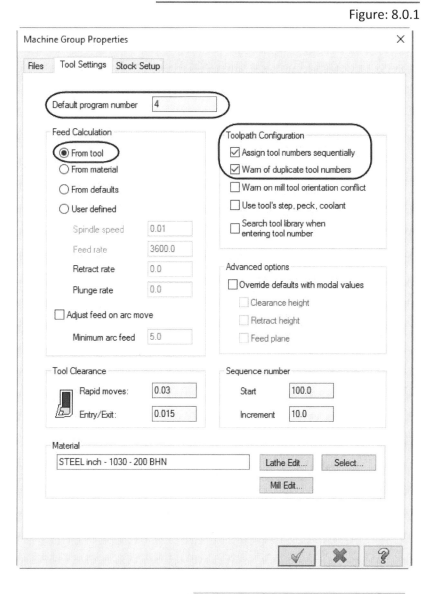

Default program number is used to enter a number if your machine requires a number for a program name.

Assign tool numbers sequentially allows you to overwrite the tool number from the library with the next available tool number.

Warn of duplicate tool numbers allows you to get a warning if you enter two tools with the same number.

Override defaults with modal values enables the system to keep the values that you enter.

Feed Calculation set to **From tool** uses the feed rate, plunge rate, retract rate and spindle speed from the tool definition.

◆ Select the **Stock Setup** tab.

◆ Choose the **Properties** button to set up the stock for the **Left Spindle**.

◆ Define the stock by setting the stock geometry to **Cylinder** and entering the stock dimensions. Ensure you enable **Use Margins** and enter in the values as shown in Figure: 8.0.2.

Figure: 8.0.2

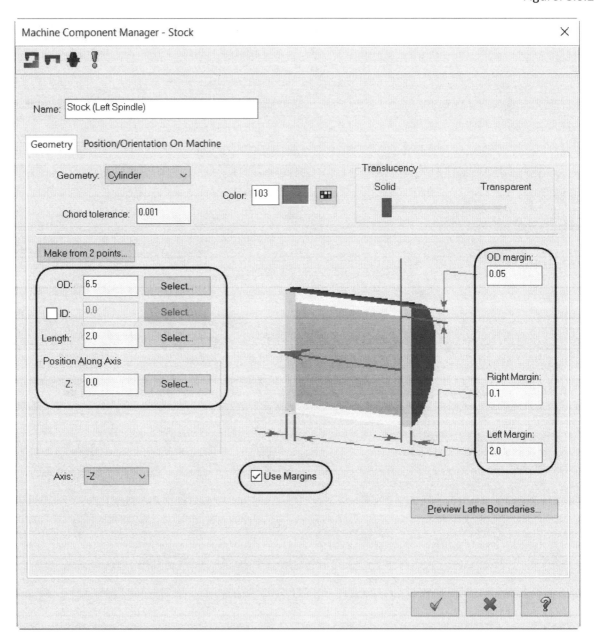

NOTE: The **stock** model that you create can be displayed with the part geometry when viewing the file or the toolpaths, during backplot, or while verifying toolpaths. You can create stock on the left or right spindle.

◆ Select the **OK** button to exit the **Machine Component Manager - Stock** dialog box.

• Ensure that **Left spindle** is selected and then select the **Properties** button in the **Chuck Jaws** area as shown.

• Make the necessary changes to define the chuck size, the clamping method and the stock position. Ensure that you choose the clamping method **OD#1** as shown in the graphic below.

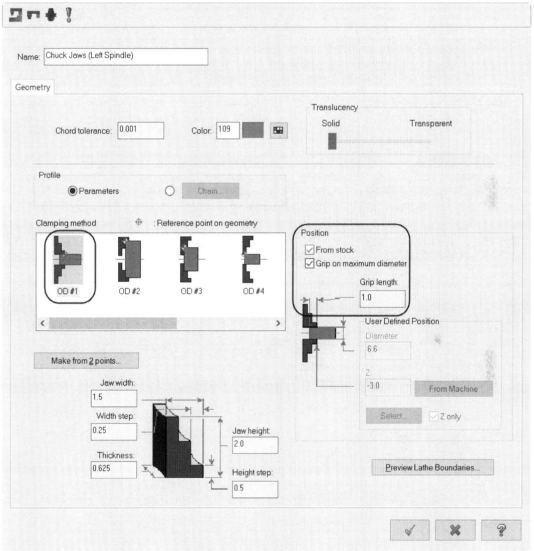

• Select the **OK** button to exit the **Machine Component Manager - Chuck Jaws** dialog box.

• Enable **Fit screen to boundaries** in the **Display Options** area.

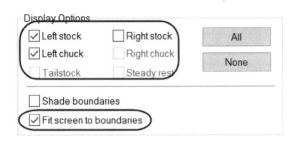

• Select the **OK** button to exit the **Machine Group Properties** dialog box.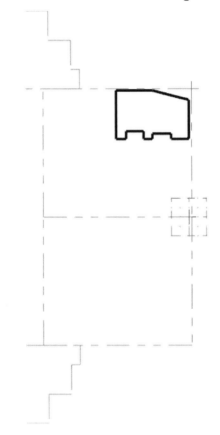
• Press **Alt + F1** to fit the geometry to the screen.
• The stock should look as shown in Figure: 8.0.3.

Figure: 8.0.3

NOTE: The stock is not geometry and cannot be selected.

STEP 9: FACE THE PART

Toolpath Preview:

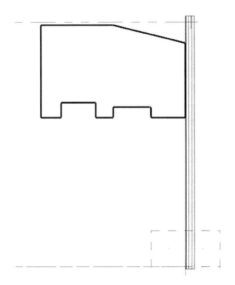

> **NOTE:** To create the **Facing** toolpath, follow **Step 9** in **Tutorial 1** on **page 46**.

♦ Press **Alt + T** to remove the toolpath display.

STEP 10: ROUGH THE OD

Toolpath Preview:

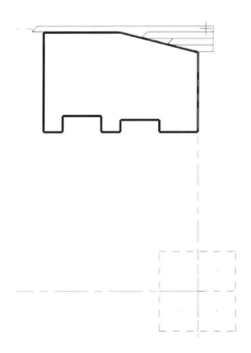

TURNING

♦ From the **General** group, select the **Rough** icon.

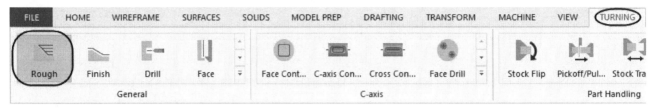

♦ Leave the default settings in the **Chaining** dialog box.

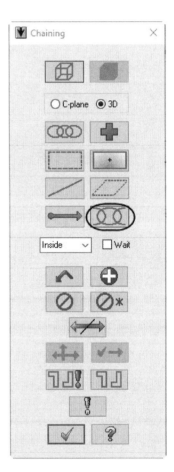

NOTE: The chaining mode is **Partial** by default. You will have to select the first entity and the last entity of the contour.

◆ Select **Entity A.**

NOTE: Make sure that the chaining direction is **CCW**; otherwise, select the **Reverse** button in the **Chaining** dialog box.

◆ Select **Entity B.**

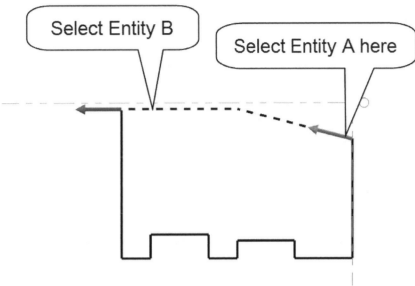

◆ Select the **OK** button to exit the **Chaining** dialog box.

• In the **Toolpath parameters** tab, select the same tool that we used in the facing operation and make any necessary changes as shown in the screenshot.

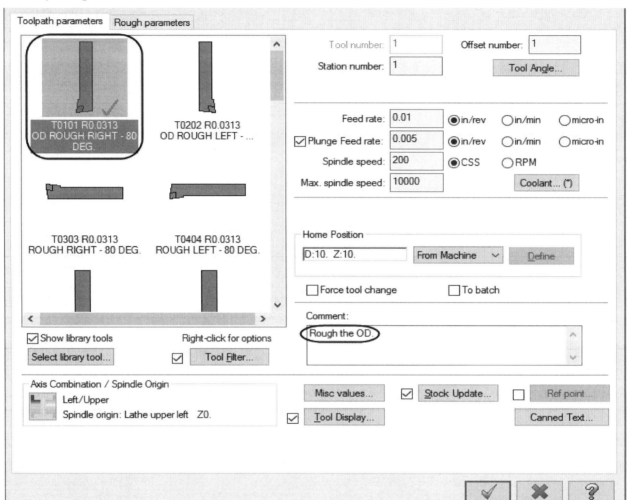

◆ Select the **Rough parameters** tab and make any necessary changes as shown.

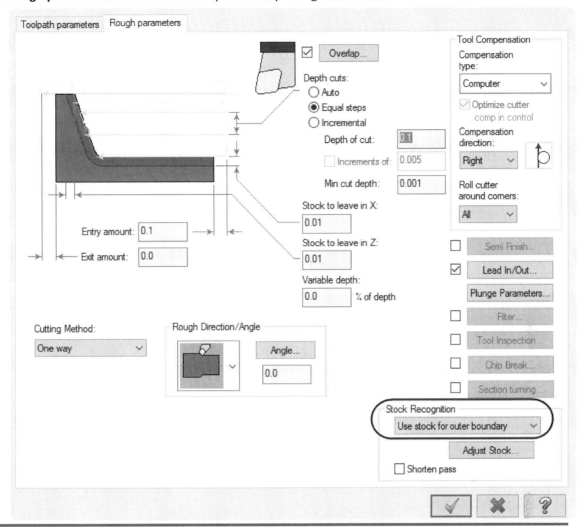

Depth of cut sets the amount of material to be removed during each pass.

Stock to leave in X sets the remaining stock in the **X axis** after the tool completes all passes.

Stock to leave in Z sets the remaining stock in the **Z axis** after the tool completes all passes.

Entry amount sets the height at which the tool rapids to or from the part.

• Select the **Lead In/Out** button and select the **Lead out** tab. Enable **Extend /shorten end of contour** and specify the length as shown.

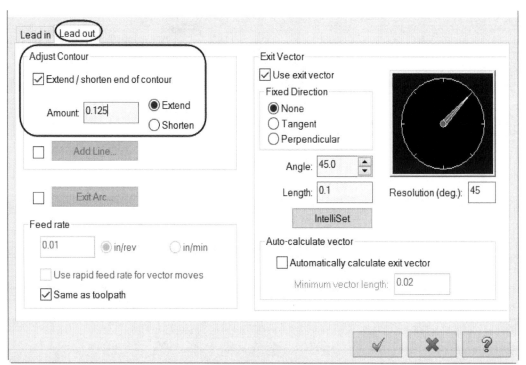

> **NOTE:** We need to extend the contour for the lead out to make sure that the tool will not crash into the part on the next finish operation that uses the rough settings. We also extend the end of the contour for a better finish.

• Select the **OK** button to exit the **Lead In/Out** dialog box.

• Select the **OK** button to exit the **Lathe Rough** dialog box.

STEP 11: BACKPLOT THE TOOLPATHS

Backplotting shows the path the tools take to cut the part. This display lets you spot errors in the program before you machine the part. As you backplot toolpaths, Mastercam displays additional information such as the X, Y, and Z coordinates, the path length, the minimum and maximum coordinates and the cycle time. It also shows any collisions between the workpiece and the tool.

♦ Select the **Backplot selected operations** icon.

♦ In the **Backplot** dialog box enable **Display with color codes**, **Display tool, Display holder** and **Display rapid moves** icons as shown.

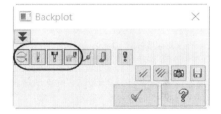

♦ To fit the workpiece to the screen, if needed, right mouse click in the graphics window and select **Fit** or press **Alt + F1**.

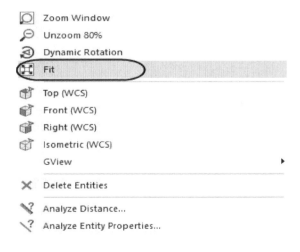

♦ You can step through the **Backplot** by using the **Step forward** ⏭ or **Step back** ⏮ buttons.

♦ You can adjust the speed of the backplot using the **Run speed slider**.

♦ Select the **Play** button to run **Backplot**.

- The toolpath should look as shown.

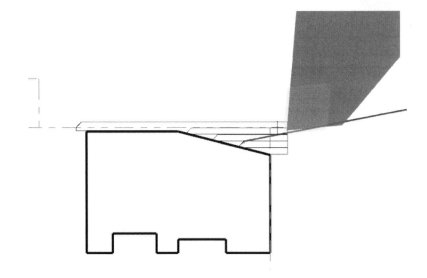

- Select the **OK** button to exit **Backplot**.

STEP 12: SIMULATE THE TOOLPATH IN VERIFY

Verify shows the path the tools take to cut the part with material removal. This display lets you spot errors in the program before you machine the part. As you verify toolpaths, Mastercam displays additional information such as the X, Y, and Z coordinates, the path length, the minimum and maximum coordinates and the cycle time. It also shows any collisions between the workpiece and the tool.

- To verify all toolpaths, from the **Toolpaths Manager**, choose the **Select all operations** icon.

- Select the **Verify selected operation**s icon.

- In the **Mastercam Simulator** window, ensure **Verify** is selected and the rest of the parameters are as shown.

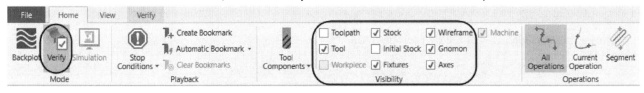

- Select the **Play Simulation** button to run **Verify**.

• To see the part from an **Isometric** view right mouse click in the graphics window and select **Isometric**.
• To fit the workpiece to the screen, right mouse click in the graphics window again and select **Fit**.

• The part should look as shown in Figure: 12.0.1.

Figure: 12.0.1

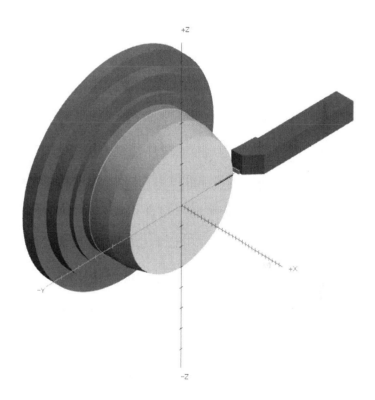

NOTE: To rotate the part, move the cursor to the center of the part and click and hold the mouse wheel and slowly move it in one direction.
To zoom in or out scroll up or down as needed.

• To go back to the Mastercam window, minimize the **Mastercam Simulator** window as shown.
• If needed, press **Alt + T** to remove the toolpath display.

STEP 13: FINISH THE OD USING A FINISH TOOLPATH

Toolpath Preview:

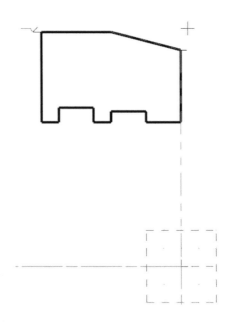

TURNING

- From the **General** group, select the **Finish** icon.

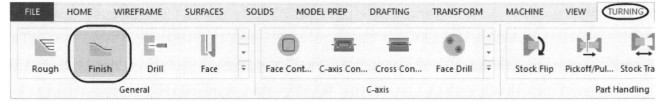

◆ Select the **Last** button in the **Chaining** dialog box as shown.

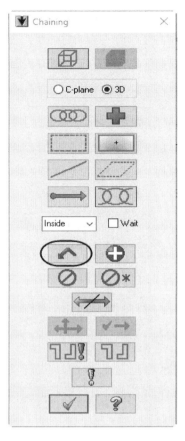

The **Last** button will automatically select the last chain that we used in the roughing toolpath.

◆ Select the **OK** button to exit the **Chaining** dialog box.

• Select the **OD Finish Right -35 Degree** tool from the tool list.

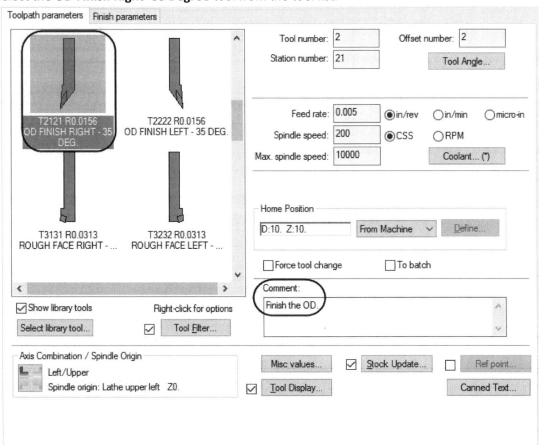

◆ Select the **Finish parameters** tab and make all of the necessary changes as shown.

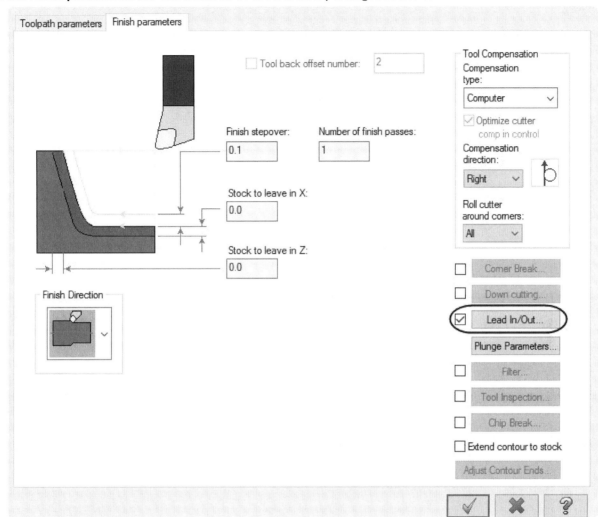

• Select the **Lead In/Out** button, select the **Lead out** tab and extend the contour as shown.

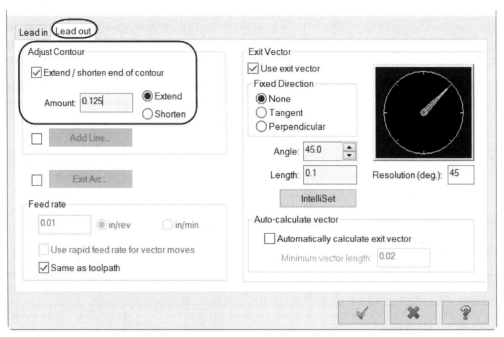

• Select the **OK** button to exit the **Lead In/Out** dialog box.

• Select the **OK** Button to exit the **Lathe Finish** dialog box.

13.1 Backplot the toolpath

• Once the operation has been regenerated **Backplot** the toolpath.
• See **page 277** to review the procedure.

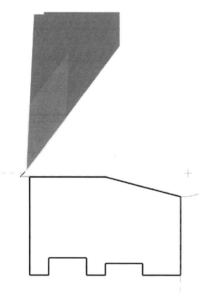

• Select the **OK** button to exit **Backplot**.

13.2 Verify the toolpaths

◆ To verify all toolpaths, from the **Toolpaths Manager**, choose the **Select all operations** icon.
◆ See **page 278** to review the procedure.

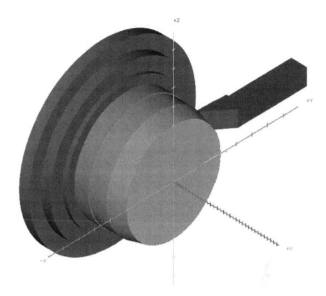

◆ To go back to the Mastercam window, minimize the **Mastercam Simulator** window as shown.

STEP 14: CENTER DRILL THE PART

Drill Toolpaths create a drilling toolpath on the face of the part along the center line. In this step, we will center drill the face before drilling the part to remove the bulk of the material on the ID.

Toolpath Preview:

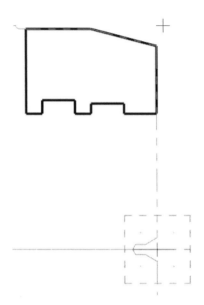

TURNING

* From the **General** group, select the **Drill** icon.

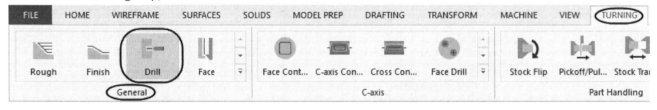

> **NOTE:** The **Lathe Drill** dialog box will automatically open. No chaining is needed because Mastercam drills along the center line to create the toolpath. Drill depths are specified within the dialog box.

◆ Select the **0.5" Diameter Center Drill** from the tool list and enter the comment as shown.

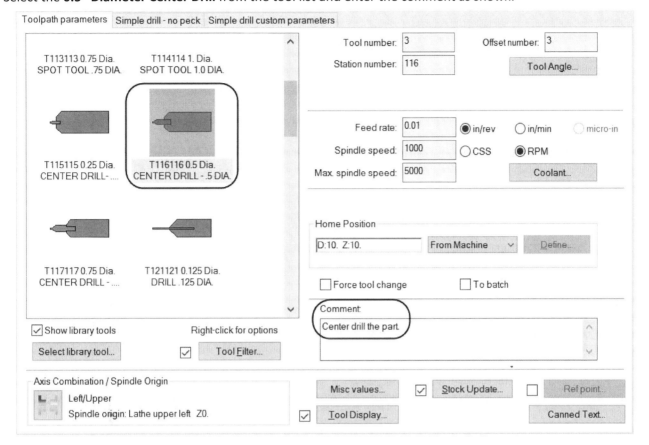

• Select the **Simple drill - no peck** tab and change the parameters to match the screenshot below.

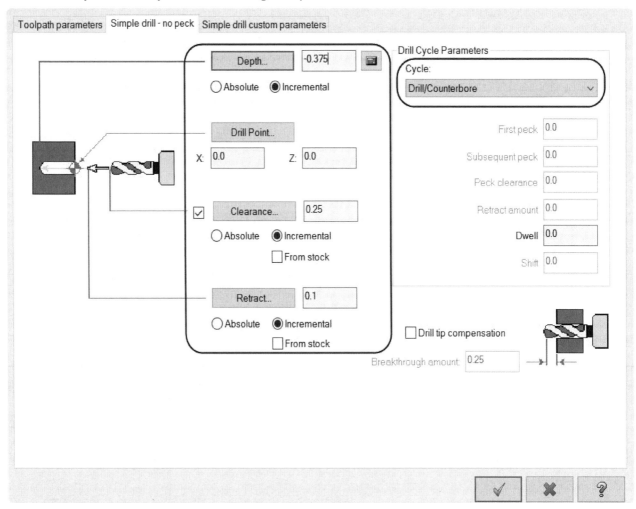

• Select the **OK** button to exit the **Lathe Drill** dialog box.

14.1 Backplot the toolpath

◆ Once the operation has been regenerated **Backplot** the toolpath.
◆ See **page 277** to review the procedure.

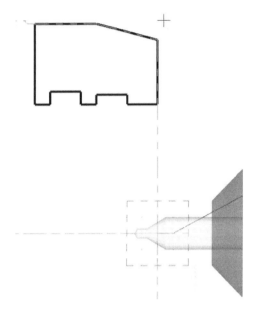

◆ Select the **OK** button to exit **Backplot**.

14.2 Verify the toolpaths

◆ To verify all toolpaths, from the **Toolpaths Manager**, choose the **Select all operations** icon.
◆ See **page 278** to review the procedure.

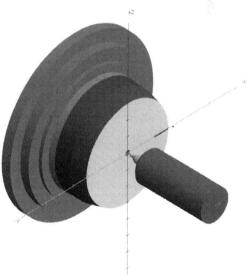

◆ To go back to the Mastercam window, minimize the **Mastercam Simulator** window as shown.

STEP 15: DRILL THE PART

In this step we will create another drilling operation to remove the bulk of the material on the ID in preparation for an ID roughing operation.

Toolpath Preview:

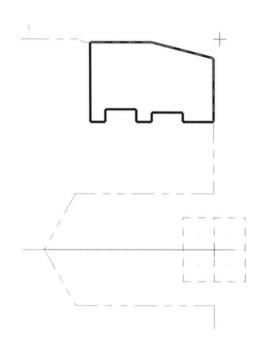

TURNING

• From the **General** group, select the **Drill** icon.

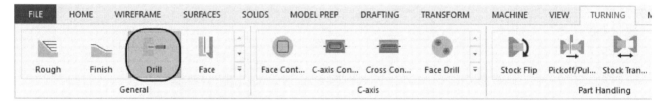

◆ Select the **1.75" Drill** from the tool list and enter the comment as shown.

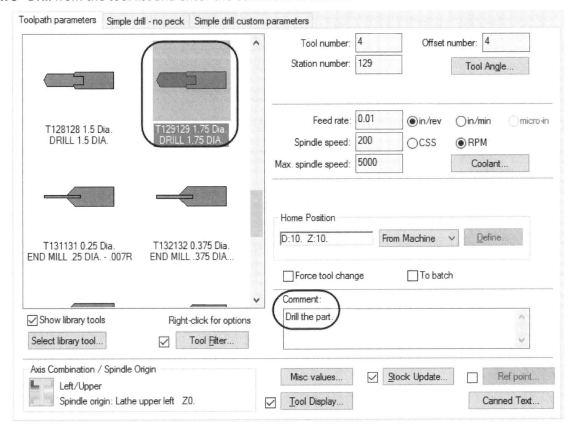

• Select the **Simple drill - no peck** tab and make the changes as shown in the graphic below.

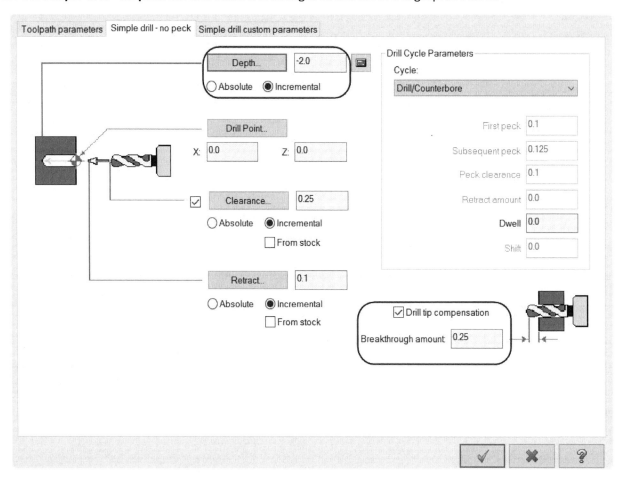

Drill tip compensation automatically adjusts the depth value by adding the tip of the drill to it.

Breakthrough amount allows you to add extra distance to the depth for through holes.

• Select the **OK** button to exit the **Lathe Drill** dialog box.

15.1 Backplot the toolpath

◆ Once the operation has been regenerated **Backplot** the toolpath.
◆ See **page 277** to review the procedure.

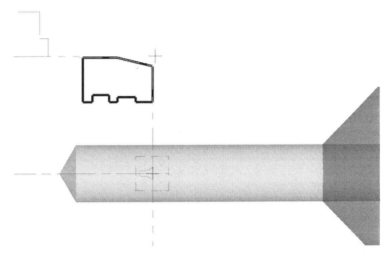

◆ Select the **OK** button to exit **Backplot**.

15.2 Verify the toolpaths

◆ To verify all toolpaths, from the **Toolpaths Manager**, choose the **Select all operations** icon.

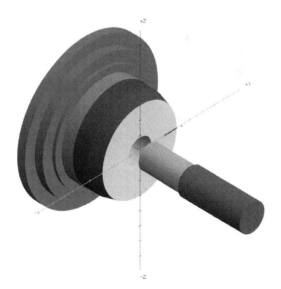

◆ To go back to the Mastercam window, minimize the **Mastercam Simulator** window as shown.

STEP 16: ROUGH THE INSIDE DIAMETER

In this step we will create a rough toolpath using an ID Tool to remove more material from the inside of the part.

Toolpath Preview:

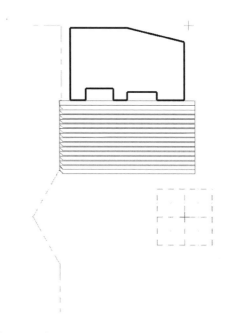

TURNING
* From the **General** group, select the **Rough** icon as shown.

◆ Leave the default settings in the **Chaining** dialog box.

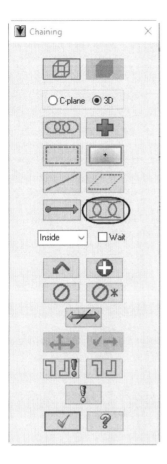

NOTE: The chaining mode is **Partial** by default. You will have to select the first entity and the last entity of the contour.

◆ Select **Entity A.**

NOTE: Make sure that the chaining direction is **CCW**; otherwise, select the **Reverse** button in the **Chaining** dialog box.

◆ Select **Entity B.**

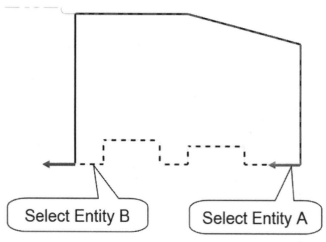

Select Entity B   Select Entity A

◆ Select the **OK** button to exit the **Chaining** dialog box.

♦ In the **Toolpath parameters** tab, select the **ID Rough Min. 1.0"Diameter - 75 Degree** tool and make any necessary changes as shown in the screenshot.

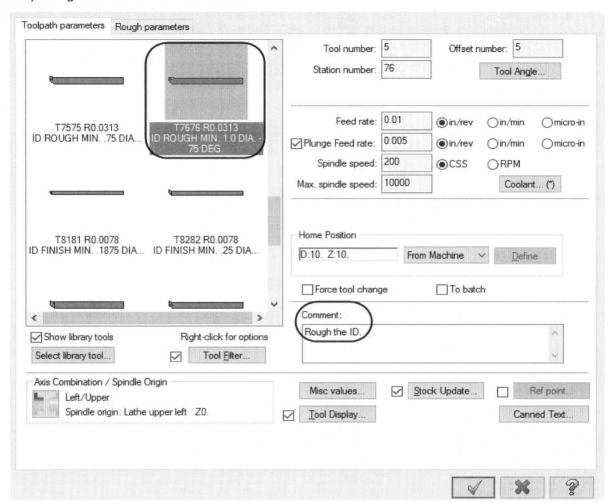

♦ Select the **Rough parameters** tab and make any necessary changes as shown.

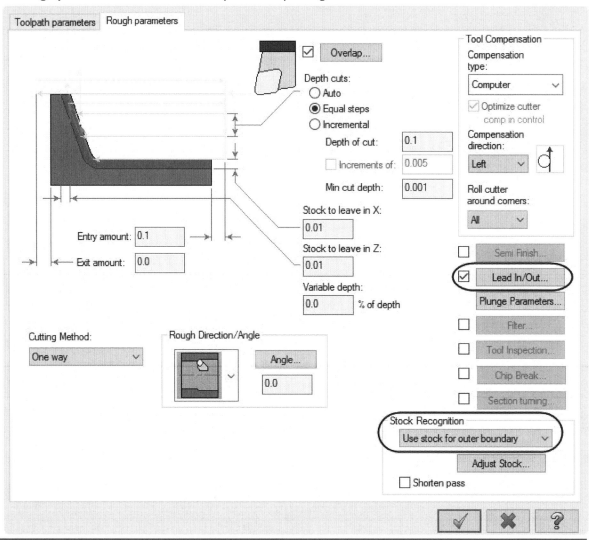

Depth of cut sets the amount of material to be removed during each pass.

Equal steps sets the **Depth of cut** value to the maximum amount of material that the tool can remove at each pass to ensure equal passes.

Min cut depth sets the minimum cut that can be taken per pass.

Stock to leave in X sets the remaining stock in the **X axis** after the tool completes all passes.

Stock to leave in Z sets the remaining stock in the **Z axis** after the tool completes all passes.

Entry amount sets the height at which the tool rapids to or from the part.

◆ Select the **Lead In/Out** button and choose the **Lead out** tab to extend the end of the contour as shown.

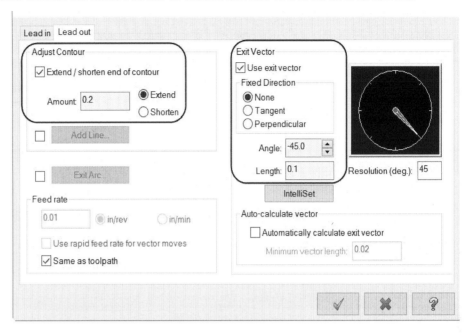

Adjust Contour allows you to extend or shorten the contour by an amount or by adding a line.

Feed rate allows you to specify a custom feed rate for the Lead In/Out.

Exit Vector allows you to create a tangent arc move or perpendicular move to start the toolpath. You can also manually define an entry/exit vector or let the system automatically calculate a vector for you.

◆ Select the **OK** button to exit the **Lead In/Out** dialog box.

◆ Select the **OK** button to exit the **Lathe Rough** dialog box.

16.1 Backplot the toolpath

* Once the operation has been regenerated **Backplot** the toolpath.
* See **page 277** to review the procedure.

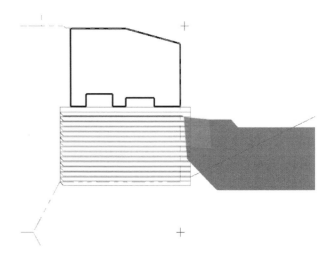

* Select the **OK** button to exit **Backplot**.

16.2 Verify the toolpaths

* To verify all toolpaths, from the **Toolpaths Manager**, choose the **Select all operations** icon.
* See **page 278** to review the procedure.

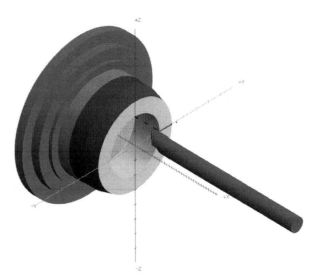

* To go back to the Mastercam window, minimize the **Mastercam Simulator** window as shown.

STEP 17: FINISH THE ID BEFORE GROOVING

In this step we will use a finishing toolpath to finish the ID before grooving the part.

Toolpath Preview:

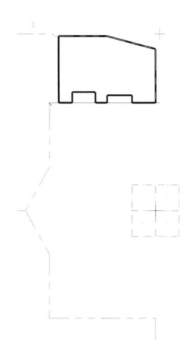

TURNING

♦ From the **General** group, select the **Finish** icon.

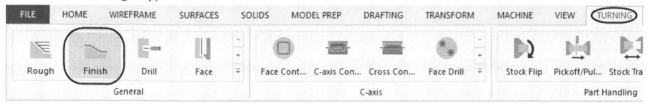

♦ Select the **Last** button in the **Chaining** dialog box.

♦ Select the **OK** button to exit the **Chaining** dialog box.

• Select the **ID Finish Min 0.375" Diameter - 55 Degree** tool from the tool list and enter the comment as shown.

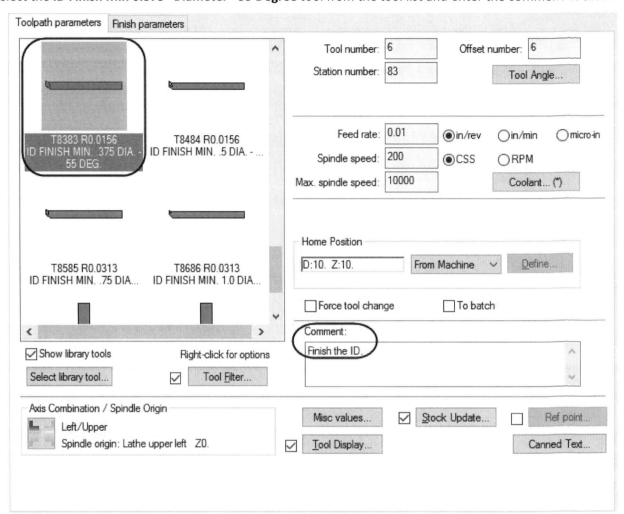

◆ Select the **Finish parameters** tab and make any changes to match the screenshot below.

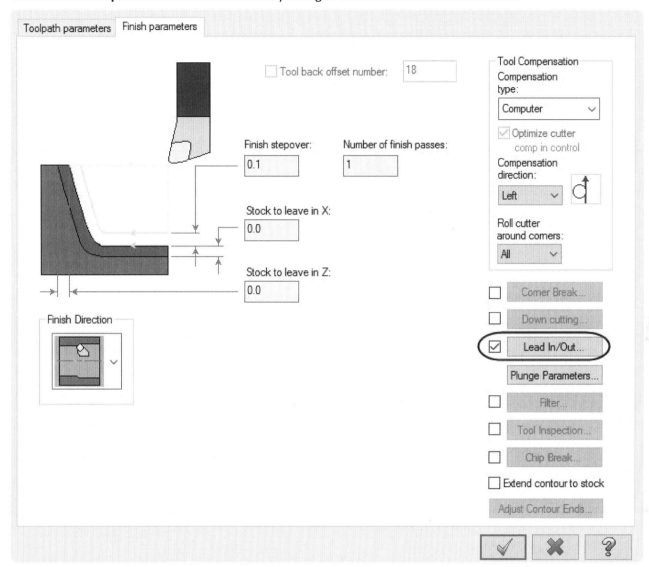

◆ Select the **Lead In/Out** button. | Lead In/Out.. |

- Select the **Lead in** tab and make sure the entry vector **Angle** is set to **180** degrees as shown.

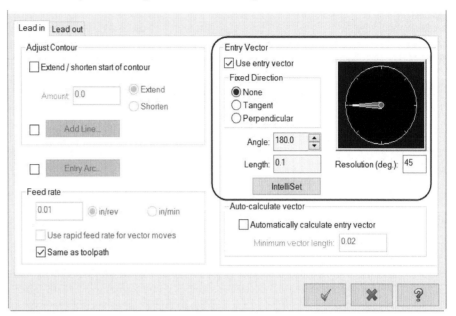

- Select the **Lead out** tab and change the exit vector **Angle** to **-45** degrees and extend the end of the contour as shown.

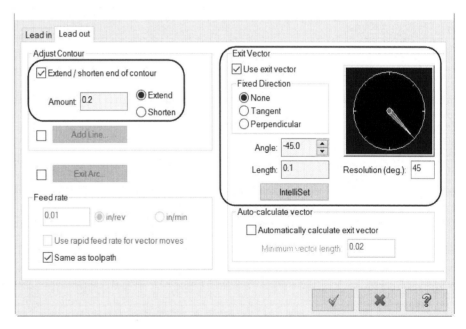

- Select the **OK** button to exit the **Lead In/Out** dialog box.

- Select the **OK** button to exit the **Lathe Finish** dialog box and generate the toolpath.

17.1 Backplot the toolpath

- Once the operation has been regenerated **Backplot** the toolpath.
- See **page 277** to review the procedure.

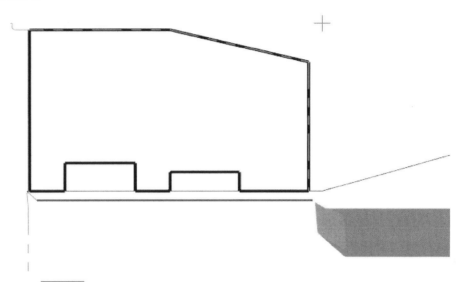

- Select the **OK** button to exit **Backplot**.

17.2 Verify the toolpaths

- To verify all toolpaths, from the **Toolpaths Manager**, choose the **Select all operations** icon.
- See **page 278** to review the procedure.

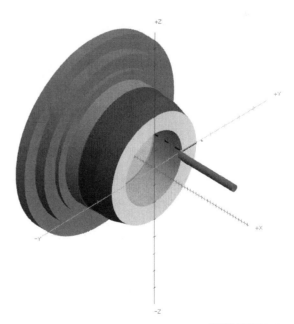

- To go back to the Mastercam window, minimize the **Mastercam Simulator** window as shown.

STEP 18: FINISH THE GROOVES ON THE ID

In this step we will create a groove toolpath to machine the grooves inside the part. We will use a grooving toolpath with multiple chains to machine both grooves in one toolpath.

Toolpath Preview:

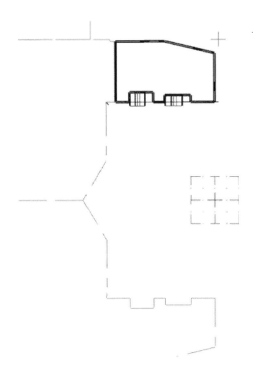

TURNING

♦ From the **General** group, click on the **Expand gallery** arrow key.

♦ Select **Groove.**

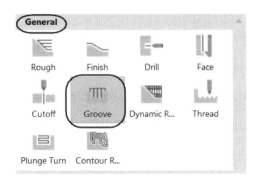

♦ Choose **Multiple chains** when the **Grooving Options** dialog box opens up.

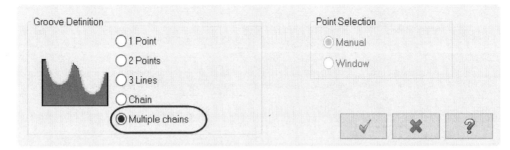

♦ Select the **OK** button to exit the **Grooving Options** dialog box.
♦ Select **Entity A** (the small vertical line) as the first entity as shown.

> **NOTE:** Make sure that the chaining direction is always the same as shown in the figures; if not, select the
>
> **Reverse** button in the **Chaining** dialog box.

♦ Select **Entity B** (the small vertical line) as the last entity as shown.

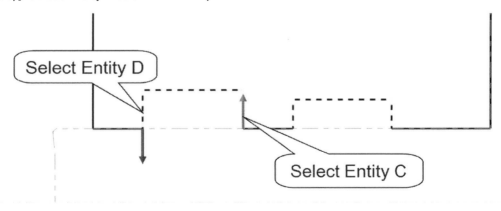

♦ [Select the entry point or chain the inner boundary]: Select **Entity C** as the first entity as shown.
♦ [Select the last entity]: Select **Entity D** as the last entity as shown.

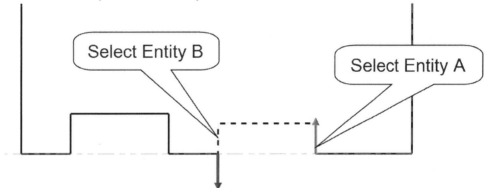

♦ Select the **OK** button to exit the **Chaining** dialog box.

• Select the **ID Groove Min 0.75 Dia.** tool from the **Tool List** and enter the comment as shown.

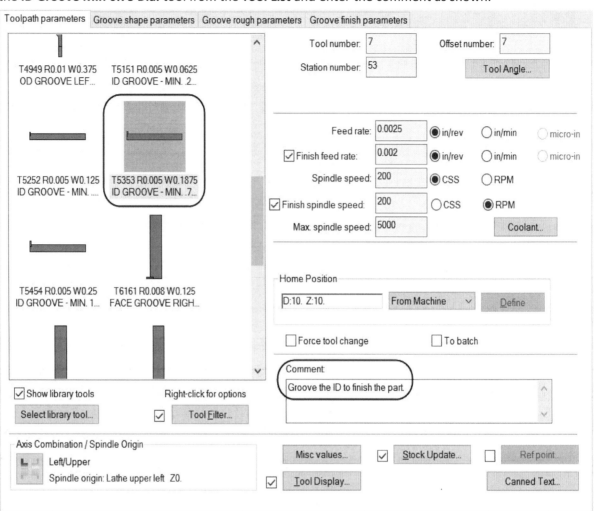

• Right click on the Tool and select **Edit tool**.

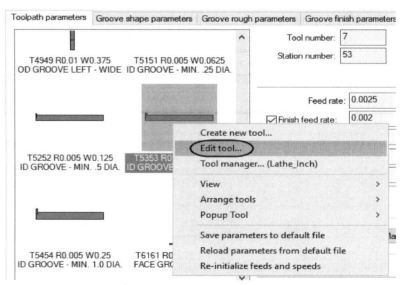

◆ Select the **Holders** tab and make the changes as shown.

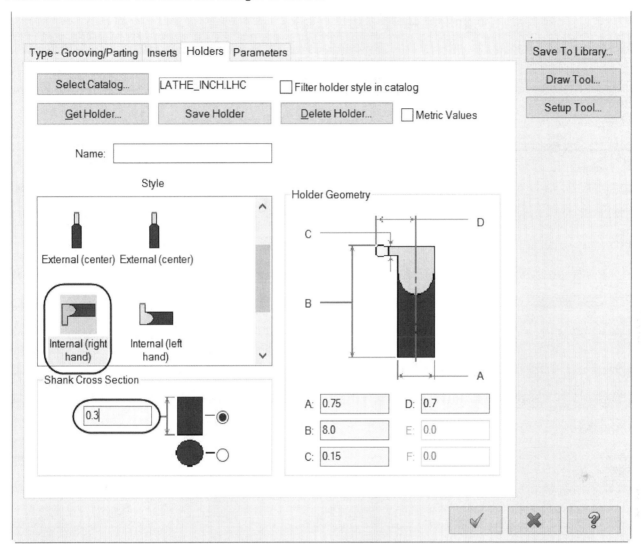

◆ Select the **OK** button to exit the **Define Tool** dialog box.
◆ Select the **Groove shape parameters** tab and enable **Use stock for outer boundary** as shown.

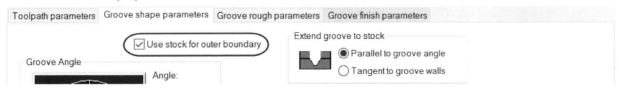

• Select the **Groove rough parameters** tab and make any necessary changes to match the screenshot below.

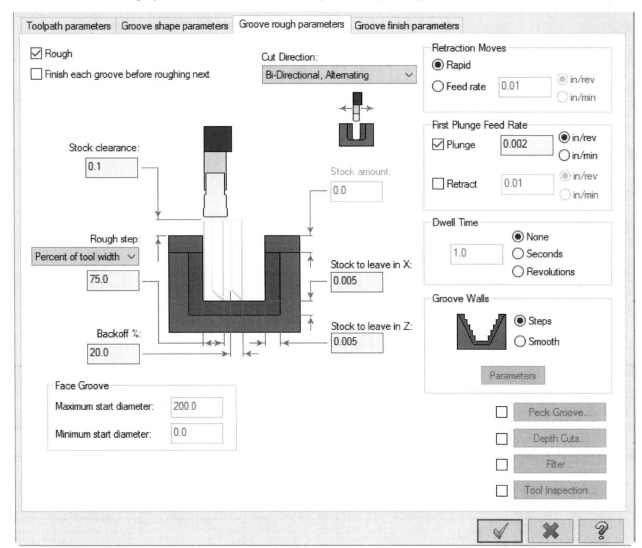

◆ Select the **Groove finish parameters** tab and make any changes as shown.

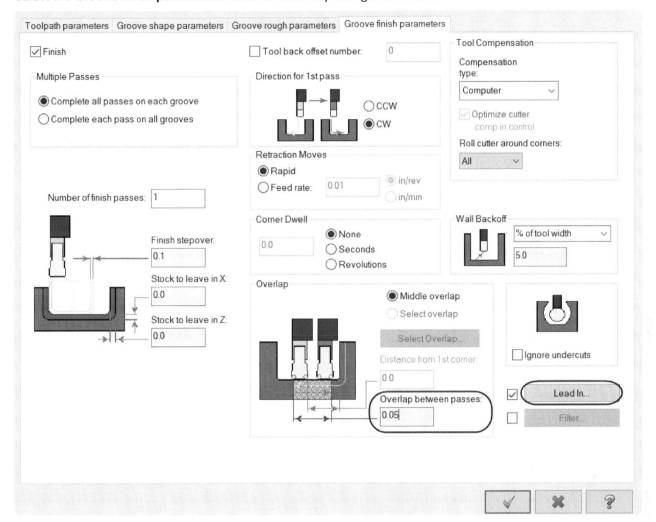

- Select the **Lead In** button and ensure the **First pass lead in** entry vector is the same as shown.

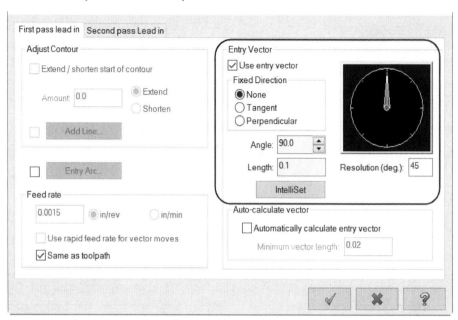

- Select the **Second pass Lead in** tab and ensure the entry vector is the same as shown.

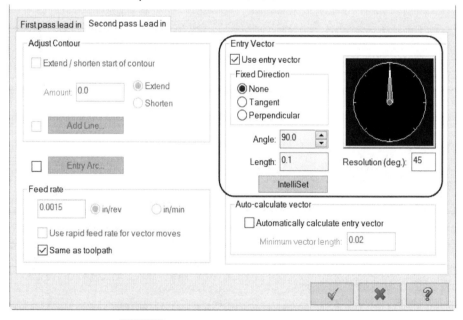

- Select the **OK** button to exit the **Lead In** dialog box.

- Select the **OK** button to exit the **Lathe Groove (Chain)** dialog box.

18.1 Backplot the toolpath

- Once the operation has been regenerated **Backplot** the toolpath.
- See **page 277** to review the procedure.

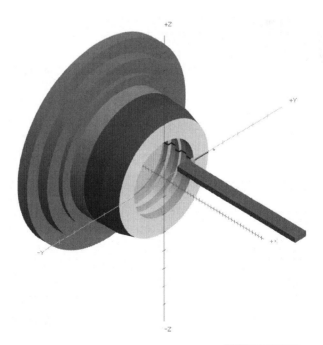

- Select the **OK** button to exit **Backplot**.

18.2 Verify the toolpaths

- To verify all toolpaths, from the **Toolpaths Manager**, choose the **Select all operations** icon.
- See **page 278** to review the procedure.

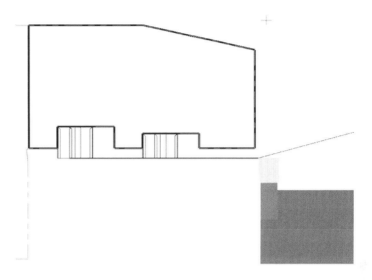

- To go back to the Mastercam window, minimize the **Mastercam Simulator** window as shown.

STEP 19: CUTOFF THE PART

Lathe Cutoff Toolpaths vertically cut off pieces of the part such as sections of bar stock.

Toolpath Preview:

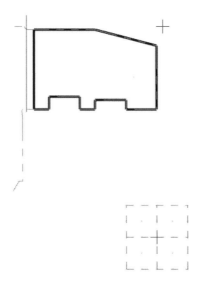

TURNING

- From the **General** group, select the **Cutoff** icon.

- [Select cutoff boundary point]: Select **Endpoint A** as shown.

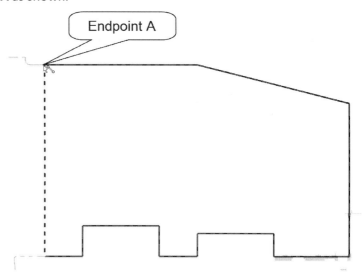

Endpoint A

• Scroll to the bottom of the tool list and choose the **OD Cutoff Right** tool and enter the comment as shown.

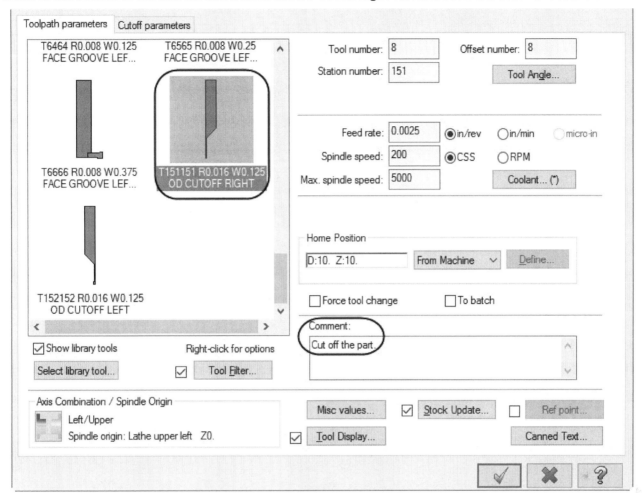

- Select the **Cutoff parameters** tab and make any changes as shown.

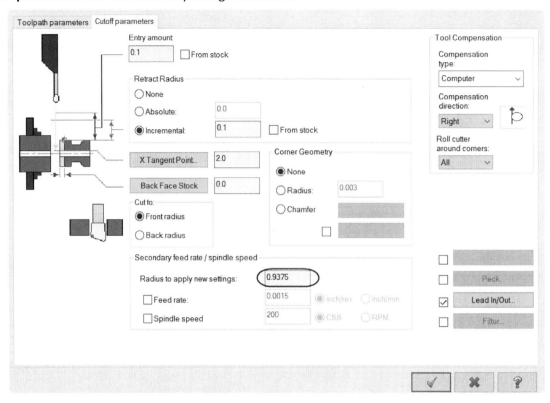

- Select the **X Tangent Point** button.   X Tangent Point...
- [Select tangent point]: Mastercam will return you to the graphical user interface. Select **Endpoint B** to determine where the cutoff should stop as shown.

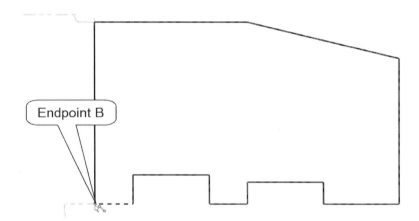

- The **X Tangent Point** should be set to **2.0** as shown.

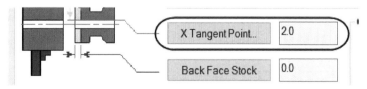

◆ Select the **OK** button to exit the **Lathe Cutoff** dialog box.

19.1 Backplot the toolpath

◆ Once the operation has been regenerated **Backplot** the toolpath.
◆ See **page 277** to review the procedure.

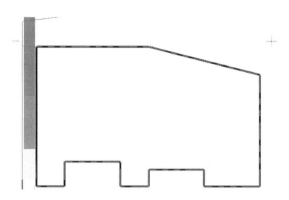

◆ Select the **OK** button to exit **Backplot**.

19.2 Verify the toolpaths

◆ To verify all toolpaths, from the **Toolpaths Manager**, choose the **Select all operations** icon.
◆ See **page 278** to review the procedure.

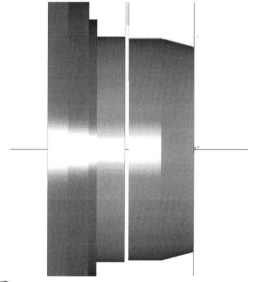

◆ To exit the Mastercam Simulator click on the **Close** icon.

STEP 20: RUN THE POST PROCESSOR TO OBTAIN THE G-CODE FILE

Post Processing refers to the process by which the toolpaths in your Mastercam part files are converted to a format that can be understood by your machine tool's controller. A special program reads your Mastercam file and writes the appropriate NC code.

- Make sure that all operations are selected, otherwise click on the **Select all operations** icon.
- Select the **Post selected operations** icon from the **Toolpaths Manager**.

- In the **Post processing** dialog box, make all of the necessary changes as shown.

NC File enabled allows you to keep the NC file and to assign the same name as the MCAM file.

Edit enabled allows you to automatically launch the default editor.

- Select the **OK** button to continue.
- Save the NC file.

• The **Mastercam Code Expert** window will be launched and the NC program will appear as shown.

```
3   (PROGRAM NAME - TUTORIAL #4 TOOLPATH)
4   (DATE=DD-MM-YY - 11-01-17 TIME=HH:MM - 15:59)
5   (MCX FILE - C:\USERS\GONG.ZHANG\DOCUMENTS\MASTERCAM\LATHE\TUTORIAL #4 TOOLPATH.MCAM)
6   (NC FILE - C:\USERS\GONG.ZHANG\DOCUMENTS\MASTERCAM\LATHE\TUTORIAL #4 TOOLPATH.NC)
7   (MATERIAL - STEEL INCH - 1030 - 200 BHN)
8   G20
9   (TOOL - 1 OFFSET - 1)
10  (OD ROUGH RIGHT - 80 DEG.  INSERT - CNMG-432)
11  ( FACE THE PART. )
12  G0 T0101
13  G18
14  G97 S114 M03
15  G0 G54 X6.7 Z.055 M8
16  G50 S3600
17  G96 S200
18  G99 G1 X-.0625 F.01
19  G0 Z.155
20  X6.7
21  Z.01
22  G1 X-.0625
23  G0 Z.11
24  X6.7
25  Z0.
26  G1 X-.0625
27  G0 Z.1
28  ( ROUGH THE OD. )
29  X6.4058
30  Z.21
31  G1 Z.11
32  Z-.7979
```

• Select the **"X"** box at the upper right corner to exit the editor.

STEP 21: SAVE THE UPDATED MCAM FILE

REVIEW EXERCISE - STUDENT PRACTICE

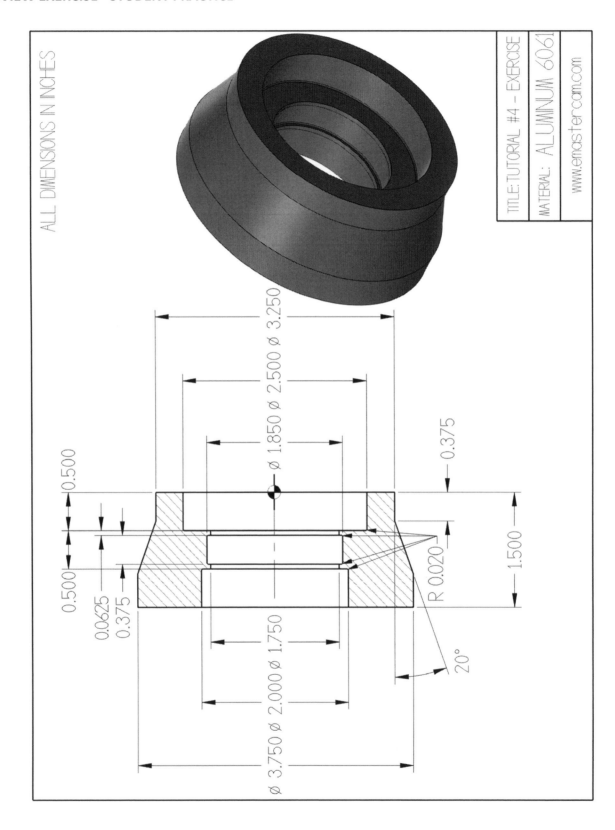

ALL DIMENSIONS IN INCHES

TITLE: TUTORIAL #4 – EXERCISE

MATERIAL: ALUMINUM 6061

www.emastercam.com

Ø 3.250

Ø 2.500

Ø 1.850

0.375

0.500

1.500

0.500

0.0625

0.375

R 0.020

Ø 1.750

Ø 2.000

20°

Ø 2.000

Ø 3.750

CREATE THE GEOMETRY FOR TUTORIAL #4 EXERCISE

Use these commands to create the top half of the geometry.

- ◆ Rectangle.
- ◆ Line Parallel.
- ◆ Line Endpoints.
- ◆ Trim Break Extend.
- ◆ Delete Entities.
- ◆ Fillet Entity.

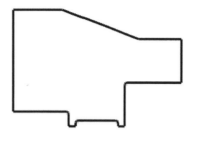

CREATE THE TOOLPATHS FOR TUTORIAL #4 EXERCISE

Create the Toolpaths for Tutorial #4 Exercise as per the instructions below.

Set the machine properties including the stock.
Rough, Face and Finish the OD.
* Use the stock setup to define the face operation.
* Use the OD Rough Right tool for roughing and facing operations.
* Use an OD Finish Right tool for the finish operation.

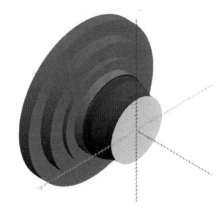

Spot Drill and Drill out the middle of the part.
* Use a large spot drill as your first operation.
* Use the depth calculator to spot drill to the appropriate depth.
* Use a large drill bit to drill the bulk of the material from the center of the part.
* Select a suitable drill cycle for drilling.
* Enable breakthrough and drill further than the end of the part.

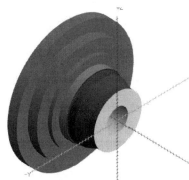

Rough and Finish the ID of the part with a boring bar.
* Chain the ID contour CW.
* Use an **ID Rough Min. 0.75"Diameter - 75 Degree** for the roughing toolpath.
* Enable **Use stock for outer boundary**.
* Select an ID Finish boring bar for the finishing toolpath.
* Use **Lead In/Out** and extend the end of the contour for both toolpaths so the tool machines past the geometry.

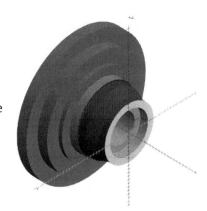

Machine the grooves.

- Select the **Multiple chains** option.
- Chain the rounded grooves CCW.
- Choose an appropriate **ID GROOVE - MIN. .25 DIA.** tool.
- Adjust the holder size if it collides with the stock.

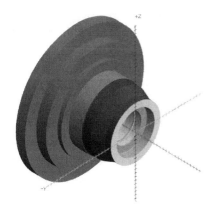

- Select **Edit tool**.

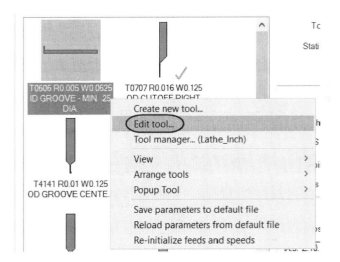

◆ Under **Holders**, change the **D** value to **0.375**.

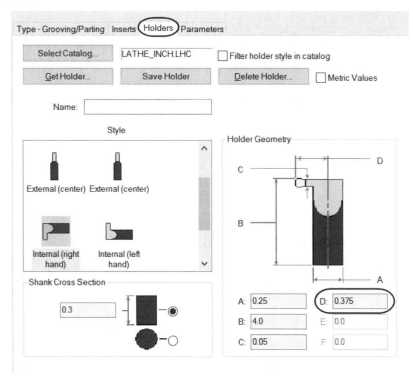

◆ Rough and Finish both grooves with the same toolpath.
◆ Change the Finish pass lead in values to **90** degrees.
◆ Use stock for outer boundary.

Cutoff the part.
◆ Choose the top left hand corner of the part as the cutoff boundary.
◆ Select the OD cutoff right tool.
◆ Select an appropriate depth to machine to.
◆ Under the Cutoff parameters set the value of the X Tangent Point to an appropriate distance.

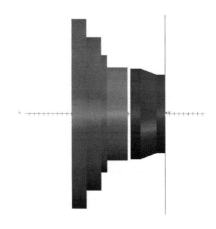

NOTES:

TUTORIAL #4 QUIZ

♦ What does the X Tangent Point button allow you to do?

♦ What does drill tip compensation do?

♦ What does a cutoff operation do?

TUTORIAL #5

OVERVIEW OF STEPS TAKEN TO CREATE THE FINAL PART:

From drawing to CAD model:
- From the drawing we can gain an idea of how to create the geometry in Mastercam.
- The student will need to create the geometry that will be used to machine the OD of the part.
- The drawing should also include relief grooves for the threads.

Create the 2D CAD Model used to generate toolpaths:
- The student will create the upper profile of the part. Only half of the geometry is needed to create the toolpaths necessary to machine the part.
- Create line will be used to make the outside profile of the part.
- The student will use the relief groove command and break some geometry to help in creating a groove toolpath.

Create the necessary toolpaths to machine the part:
- The student will face the part, then rough and finish the part from both sides.
- The student will drill the part halfway from both sides.
- Grooving and threading toolpaths will be created to machine the relief grooves and machine the threads.
- A stock flip operation will be created to flip the stock to a specified location in the chuck.

Backplot and Verify the file:
- The Backplot will be used to simulate a step by step process of the tool's movements.
- The Verify will be used to watch a tool machine the part out of a solid model.

Post Process the file to generate the G-code:
- The student will then post process the file to obtain an NC file containing the necessary code for the machine.

 This tutorial takes approximately one hour to complete.

ALL DIMENSIONS IN INCHES

TITLE: TUTORIAL #5

MATERIAL: ALUMINUM 6061

www.emastercam.com

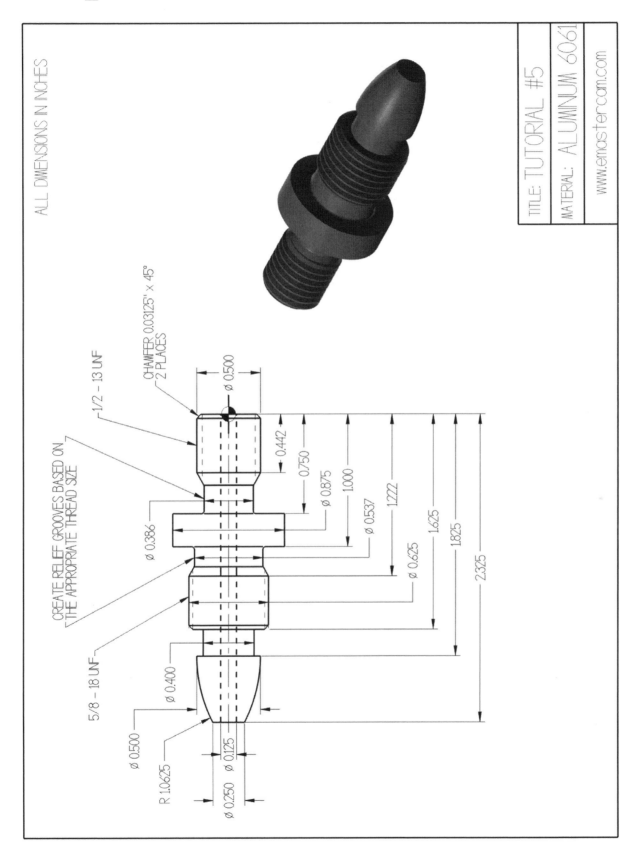

1/2 – 13 UNF

CHAMFER 0.03125" × 45°
2 PLACES

CREATE RELIEF GROOVES BASED ON
THE APPROPRIATE THREAD SIZE

5/8 – 18 UNF

Ø 0.500

Ø 0.386

Ø 0.400

R 1.0625

Ø 0.250

Ø 0.125

Ø 0.500

0.442

0.750

Ø 0.875

1.000

Ø 0.537

1.222

Ø 0.625

1.625

1.825

2.325

GEOMETRY CREATION

STEP 1: SETTING UP THE GRAPHIC USER INTERFACE

Please refer to the **Getting Started** section to set up the graphical user interface accordingly.

STEP 2: SELECT THE LATHE DEFAULT

In this step you will select the machine, in your case the Lathe default. This allows you to set the plane to the Lathe +D +Z and to be able to enter the coordinates based on the lathe axes.

MACHINE

• From the **Machine Type,** select the drop down arrow below the **Lathe** and select **Default** as shown.

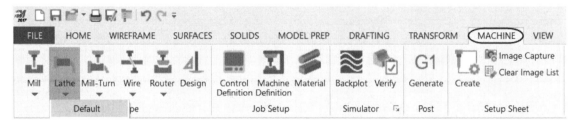

STEP 3: SET UP THE LATHE PLANE +D +Z

In this step you will learn how to set up the **Lathe Plane +D +Z** to be able to enter coordinates using this plane.

3.1 Set the Construction plane and Tool plane to +D +Z

• To set the **Construction plane** and **Tool plane** to +D +Z see **page 78**.

STEP 4: CREATE LINES TO REPRESENT THE OUTSIDE PROFILE

In this step you will create lines to represent the profile of the part given their length and angles.

Step Preview:

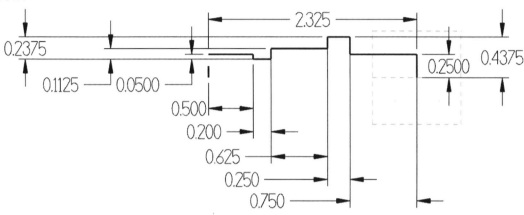

4.1 Create the horizontal and vertical lines

WIREFRAME

♦ From the **Lines** group, select **Line Endpoints**.

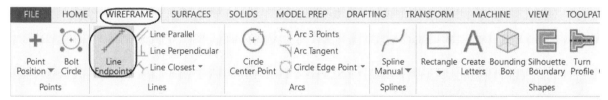

♦ Enter the **Length** then press tab on your keyboard and enter the **Angle** as shown (**Enter**).

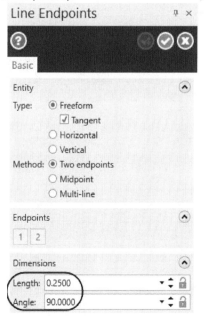

• To select the position of the base point, from the **General Selection** toolbar, click on the drop down arrow next to **AutoCursor** as shown.

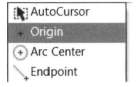

• From the fly-out menu select **Origin**.

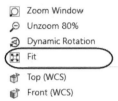

• To focus on the line, right mouse click in the graphics window and select **Fit** as shown.

> **NOTE:** To fit the geometry to the screen you can also press **Alt + F1**.

• Scroll down on the mouse wheel to unzoom the geometry.
• Press **Enter** to finish the line.
• The geometry should look as shown.

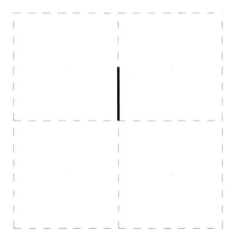

> **NOTE:** While creating the geometry for this tutorial, if you make a mistake you can undo the last step using the
>
> **Undo** icon. � You can undo as many steps as needed. If you delete or undo a step by mistake, just use the
>
> **Redo** icon. ↻
>
> To delete unwanted geometry, select the geometry first and then press **Delete** from the keyboard.

♦ In the **Line Endpoints** panel, enter the **Length** then press tab on your keyboard and enter the **Angle** as shown (**Enter**).

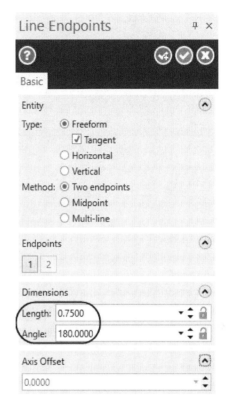

♦ [Specify the first endpoint]: Select **Endpoint A** as shown.

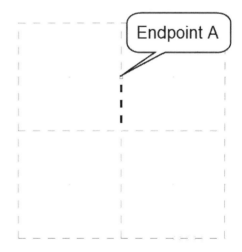

♦ Press **Enter** to finish the line and stay within the command.
♦ Press **Alt + F1** to fit the geometry to the graphics window.

• In the **Line Endpoints** panel, enter the **Length** then press tab on your keyboard and enter the **Angle** as shown (**Enter**).

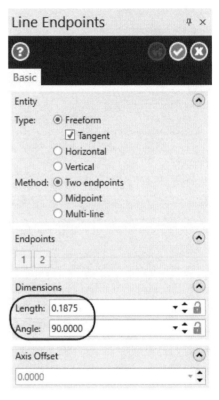

• [Specify the first endpoint]: Select **Endpoint B** as shown.

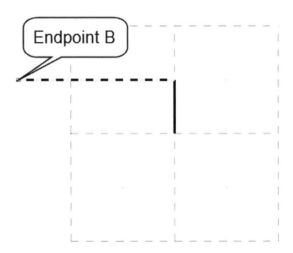

• Press **Enter** to stay within the command.
• Scroll down on the mouse wheel to unzoom the geometry.

• In the **Line Endpoints** panel, enter the **Length** then press tab on your keyboard and enter the **Angle** as shown (**Enter**).

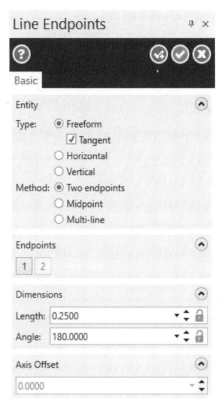

• [Specify the first endpoint]: Select **Endpoint C** as shown.

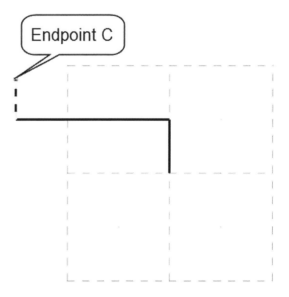

• Press **Enter** to finish the line and stay within the command.

• In the **Line Endpoints** panel, enter the **Length** then press tab on your keyboard and enter the **Angle** as shown (**Enter**).

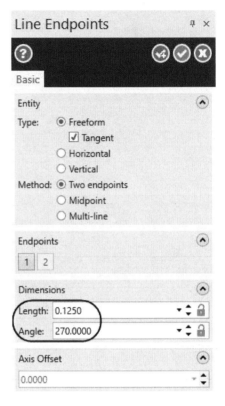

• [Specify the first endpoint]: Select **Endpoint D** as shown.

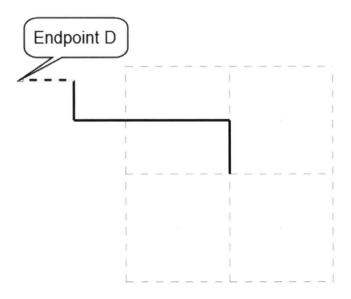

• Press **Enter**.

• In the **Line Endpoints** panel, enter the **Length** then press tab on your keyboard and enter the **Angle** as shown (**Enter**).

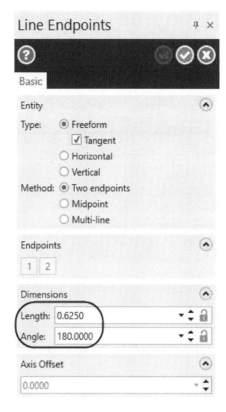

• [Specify the first endpoint]: Select **Endpoint E** as shown.

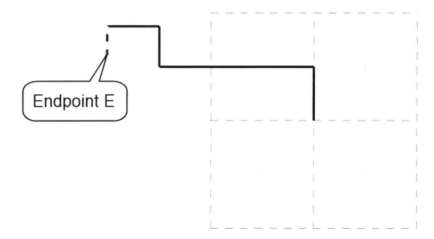

• Press **Enter**.

+ To center the part if needed, hold down the **Shift** key and, while holding down the mouse wheel, move the cursor in the desired direction to see the geometry as shown.

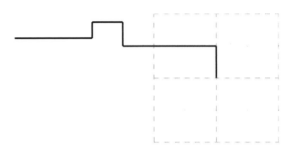

+ In the **Line Endpoints** panel, enter the **Length** then press tab on your keyboard and enter the **Angle** as shown **(Enter)**.

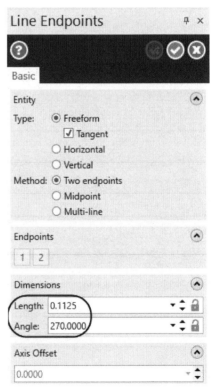

- [Specify the first endpoint]: Select **Endpoint F** as shown.

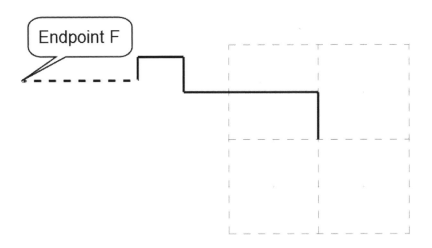

Endpoint F

- Press **Enter**.
- Enter the **Length** then press tab on your keyboard and enter the **Angle** as shown (**Enter**).

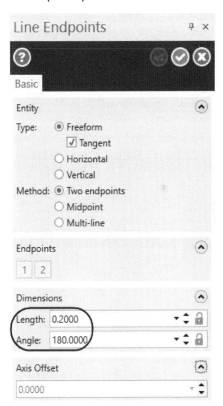

- [Specify the first endpoint]: Select **Endpoint G** as shown.

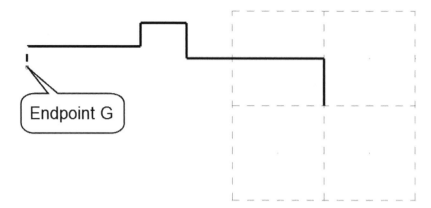

Endpoint G

- Press **Enter**.
- Enter the **Length** then press tab on your keyboard and enter the **Angle** as shown (**Enter**).

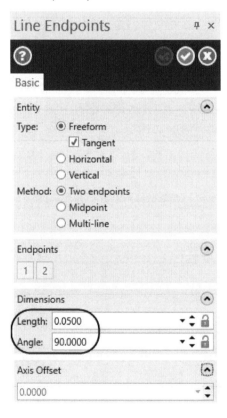

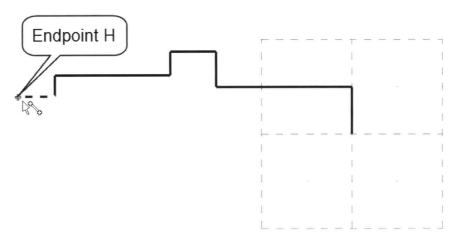

- [Specify the first endpoint]: Select **Endpoint H** as shown.

- Press **Enter**.
- In the **Line Endpoints** panel, enter the **Length** then press tab on your keyboard and enter the **Angle** as shown (**Enter**).

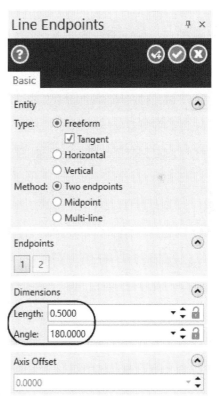

♦ [Specify the first endpoint]: Select **Endpoint I** as shown.

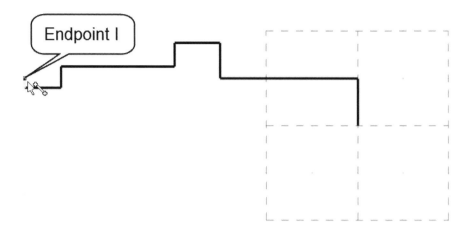

♦ Press **Enter**.
♦ In the **Line Endpoints** panel, enter the **Length** then press tab on your keyboard and enter the **Angle** as shown (**Enter**).

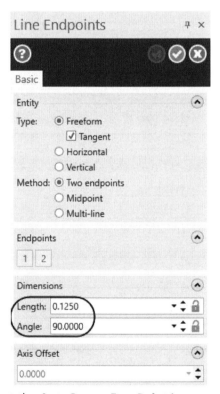

♦ [Specify the first endpoint]: Press the **Space Bar** from the keyboard or select the **AutoCursor Fast Point** icon from the **General Selection** toolbar and the field where you can type the coordinates will open at the upper left corner of the graphics window as shown.

◆ Enter in the coordinates **0,-2.325** (**Enter**).

0,-2.325

> **NOTE:** When working with the **+D +Z** plane, enter in the coordinates in this order (D,Z).

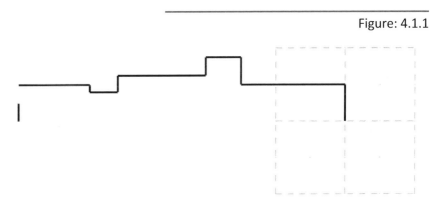

◆ Select the **OK** button to exit the command.
◆ Press **Alt + F1** to fit the geometry to the screen then use the mouse wheel and scroll down to unzoom. The geometry should appear as shown in Figure: 4.1.1.

Figure: 4.1.1

STEP 5: CREATE AN ARC TANGENT WITH DYNAMIC TANGENCY

In this step, we will use the **Arc dynamic** command to dynamically create an arc tangent to an existing entity.

Step Preview:

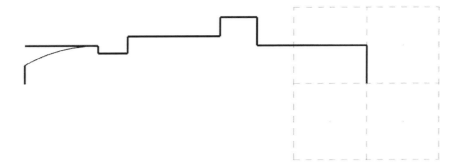

WIREFRAME

◆ From the **Arcs** group, select **Arc Tangent**.

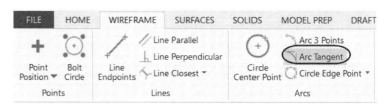

◆ Under **Method** select **Arc dynamic** as shown.

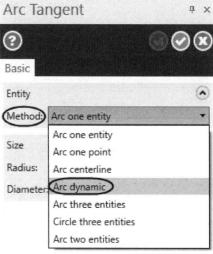

◆ [Select the entity that the arc is to be tangent to]: Select **Entity A** as shown.

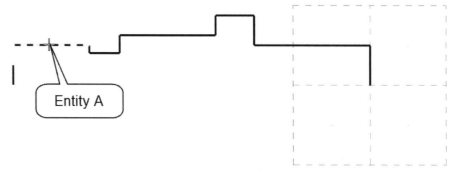

Entity A

◆ [Slide Arrow to position to be tangent to]: Select **Endpoint A** as shown.

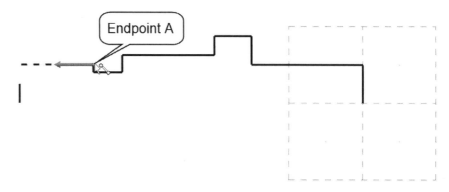

Endpoint A

Lathe Training Tutorial

Mastercam 2018

• Sketch the arc to **Endpoint B**, click to select it as shown.

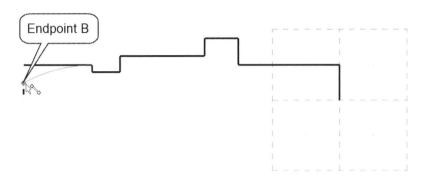

Endpoint B

• Select the **OK** button to exit the command.
• The part should appear as shown in Figure: 5.0.1.

Figure: 5.0.1

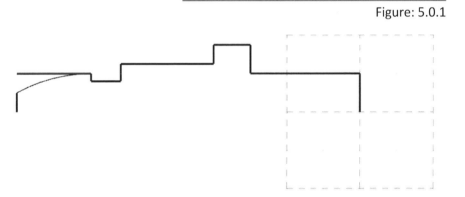

STEP 6: DELETE THE EXTRA CONSTRUCTION LINE

In this step we will delete the extra horizontal line.

Step Preview:

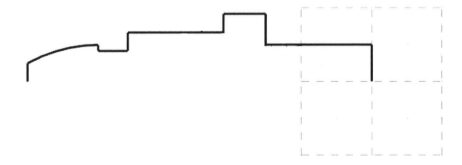

- Select **Entity A** as shown.

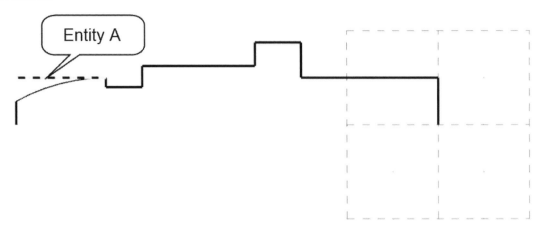

- Press the **Delete** key.

STEP 7: CREATE RELIEF GROOVES

The **Relief Groove** command will create geometry based on the thread size and orientation information you provide. Thread relief grooves provide clearance for threading tools to retract at the end of the cut and relieve stress concentrations at the end of the part to make the part stronger.

Step Preview:

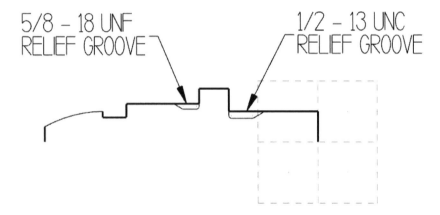

7.1 Create the 1/2" - 13 UNC Relief Groove

WIREFRAME

* From the **Shapes** group, select **Relief Groove**.

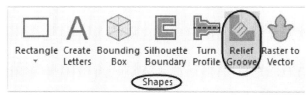

* The **DIN Relief Groove Parameters** dialog box will appear. Enable **OD thread** and select the **Select From Table** button as shown below.

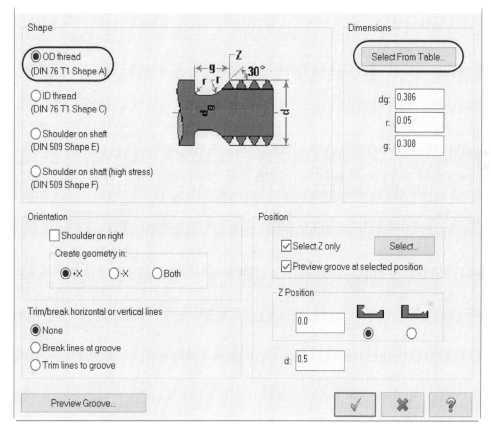

• Scroll through the list and select the **1/2 - 13 UNC** thread.

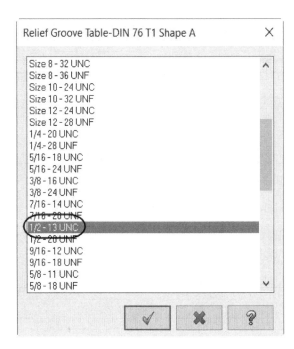

Relief Groove Table-DIN 76 T1 Shape A   ✕

```
Size 8 - 32 UNC
Size 8 - 36 UNF
Size 10 - 24 UNC
Size 10 - 32 UNF
Size 12 - 24 UNC
Size 12 - 28 UNF
1/4 - 20 UNC
1/4 - 28 UNF
5/16 - 18 UNC
5/16 - 24 UNF
3/8 - 16 UNC
3/8 - 24 UNF
7/16 - 14 UNC
7/16 - 20 UNF
1/2 - 13 UNC
1/2 - 20 UNF
9/16 - 12 UNC
9/16 - 18 UNF
5/8 - 11 UNC
5/8 - 18 UNF
```

• Select the **OK** button to exit the dialog box.

• Change the **Orientation, Trim/break horizontal or vertical lines** and **Position** values as shown.

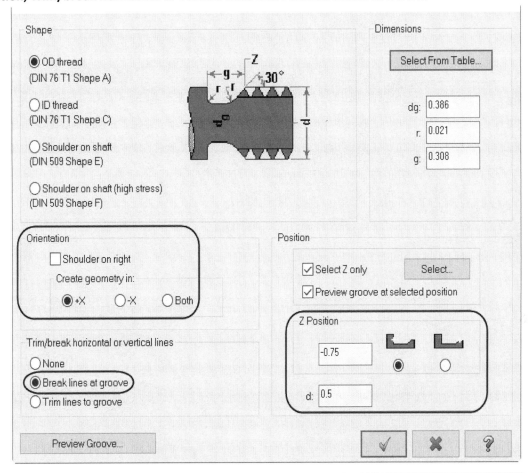

Shape determines what type of relief groove you would like to create. You can select **OD** or **ID Thread** relief grooves, or **Shoulder on shaft** types.

Orientation establishes where on the **X axis** you would like to create the geometry, or the direction the geometry is created in.

Trim/Break horizontal or vertical lines - use this option to either trim or break the geometry the groove is created with, or you can select **None** to make no trimming or breaking changes.

Position tells Mastercam where the relief groove will be created. You can also specify the Z Position of the front of the relief groove or the back by selecting one of the geometry entities.

• Select the **OK** button to create the relief groove.

- The part should appear as shown in Figure: 7.1.1.

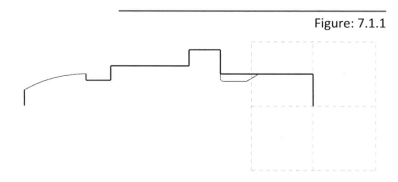

7.2 Create the 5/8" - 18 UNF Relief Groove

WIREFRAME

- From the **Shapes** group, select **Relief Groove**.

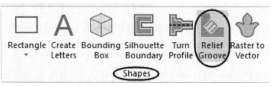

- Ensure **OD thread** is enabled. Then click on the **Select From Table** button as shown.

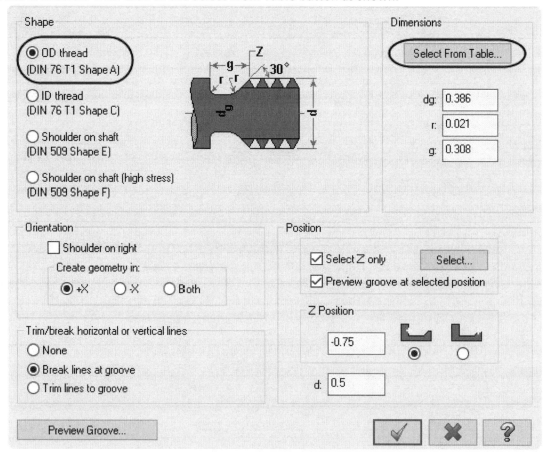

◆ Scroll through the list and select the **5/8 - 18 UNF** thread.

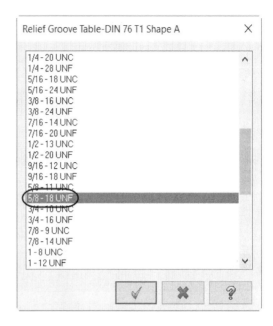

◆ Select the **OK** button to exit the dialog box.
◆ Change the **Orientation**, **Trim/break horizontal or vertical lines**, and **Z Position** as shown below.

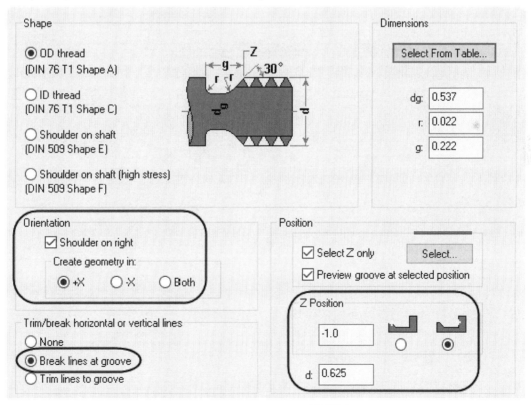

◆ Select the **OK** button to exit the command and create the relief groove.

• The part should appear as shown in <u>Figure: 7.2.1</u>.

Figure: 7.2.1

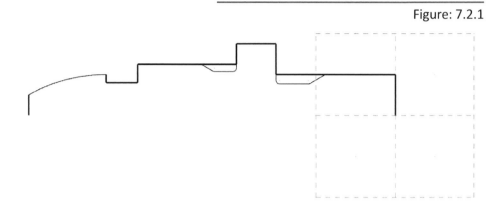

STEP 8: CHAMFER THE PART

In this step we will create two chamfers to complete the part.

Step Preview:

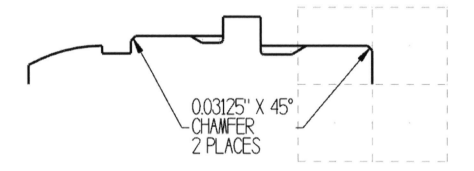

WIREFRAME
• From the **Modify** group, select **Chamfer Entities**.

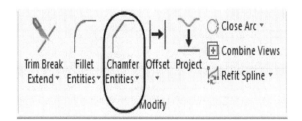

◆ Enter the **Distance** and change the **Method** to **1 Distance** as shown.

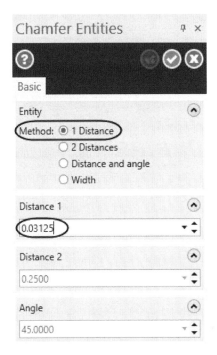

◆ [Select line or arc]: Select **Entity A** as shown in Figure: 8.0.1.
◆ [Select line or arc]: Select **Entity B** as shown in Figure: 8.0.1.

Figure: 8.0.1

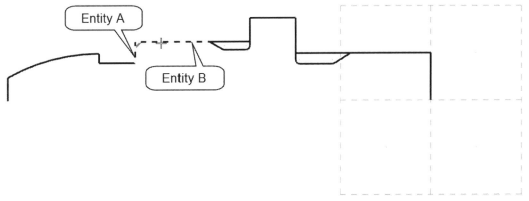

- [Select line or arc]: Select **Entity C** as shown in <u>Figure: 8.0.2</u>.
- [Select line or arc]: Select **Entity D** as shown in <u>Figure: 8.0.2</u>.

Figure: 8.0.2

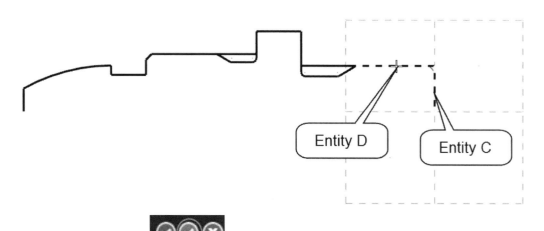

- Select the **OK** button to exit the command.
- The part should appear as shown in <u>Figure: 8.0.3</u>.

Figure: 8.0.3

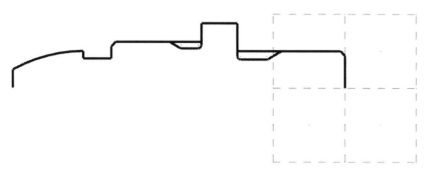

> **NOTE:** The lines at the top of the grooves are not removed as we want do not want the rough and finish toolpaths to cut inside the grooves.

STEP 9: SAVE THE FILE

FILE
- **Save As.**

- Click on the **Browse** icon as shown.
- Find a location on the computer to save your file.
- File name: "Your Name_5".

TOOLPATH CREATION

PART SETUP:

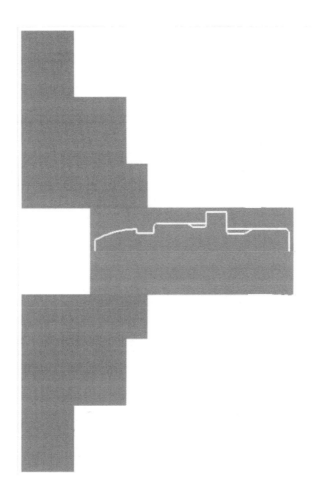

SETUP SHEET:

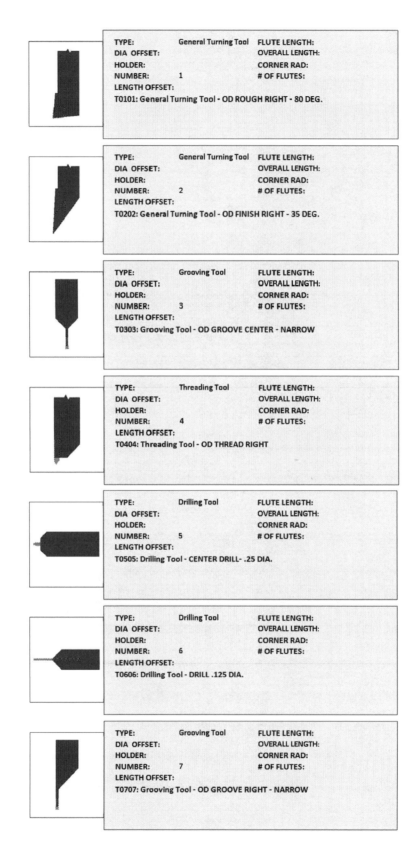

TYPE:	General Turning Tool	FLUTE LENGTH:
DIA OFFSET:		OVERALL LENGTH:
HOLDER:		CORNER RAD:
NUMBER:	1	# OF FLUTES:
LENGTH OFFSET:		

T0101: General Turning Tool - OD ROUGH RIGHT - 80 DEG.

TYPE:	General Turning Tool	FLUTE LENGTH:
DIA OFFSET:		OVERALL LENGTH:
HOLDER:		CORNER RAD:
NUMBER:	2	# OF FLUTES:
LENGTH OFFSET:		

T0202: General Turning Tool - OD FINISH RIGHT - 35 DEG.

TYPE:	Grooving Tool	FLUTE LENGTH:
DIA OFFSET:		OVERALL LENGTH:
HOLDER:		CORNER RAD:
NUMBER:	3	# OF FLUTES:
LENGTH OFFSET:		

T0303: Grooving Tool - OD GROOVE CENTER - NARROW

TYPE:	Threading Tool	FLUTE LENGTH:
DIA OFFSET:		OVERALL LENGTH:
HOLDER:		CORNER RAD:
NUMBER:	4	# OF FLUTES:
LENGTH OFFSET:		

T0404: Threading Tool - OD THREAD RIGHT

TYPE:	Drilling Tool	FLUTE LENGTH:
DIA OFFSET:		OVERALL LENGTH:
HOLDER:		CORNER RAD:
NUMBER:	5	# OF FLUTES:
LENGTH OFFSET:		

T0505: Drilling Tool - CENTER DRILL- .25 DIA.

TYPE:	Drilling Tool	FLUTE LENGTH:
DIA OFFSET:		OVERALL LENGTH:
HOLDER:		CORNER RAD:
NUMBER:	6	# OF FLUTES:
LENGTH OFFSET:		

T0606: Drilling Tool - DRILL .125 DIA.

TYPE:	Grooving Tool	FLUTE LENGTH:
DIA OFFSET:		OVERALL LENGTH:
HOLDER:		CORNER RAD:
NUMBER:	7	# OF FLUTES:
LENGTH OFFSET:		

T0707: Grooving Tool - OD GROOVE RIGHT - NARROW

STEP 10: SET UP THE TOOL SETTINGS AND THE STOCK

In this step you will learn how to assign tool numbers, tool offset numbers, and default values for feeds, speeds, and other toolpath parameters. You will also learn how to define the stock and chuck jaws using the lathe machine groups.

- ◆ Press **Alt + F1** to fit the drawing to the screen.
- ◆ To display the **Toolpaths Manager** panel select the **Toolpaths** tab as shown.

> **NOTE:** If the **Lathe Machine Group** is not displayed in the **Toolpaths Manager,** see **Tutorial 2 page 78.**
> If another machine is already selected, to remove it see **Tutorial 2 page 102.**

- ◆ Select the plus sign in front of **Properties** in the **Toolpaths Manager** to expand the **Toolpaths Group Properties.**

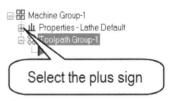

- ◆ Select **Tool settings** to set the tool parameters.

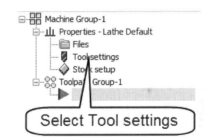

● Change the parameters to match the screenshot in <u>Figure: 10.0.1</u>.

Figure: 10.0.1

Default program number is used to enter a number if your machine requires a number for a program name.

Assign tool numbers sequentially allows you to overwrite the tool number from the library with the next available tool number.

Warn of duplicate tool numbers allows you to get a warning if you enter two tools with the same number.

Override defaults with modal values enables the system to keep the values that you enter.

Feed Calculation set to **From tool** uses the feed rate, plunge rate, retract rate and spindle speed from the tool definition.

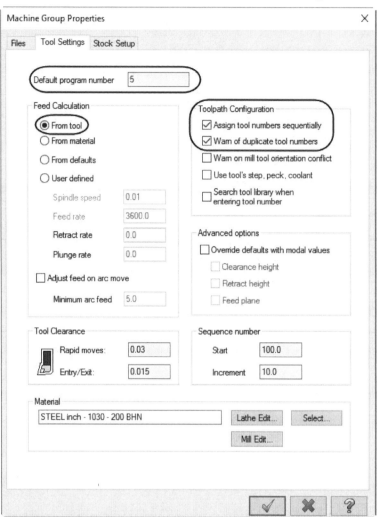

● Select the **Stock Setup** tab.

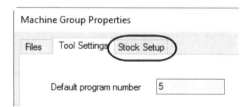

● Choose the **Properties** button to set up the stock for the **Left Spindle**.

• Define the stock by setting the stock geometry to **Cylinder** and entering the stock dimensions. Ensure you enable **Use Margins** and enter in the values as shown in Figure: 10.0.2.

Figure: 10.0.2

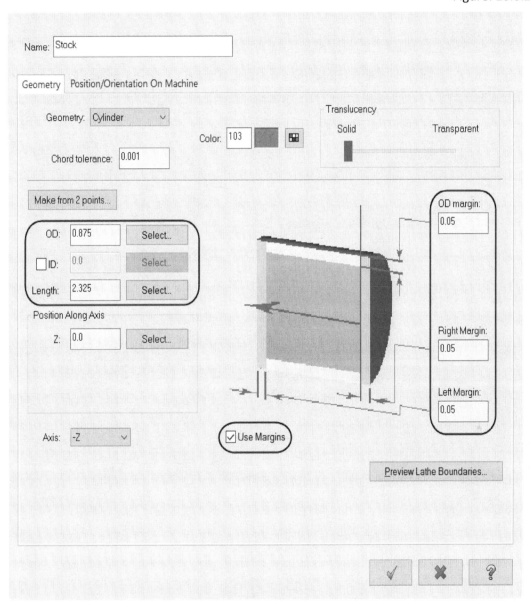

NOTE: The **stock** model that you create can be displayed with the part geometry when viewing the file or the toolpaths, during backplot, or while verifying toolpaths. You can create stock on the left or right spindle.

• Select the **OK** button to exit the **Machine Component Manager - Stock** dialog box.

- Ensure that **Left Spindle** is selected and then select the **Properties** button in the **Chuck Jaws** area as shown.

- Make the necessary changes to define the chuck size, the clamping method and the stock position. Ensure that you choose the clamping method **OD#1** as shown in the graphic below.

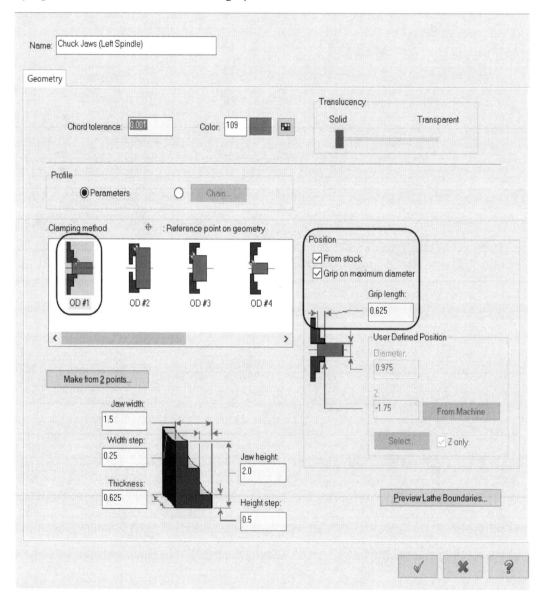

- Select the **OK** button to exit the **Machine Component Manager - Chuck Jaws** dialog box.

♦ Enable **Fit screen to boundaries** in the **Display Options** area.

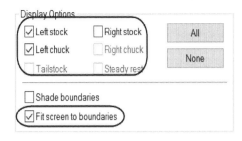

♦ Select the **OK** button to exit the **Machine Group Properties** dialog box.

♦ Press **Alt + F1** to fit the geometry to the screen.

♦ The stock should look as shown in <u>Figure: 10.0.3</u>.

Figure: 10.0.3

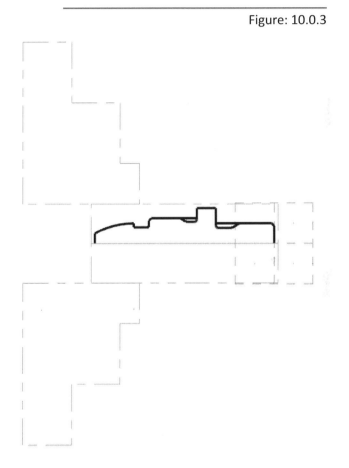

NOTE: The stock is not geometry and cannot be selected.

STEP 11: FACE THE PART

> **NOTE:** To create the **Facing** toolpath, follow the steps in **Tutorial 1** on **page 46**.

Toolpath Preview:

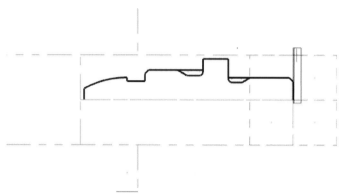

* Press **Alt + T** to remove the toolpath display.

STEP 12: ROUGH THE OD

Rough Toolpaths quickly remove large amounts of stock in preparation for a finish pass. Roughing passes are typically straight cuts parallel to the **Z axis**.

Toolpath Preview:

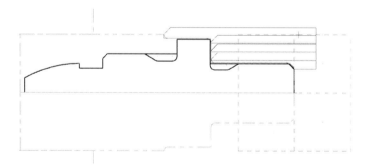

TURNING
* From the **General** group, select the **Rough** icon as shown.

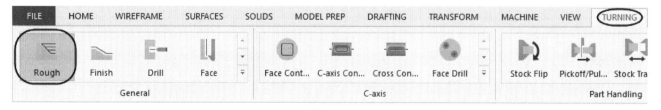

◆ Leave the default parameters in the **Chaining** dialog box.

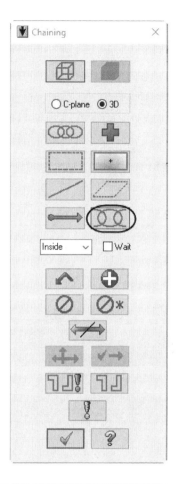

NOTE: The chaining mode is **Partial** by default. You will have to select the first entity and the last entity of the contour.

♦ [Select the entry point or chain the inner boundary]: Select **Entity A.**

NOTE: Make sure that the chaining direction is **CCW**, otherwise select the **Reverse** button in the **Chaining** dialog box.

♦ [Select the last entity]: Select **Entity B.**

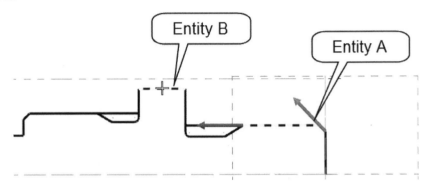

NOTE: A **branch point** will be encountered. This is because the geometry is broken and Mastercam has reached an intersection point and needs to know which path to take to complete the chain.

♦ [Branch point reached. Select next branch.]: Select **Branch A.**

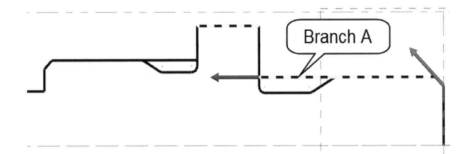

♦ [Branch point reached. Select next branch.]: Select **Branch B.**

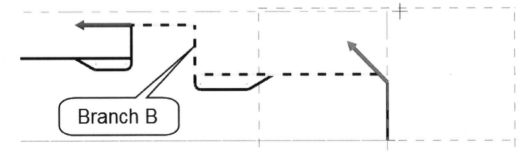

♦ Select the **OK** button to exit the **Chaining** dialog box.

• In the **Toolpath parameters** tab, select the same tool that we used in the facing operation and make all of the necessary changes as shown below.

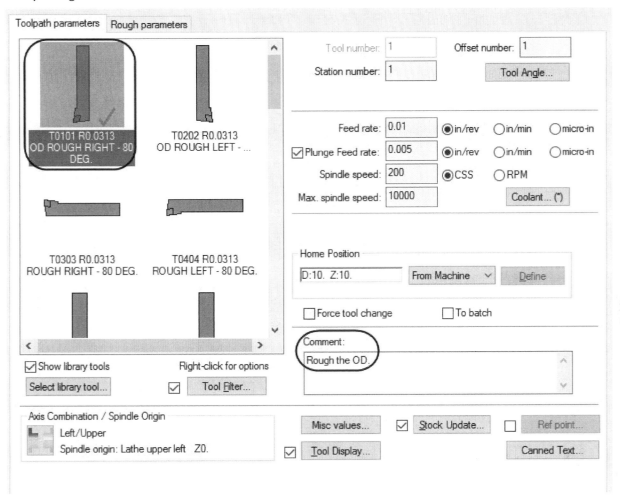

● Select the **Rough parameters** tab and make any changes as shown.

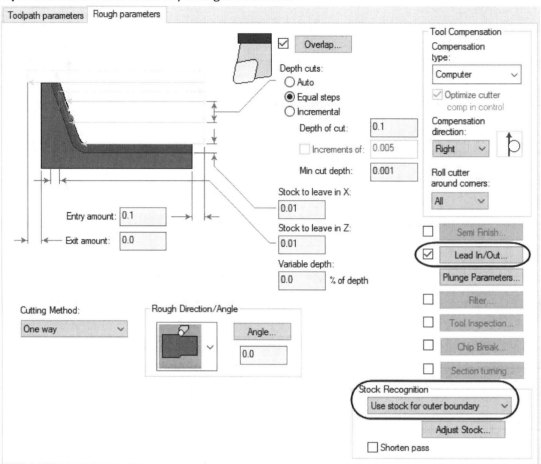

● Select the **Lead In/Out** button as outlined above.
● Select the **Lead out** tab and enable **Add Line** then select the button.

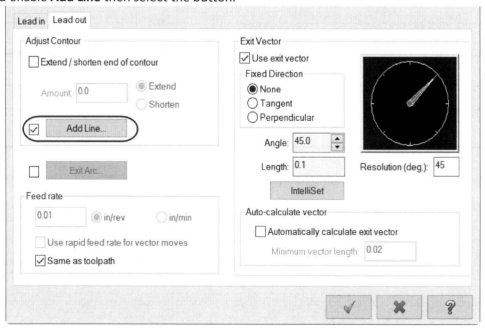

♦ Add a line with a length of **0.125** at an angle of **180 Degrees.**

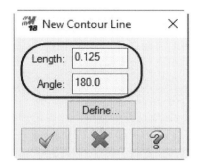

> **NOTE:** Adding a line in the lead out is another way in which you can extend the area that will be machined. This option allows you to create a line that will be added at the end of the chain.

♦ Select the **OK** button to exit the **New Contour Line** dialog box.

♦ Select the **OK** button to exit the **Lead In/Out** dialog box.

♦ Select the **OK** button to exit the **Lathe Rough** dialog box.

12.1 Backplot the toolpaths

♦ Select the **Backplot selected operations** icon.

♦ See **page 49** to review the procedure.

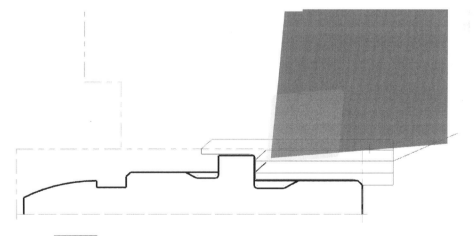

♦ Select the **OK** button to exit **Backplot.**

12.2 Verify the toolpaths

◆ To verify all toolpaths, from the **Toolpaths Manager**, choose the **Select all operations** icon.

◆ Select the **Verify selected operation**s icon.

◆ See **page 51** to review the procedure

• The part should look as shown in <u>Figure: 12.2.1</u>.

Figure: 12.2.1

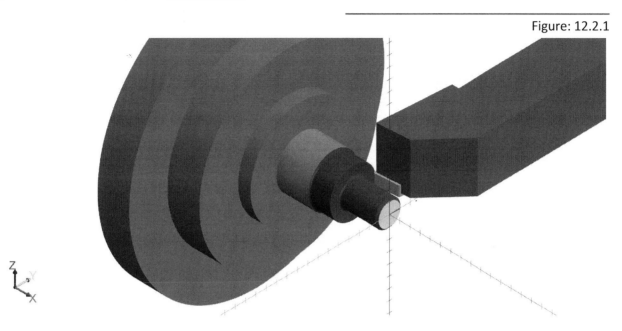

> **NOTE:** To rotate the part, move the cursor to the center of the part and click and hold the mouse wheel and slowly move it in one direction.
> To zoom in or out scroll up or down as needed.

• To go back to the Mastercam window, minimize the **Mastercam Simulator** window as shown.
• Press **Alt + T** to remove the toolpath display.

STEP 13: FINISH THE OD

The **Finish Toolpath** follows the contour of the chained geometry. Typically a finish toolpath follows a roughing toolpath.

Toolpath Preview:

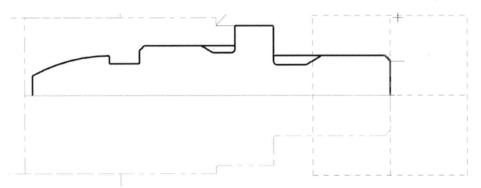

TURNING

♦ From the **General** group, select the **Finish** icon as shown.

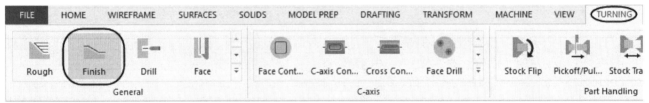

♦ Select the **Last** button in the **Chaining** dialog box to select the chain we selected in the roughing operation.

♦ Select the **OK** button to exit the **Chaining** dialog box.

• Select the **OD Finish Right -35 Degree** tool and enter the comment as shown.

• Select the **Finish parameters** tab and make any changes as shown.

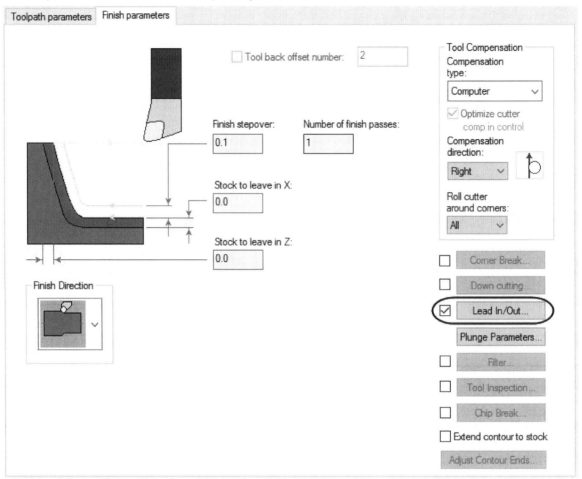

• Select the **Lead In/Out** button as outlined above.
• Select the **Lead out** tab and add a line as outlined on **page 367** to extend the finish operation up to the point that the roughing operation machined to.

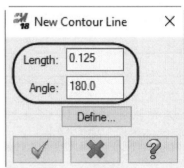

• Select the **OK** button to exit the **New Contour Line** dialog box.
• Select the **OK** button to exit the **Lead In/Out** dialog box.
• Select the **OK** button to exit the **Lathe Finish** dialog box.

13.1 Backplot the toolpath

• Once the operation has been regenerated **Backplot** the toolpath.
• See **page 49** to review the procedure.

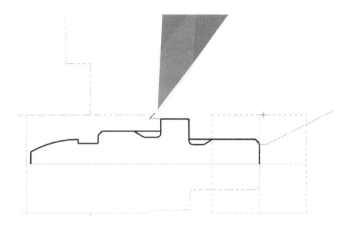

• Select the **OK** button to exit **Backplot**.

13.2 Verify the toolpaths

• To verify all toolpaths, from the **Toolpaths Manager**, choose the **Select all operations** icon.
• Select the **Verify selected operations** icon.

• See **page 51** to review the procedure.

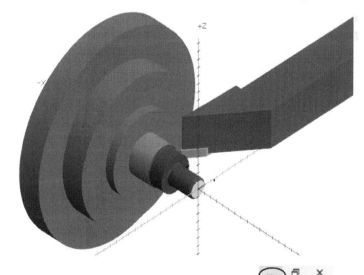

• To go back to the Mastercam window, minimize the **Mastercam Simulator** window as shown.

STEP 14: MACHINE THE 1/2" - 13 UNC RELIEF GROOVE

In this step we will create a groove toolpath to machine the groove behind the area we will thread.

Toolpath Preview:

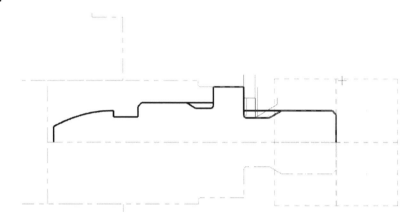

TURNING

- From the **General** group, click on the **Expand gallery** arrow key.

- Select the **Groove** icon.

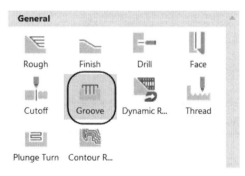

- When the **Grooving Options** dialog box appears choose **Chain** as shown.

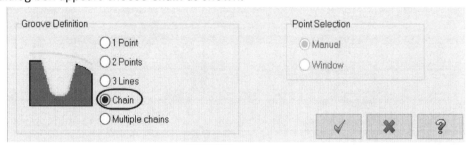

- Select the **OK** button to exit the **Grooving Options** dialog box.

♦ [Select the entry point or chain the inner boundary]: Select **Entity A** (the front of the relief groove) as your first entity as shown.

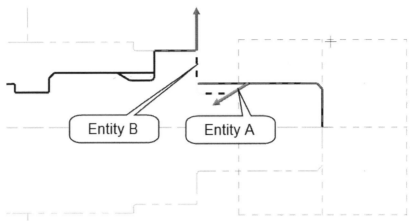

♦ [Select the last entity]: Select **Entity B** (the vertical line) as the last entity as shown above. (You might need to select a branch between **Entity A** and **Entity B**).

♦ Select the **OK** button to exit the **Chaining** dialog box.

♦ Select the **OD Groove Center - Narrow** tool from the tool list and enter the comment as shown.

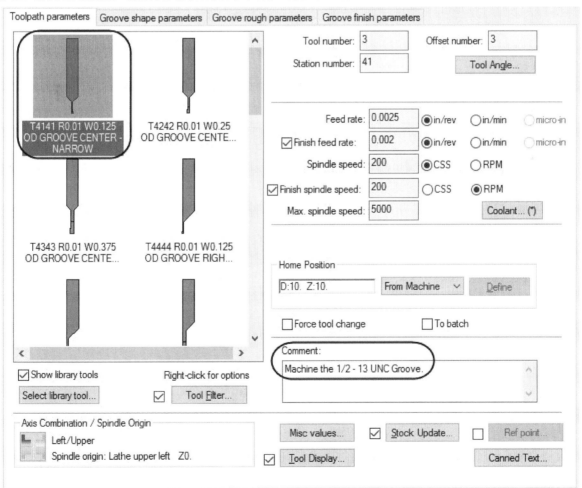

- Select the **Groove shape parameters** tab and enable **Use stock for outer boundary**.

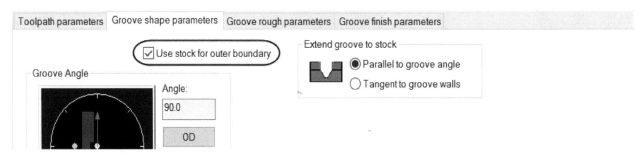

- Select the **Groove rough parameters** tab and make any necessary changes to match the screenshot below.

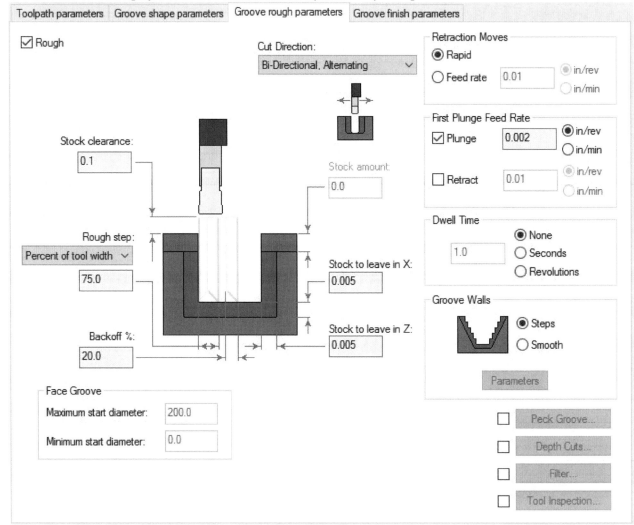

♦ Select the **Groove finish parameters** tab and make any changes as shown.

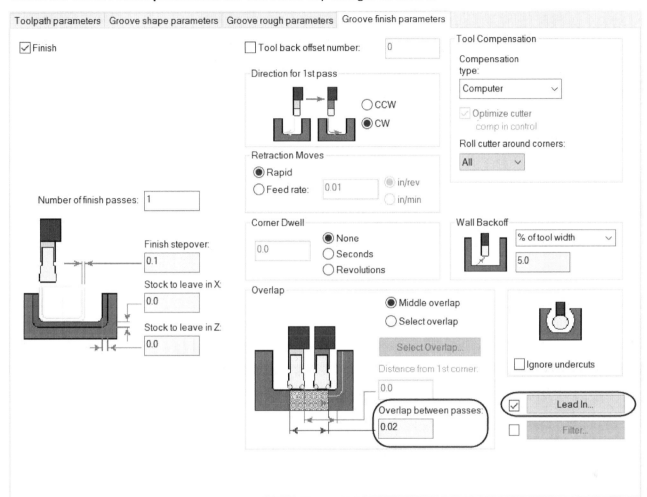

• Select the **Lead In** button and ensure the **First pass lead in** entry vector is set to **Tangent** as shown.

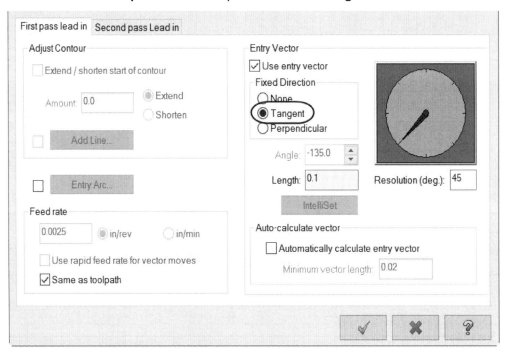

• Select the **Second pass Lead in** tab and ensure the entry vector is the same as shown.

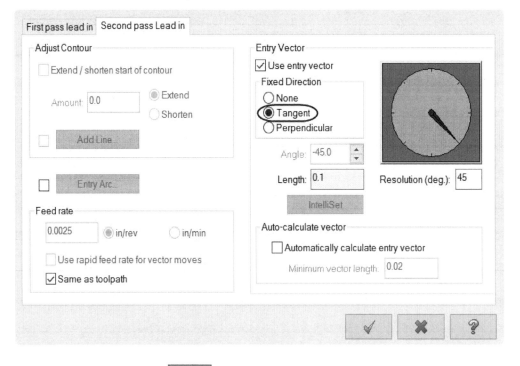

• Select the **OK** button to exit the **Lead In** dialog box.

• Select the **OK** button to exit the **Lathe Groove (Chain)** dialog box.

14.1 Backplot the toolpath

- Once the operation has been regenerated **Backplot** the toolpath.
- See **page 49** to review the procedure.

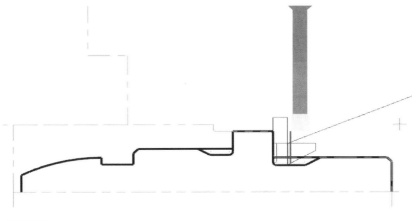

- Select the **OK** button to exit **Backplot**.

14.2 Verify the toolpaths

- To verify all toolpaths, from the **Toolpaths Manager**, choose the **Select all operations** icon.
- See **page 51** to review the procedure.

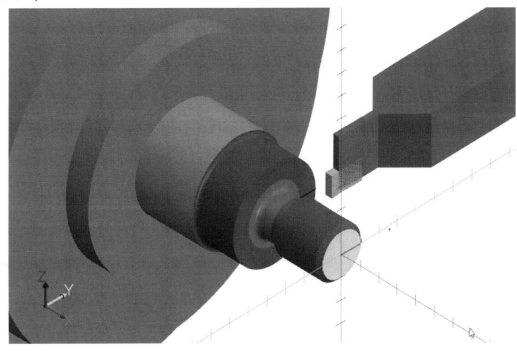

- To go back to the Mastercam window, minimize the **Mastercam Simulator** window as shown.

STEP 15: MACHINE THE 1/2" - 13 UNC THREAD

Thread Toolpaths give you the option to create a screw, bolt or nut. You can program straight threads on the outside, inside, or face of the part. You can also program multiple lead threads.

Toolpath Preview:

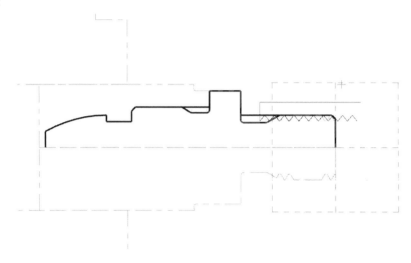

TURNING

◆ From the **General** group, select **Thread**.

NOTE: The toolpath dialog box will open automatically.

◆ Select the **OD Thread Right** tool from the tool list and enter the comment as shown.

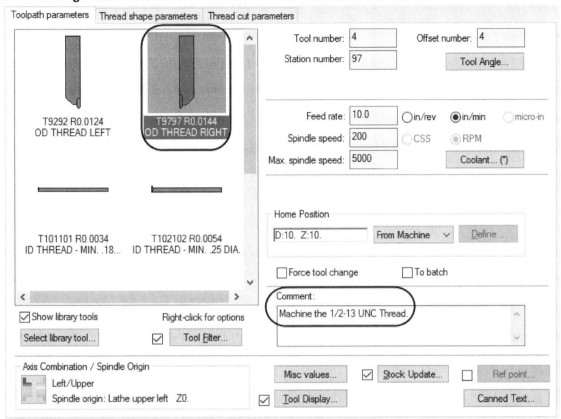

◆ Select the **Thread shape parameters** tab and in the **Thread Form** area click on the **Select from table** button.

Select from table...

◆ Change the **Thread Form** if necessary and select the proper thread from the list as shown.

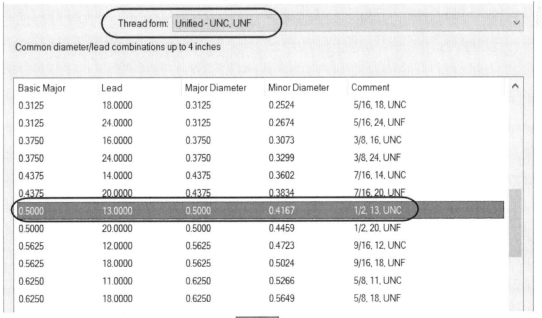

◆ Select the **OK** button to exit the **Thread Table** dialog box.

• Ensure that your parameters match the parameters shown below.

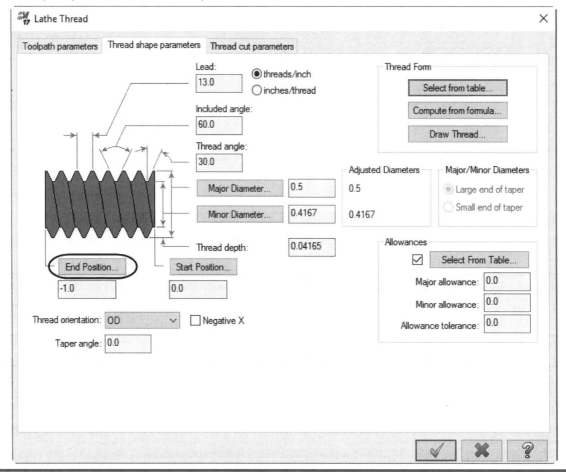

Lead sets the distance a nut would travel if turned once on a bolt of the given thread.

Included angle determines the angle between sides of a thread measured in an axial plane.

Thread angle determines the angle between one side of the thread and a line perpendicular to the thread axis.

Major Diameter sets the thread's largest diameter.

Minor Diameter sets the thread's smallest diameter.

Start Position determines where, on the **Z axis** for OD/ID threads or on the **X axis** for Face/Back threads, the thread will start.

End Position determines where, on the **Z axis** for OD/ID threads or on the **X axis** for Face/Back threads, the thread will end.

• Select the **End Position** button as outlined above.

♦ [End Z: select point]: Mastercam will return you to the graphical user interface, select the **Midpoint** as shown.

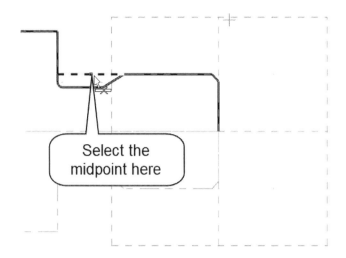

♦ Select the **Start Position** button. Start Position...

♦ [Start Z: select point]: Mastercam will return you to the graphical user interface, select the **Endpoint** as shown.

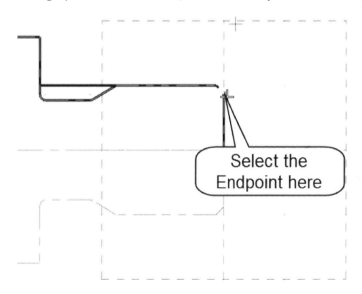

♦ The **Starting Point** and **Ending Point** should appear as shown.

End Position...	Start Position...
-0.596	0.0

♦ Select the **Thread cut parameters** tab and ensure the parameters match the screenshot below.

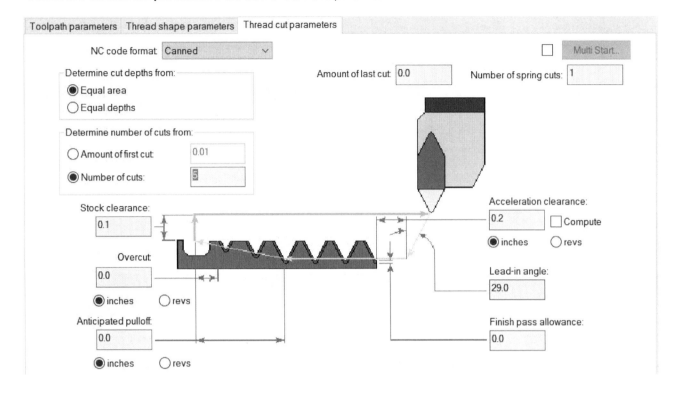

NC Code determines the G-code that displays in the NC file depending on the toolpath you choose; Longhand, Box, Canned or Alternating.

Determine cut depths from determines how the material will be removed; equal amounts of material at each cut or equal depths.

Determine number of cuts from can be set to the amount of the first cut or based on the number of cuts. If you choose the **Amount of the first cut**, the system automatically calculates the number based on the **Amount of the last cut**, the thread shape and the depth of thread.

Stock clearance sets how far above the top of stock the tool retracts between passes.

Overcut sets how far past the end of the thread the tool moves before retracting.

Anticipated pulloff sets the distance from the end of the thread that the tool begins to pull away from the thread.

Acceleration clearance sets the necessary distance in the Z direction for the tool to accelerate to full speed before it starts cutting the thread.

♦ Select the **OK** button to exit the **Lathe Thread** dialog box.

15.1 Verify the toolpaths

◆ To verify all toolpaths, from the **Toolpaths Manager**, choose the **Select all operations** icon.

◆ Click on the **Verify selected operations** icon.

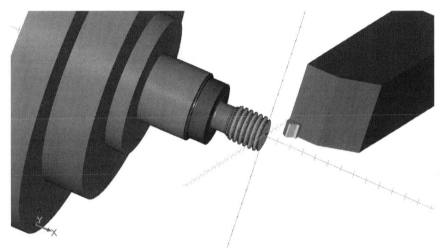

◆ To rotate the part, hold down the mouse wheel and slightly drag the mouse.

◆ See **page 51** to review the procedure.

STEP 16: CENTER DRILL THE PART

The **Drill Toolpath** creates a drilling toolpath on the face of the part along the center line. In this step, we will center drill the face before drilling the part.

Toolpath Preview:

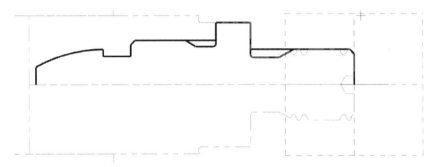

TURNING

• From the **General** group, click on the **Expand gallery** arrow key.

• Select **Drill**.

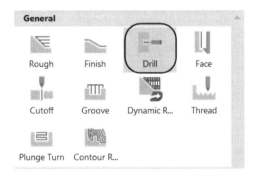

> **NOTE:** The **Lathe Drill Parameters** dialog box will automatically open. No chaining is required because Mastercam drills along the center line to create the toolpath. The drill depths are specified within the dialog box.

• Select the **0.25" Diameter Center Drill** from the tool list and enter the comment as shown.

• Select the **Simple drill - no peck** tab and change the parameters to match the screenshot below.

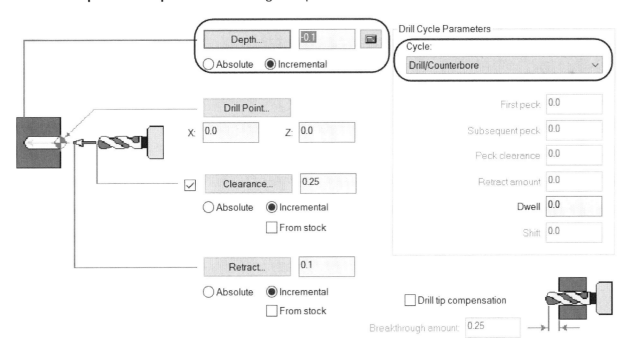

• Select the **OK** button to exit the **Lathe Drill** dialog box.

16.1 Backplot the toolpath

* Once the operation has been regenerated **Backplot** the toolpath.
* See **page 49** to review the procedure.

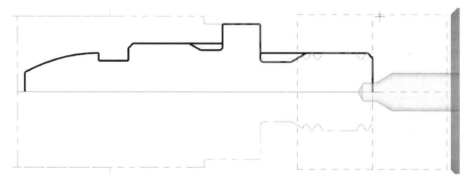

* Select the **OK** button to exit **Backplot**.

16.2 Verify the toolpaths

* To verify all toolpaths, from the **Toolpaths Manager**, choose the **Select all operations** icon.
* See **page 51** to review the procedure.

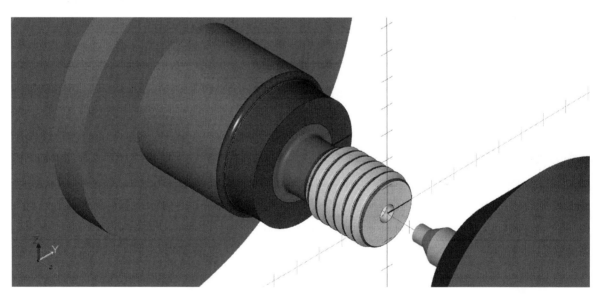

* To go back to the Mastercam window, minimize the **Mastercam Simulator** window as shown.

STEP 17: DRILL THE PART

In this step we will create another drilling operation to drill the part to size from one side. The part will be drilled to just past half of its overall length.

Toolpath Preview:

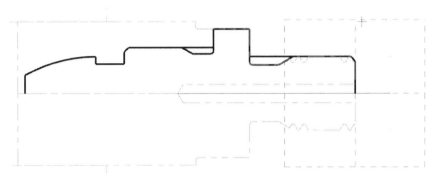

TURNING

* From the **General** group, select the **Drill** icon.

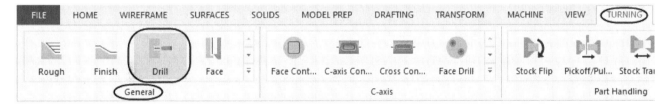

◆ Select the **0.125" Drill** from the tool list and enter the comment as shown.

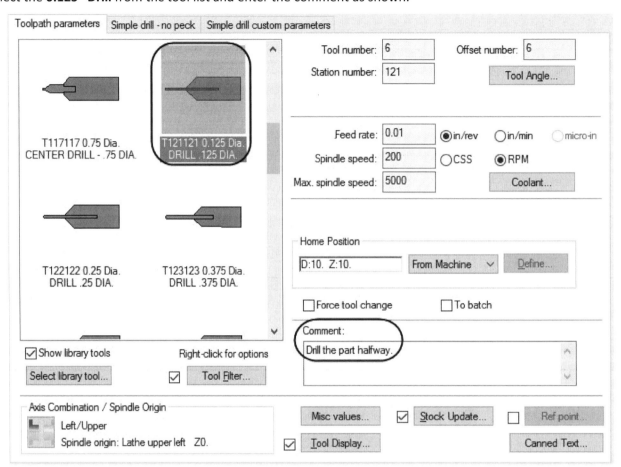

- Select the **Simple drill - no peck** tab and make the changes as shown in the graphic below
- Once Peck Drill is selected, the tab label will change to "Peck drill - full retract".

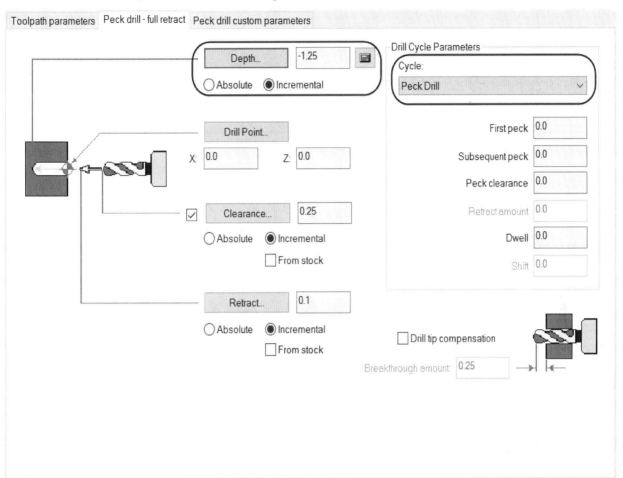

- Select the **OK** button to exit the **Lathe Drill** dialog box.

17.1 Backplot the toolpath

* Once the operation has been regenerated **Backplot** the toolpath.
* See **page 49** to review the procedure.

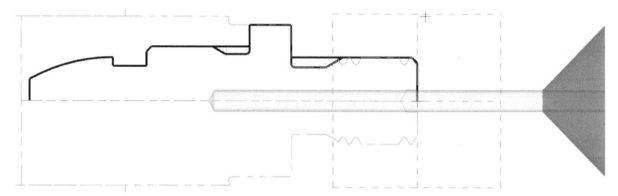

* Select the **OK** button to exit **Backplot**.

17.2 Verify the toolpaths

* To verify all toolpaths, from the **Toolpaths Manager**, choose the **Select all operations** icon.
* See **page 51** to review the procedure.

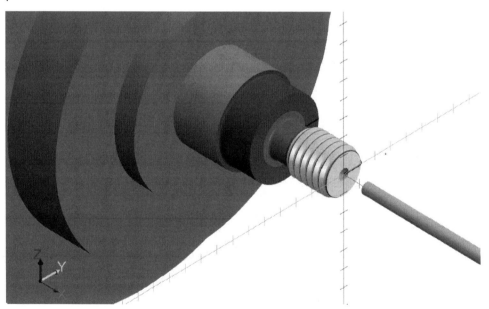

- To see a section through the part, select the **Verify** tab.
- In the **Clipping** group click on the drop down arrow below **XY Clipping Plane** and select **Clip Top** as shown.

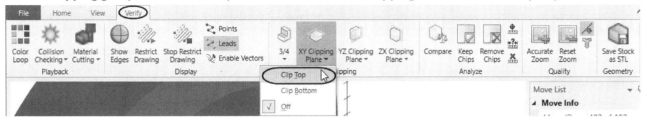

- The geometry should look as shown.

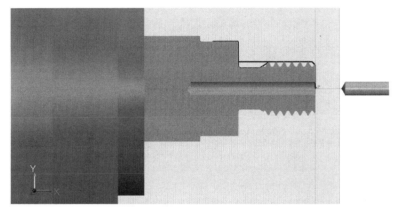

- To remove the section, click on the drop down arrow below **XY Clipping** and select **Off.**

- To go back to the Mastercam window, minimize the **Mastercam Simulator** window as shown.
- Save the file.

STEP 18: FLIP THE PART USING STOCK FLIP

Stock Flip: This option is used if you wish to machine half of the part and then flip the stock to finish the second half (backside) of the part.

Toolpath Preview:

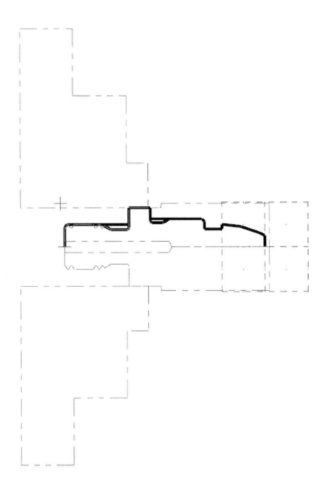

TURNING
• From the **Part Handling** group, select **Stock Flip**.

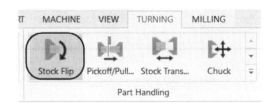

Mastercam 2018

♦ The **Lathe Stock Flip** dialog box will open automatically. Click on the **Select** button as shown.

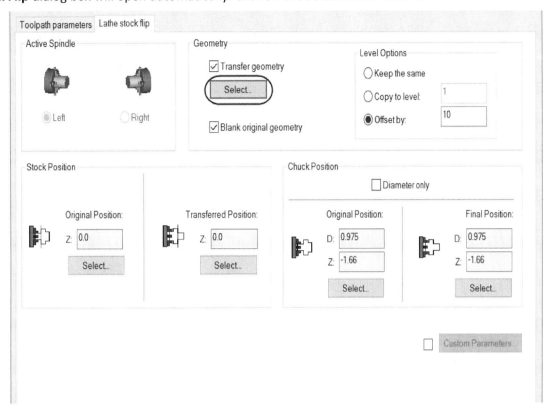

Geometry allows you to select the geometry you wish to include in the stock flip and how you would like to manipulate it. You can keep the original geometry the same, copy the geometry to a certain level or offset the geometry by a number of levels. **Blank original geometry** will hide the original geometry after you create the stock flip.

Stock Position allows you to enter or select values to specify where the stock was originally located and where the stock will be repositioned.

Chuck Position allows you to enter or select values to specify where the chuck was originally located and where the stock will be repositioned.

- [Select entities to transfer]: Click on the **Select all advanced** button on the top left half of the button as shown.

- Click on the **All Entities** button in the dialog box.

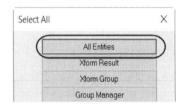

- Press **Enter**.
- When the **Lathe Stock Flip** dialog box appears, click on the **Select** button underneath **Transferred Position** in the **Stock Position** area.

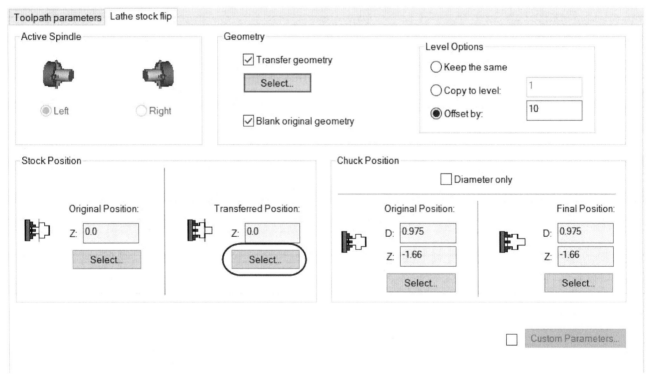

- After clicking on the **Select** button, Mastercam will return you to the graphical user interface to select the geometry you wish to transfer. Select a point to transfer the stock to.

◆ [Select Z position to transfer to]: Select **Endpoint A** as shown.

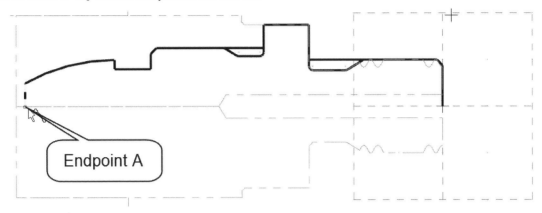

Endpoint A

◆ Enter in the **Final Position** values to specify the new chuck location as shown.

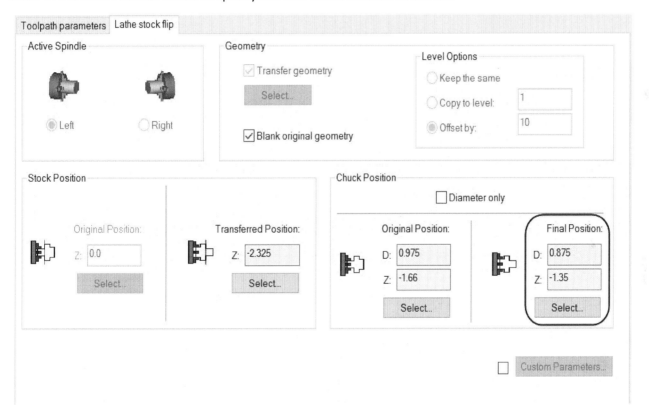

NOTE: The **Final Position** values are based on the drawing. The chuck should grip on the **0.875** diameter.

◆ Select the **OK** button to exit the **Lathe Stock Flip** dialog box.

♦ The Stock Flip should appear as shown.

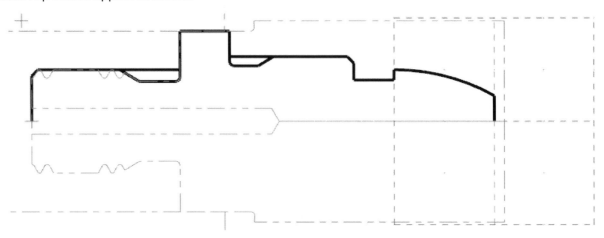

STEP 19: FACE THE FLIPPED PART

> **NOTE:** To create the **Facing** toolpath, follow **Step 9** in **Tutorial 1** on **page 46**.

Toolpath Preview:

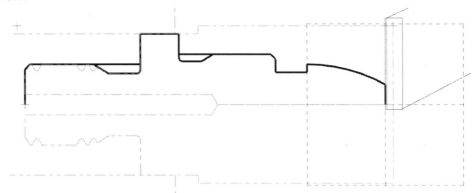

♦ Press **Alt + T** to remove the toolpath display.

STEP 20: ROUGH THE OD OF THE FLIPPED PART

In this step we will rough the OD of the flipped part.

Toolpath Preview:

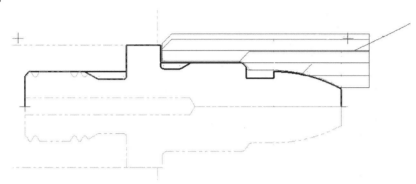

TURNING

• From the **General** group, select the **Rough** icon.

• Leave the default settings in the **Chaining** dialog box.

NOTE: The chaining mode is **Partial** by default. You will have to select the first entity and the last entity of the contour.

- [Select the entry point or chain the inner boundary]: Select **Entity A**.

> **NOTE:** Make sure that the chaining direction is **CCW**, otherwise select the **Reverse** button in the **Chaining** dialog box.

- [Select the last entity]: Select **Entity B**.

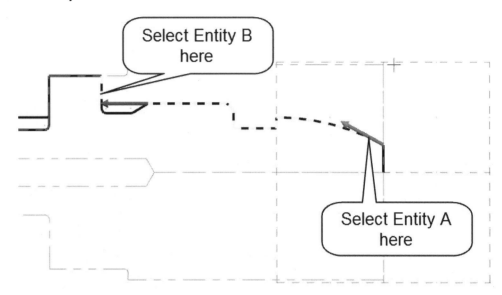

> **NOTE:** A **branch point** will be encountered. This is because the geometry is broken and Mastercam has reached an intersection point and needs to know which path to take to complete the chain.

- [Branch point reached. Select next branch.]: Select **Branch A.**

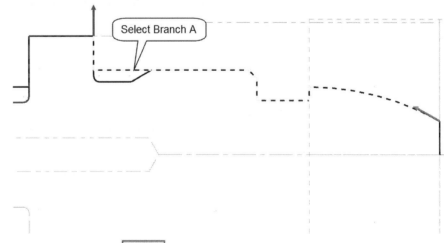

- Select the **OK** button to exit the **Chaining** dialog box.

♦ In the **Toolpath parameters** tab, select the same tool that we used in the facing operation and make all of the necessary changes as shown in the screenshot.

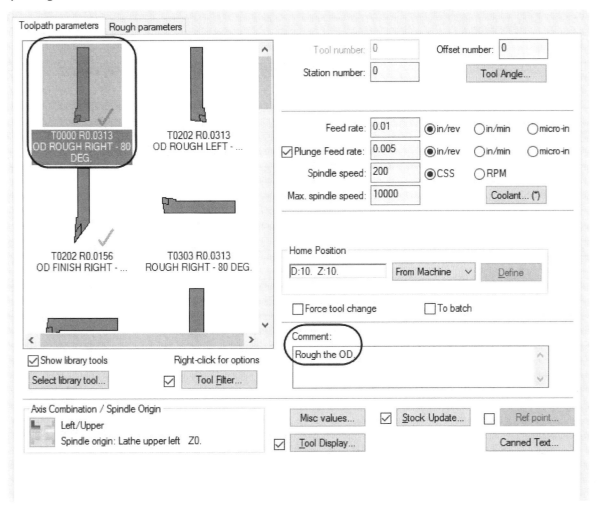

• Select the **Rough parameters** tab and make any changes as shown.

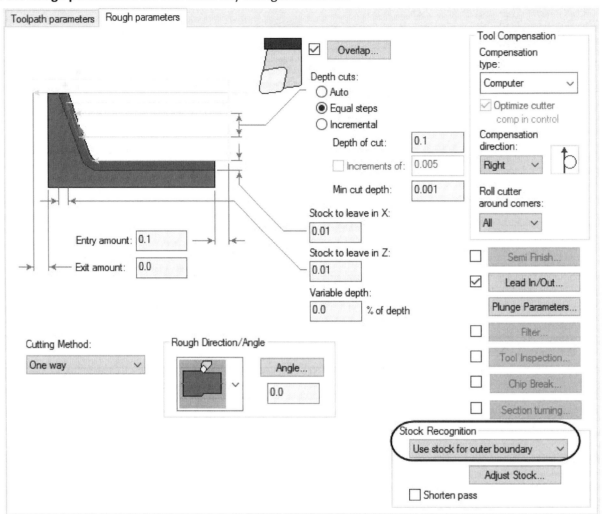

• Select the **OK** button to exit the **Lathe Rough** dialog box.

20.1 Backplot the toolpath

- Once the operation has been regenerated **Backplot** the toolpath.
- See **page 49** to review the procedure.

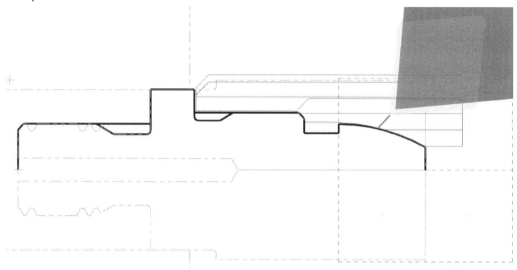

- Select the **OK** button to exit **Backplot**.

20.2 Verify the toolpaths

- Verify operations 9 and 10 from the **Toolpaths Manager**.
- To verify these operations hold down the **Ctrl** key and select the operations accordingly.
- See **page 51** to review the procedure.

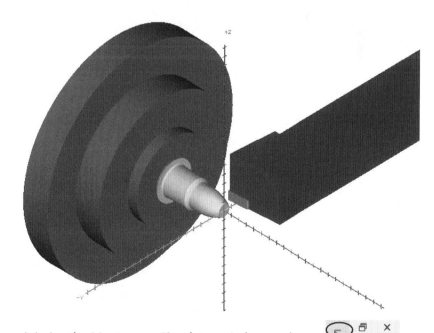

- To go back to the Mastercam window, minimize the **Mastercam Simulator** window as shown.
- If needed, press **Alt + T** to remove the toolpath display.

STEP 21: FINISH THE OD OF THE FLIPPED PART

Toolpath Preview:

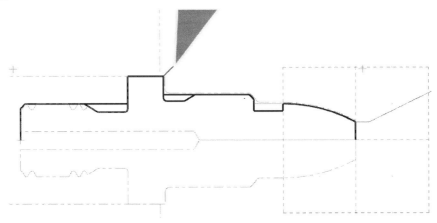

> **NOTE:** To create the **Finish** toolpath, follow **Step 13** on **page 370**. In the **Lead out** tab, disable **Add Line** if necessary.

STEP 22: MACHINE THE GROOVES OF THE FLIPPED PART

In this step we will create a grooving operation with multiple chains to machine both grooves in the same toolpath.

Toolpath Preview:

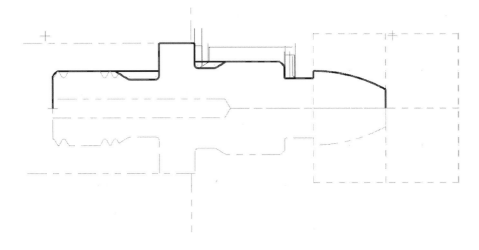

TURNING

- From the **General** group, click on the **Expand gallery** arrow key.

- Select **Groove.**

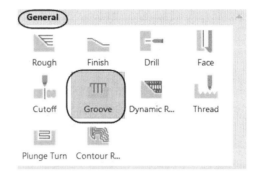

- When the **Grooving Options** dialog box appears choose **Multiple chains** as shown.

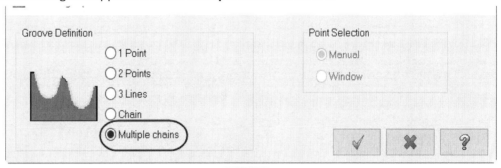

- Select the **OK** button to exit the **Grooving Options** dialog box.
- The **Chaining** dialog box will open; leave **Partial** as the chaining method.

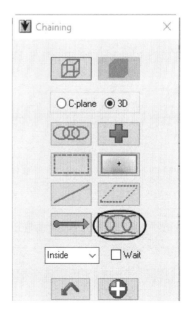

- [Select the entry point or chain the inner boundary]: Select **Entity A** as shown.
- [Select the last entity]: Select **Entity B** as shown.

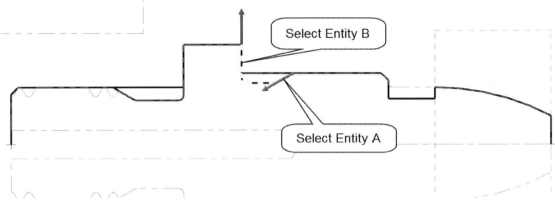

- [Select the inner boundary or select the retraction point or select done]: Select **Entity C** as shown.
- [Select the last entity]: Select **Entity D** as shown.

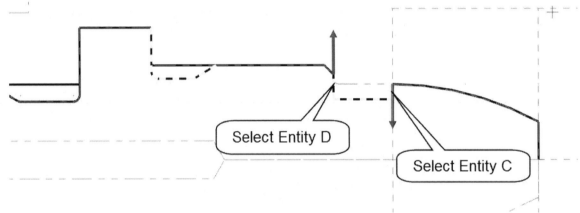

- Select the **OK** button to exit the **Chaining** dialog box.

◆ Select the **OD Groove Right - Narrow** tool from the tool list and enter the comment as shown.

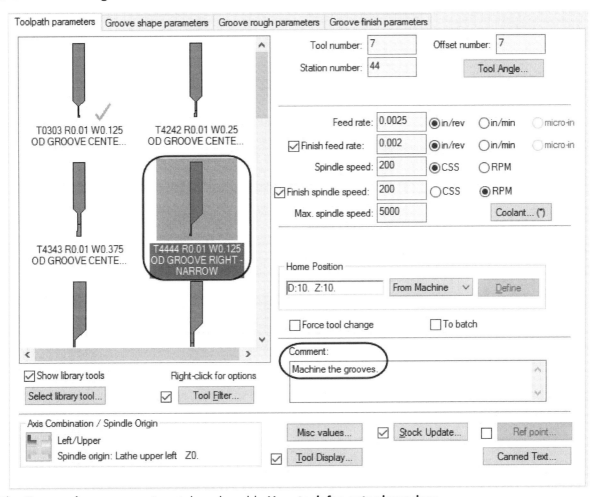

◆ Select the **Groove shape parameters** tab and enable **Use stock for outer boundary.**

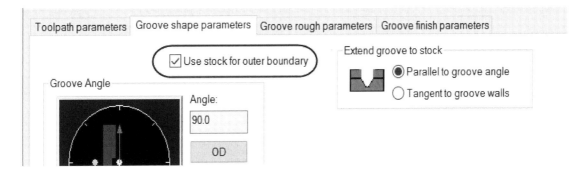

◆ Select the **Groove rough parameters** tab and make any necessary changes as shown.

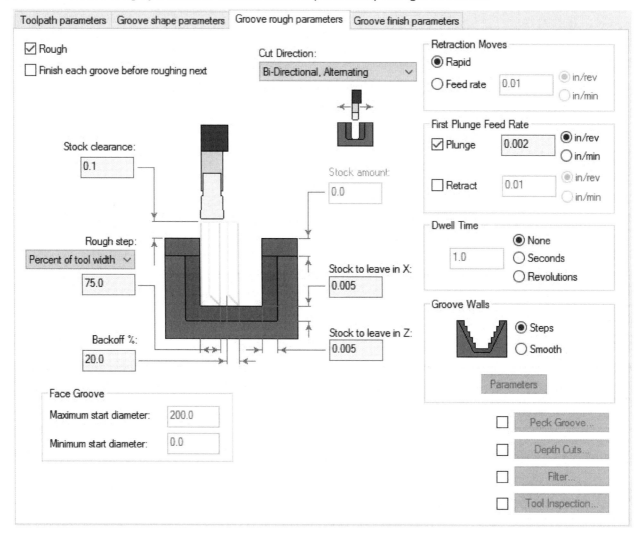

Toolpath parameters | Groove shape parameters | Groove rough parameters | Groove finish parameters

☑ Rough

☐ Finish each groove before roughing next

Cut Direction:

Bi-Directional, Alternating ▽

Retraction Moves

◉ Rapid

◯ Feed rate | 0.01 | ◉ in/rev ◯ in/min

First Plunge Feed Rate

☑ Plunge | 0.002 | ◉ in/rev ◯ in/min

☐ Retract | 0.01 | ◉ in/rev ◯ in/min

Stock clearance: 0.1

Stock amount: 0.0

Dwell Time | 1.0 | ◉ None ◯ Seconds ◯ Revolutions

Rough step: Percent of tool width ▽ | 75.0

Stock to leave in X: 0.005

Groove Walls | ◉ Steps ◯ Smooth | Parameters

Backoff %: 20.0

Stock to leave in Z: 0.005

Face Groove

Maximum start diameter: 200.0

Minimum start diameter: 0.0

☐ Peck Groove...

☐ Depth Cuts...

☐ Filter...

☐ Tool Inspection...

• Select the **Groove finish parameters** tab and make any necessary changes as shown.

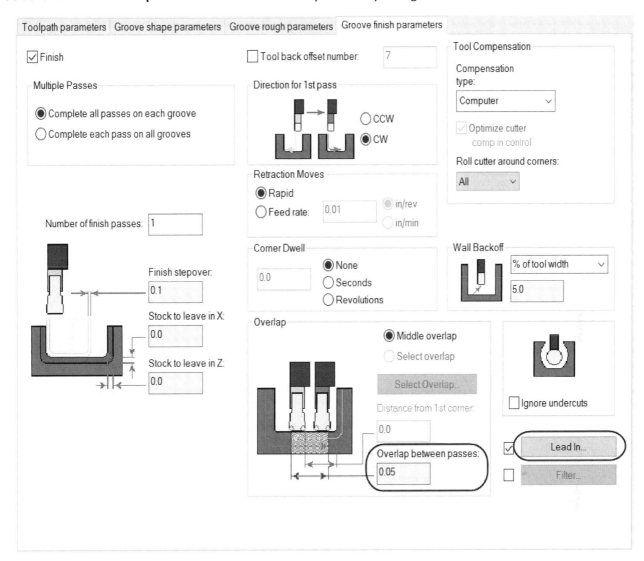

◆ Select the **Lead In** button and ensure the **First pass lead in** entry vector is set as shown.

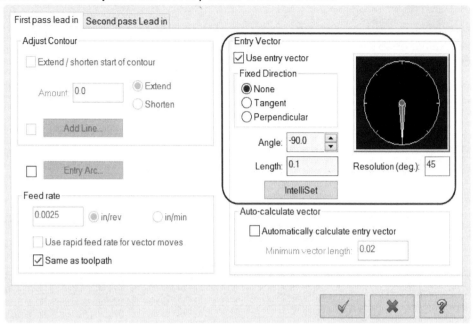

◆ Select the **Second pass Lead in** tab and ensure the entry vector is the same as shown.

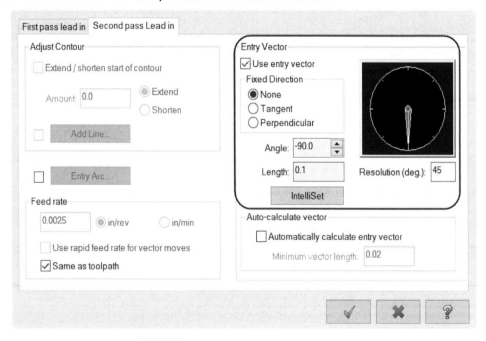

◆ Select the **OK** button to exit the **Lead In** dialog box.

◆ Select the **OK** button to exit the **Lathe Groove (Chain)** dialog box.

22.1 Backplot the toolpath

- Once the operation has been regenerated **Backplot** the toolpath.
- See **page 49** to review the procedure.

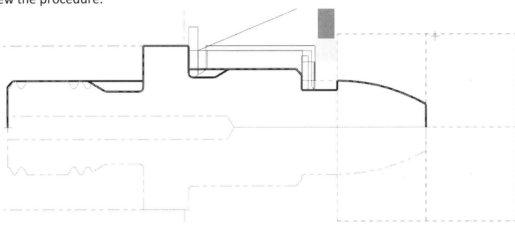

- Select the **OK** button to exit **Backplot**.

22.2 Verify the toolpaths

- Verify operations 9, 10, 11, and 12 from the **Toolpaths Manager**.
- See **page 51** review the procedure.

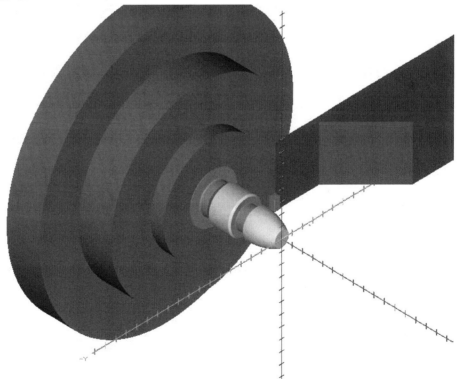

- To go back to the Mastercam window, minimize the **Mastercam Simulator** window as shown.

STEP 23: MACHINE THE 5/8" - 18 UNF THREAD

Thread Toolpaths give you the option to create a screw, bolt or nut. You can program straight threads on the outside, inside, or face of the part. You can also program multiple lead threads.

Toolpath Preview:

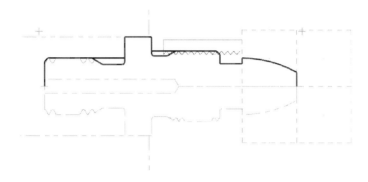

TURNING

◆ From the **General** group, select **Thread**.

> **NOTE:** The toolpath dialog box will open automatically.

• Select the **OD Thread Right** tool from the tool list and enter the comment as shown.

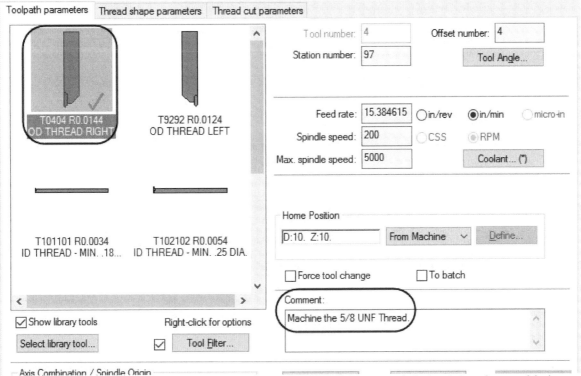

• Select the **Thread shape parameters** tab and from the **Thread Form** group click the **Select from table** button.

Select from table...

• Change the **Thread Form** and select the proper thread from the list as shown.

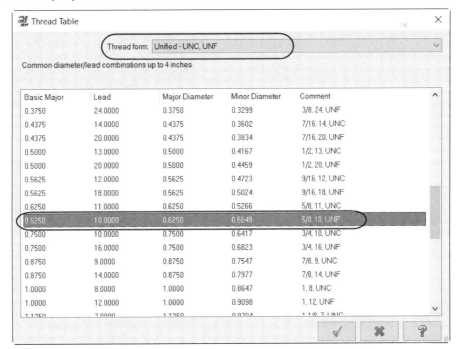

• Select the **OK** button to exit the **Thread Table** dialog box.

• Ensure that the parameters on the **Thread shape parameters** tab match the screenshot below.

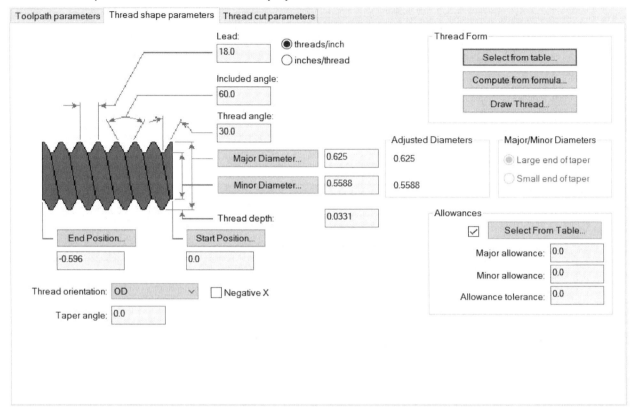

• Select the **End Position** button.

• Mastercam will return you to the graphic user interface. Select the **Midpoint** as shown.

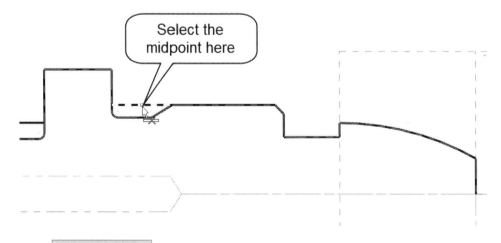

Select the midpoint here

• Select the **Start Position** button.

• Mastercam will return you to the graphic user interface. Select the **Endpoint** as shown.

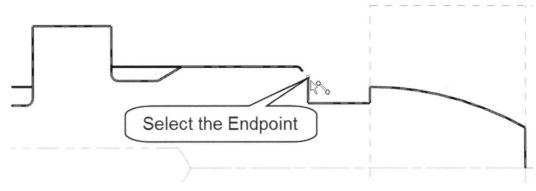

Select the Endpoint

• The **Start Position** and **End Position** should appear as shown.

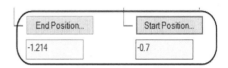

End Position... | Start Position...
-1.214 | -0.7

• Select the **Thread cut parameters** tab and make the changes as shown in the screenshot below.

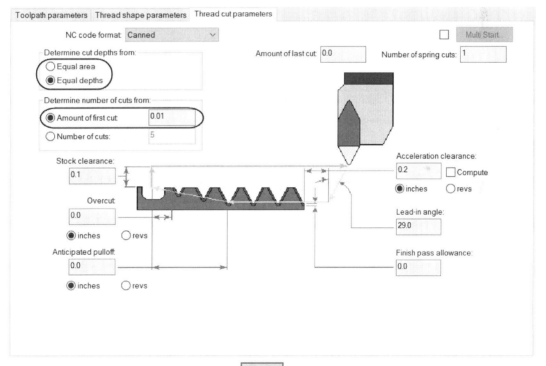

• Select the **OK** button to exit the **Lathe Thread** dialog box.

23.1 Verify the toolpaths

- To verify only operations 9, 10, 11, 12, and 13, hold down the **Ctrl** key and select them from the **Toolpaths Manager**.
- See **page 51** to review the procedure.

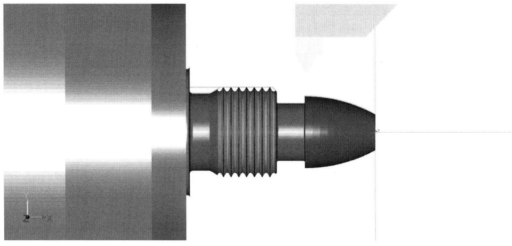

- To go back to the Mastercam window, minimize the **Mastercam Simulator** window as shown.

STEP 24: CENTER DRILL THE FLIPPED PART

Drill Toolpaths create a drilling toolpath on the face of the part along the center line. In this step we will center drill the face before drilling the part.

Toolpath Preview:

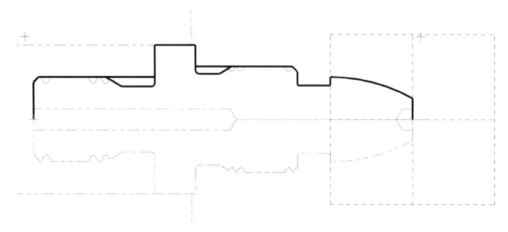

TURNING

- From the **General** group, click on the **Expand gallery** arrow key.
- Select the **Drill** icon.

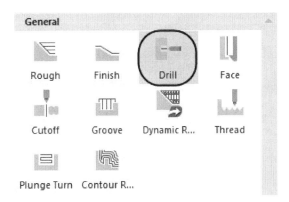

NOTE: The **Lathe Drill** dialog box will automatically open. No chaining is required because Mastercam drills along the center line to create the toolpath. The drill depths are specified within the dialog box.

- Select the **0.25" Diameter Center Drill** from the tool list and enter the comment as shown.

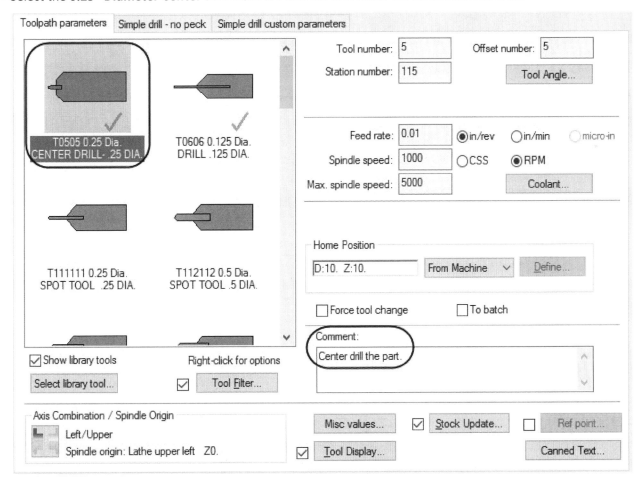

♦ Select the **Simple drill - no peck** tab and change the parameters to match the screenshot below.

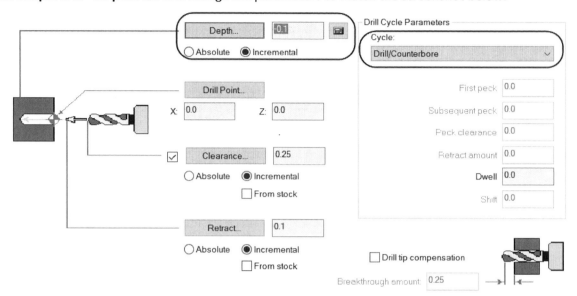

♦ Select the **OK** button to exit the **Lathe Drill** dialog box. ✓

24.1 Backplot the toolpath

♦ Once the operation has been regenerated **Backplot** the toolpath.
♦ See **page 49** to review the procedure.

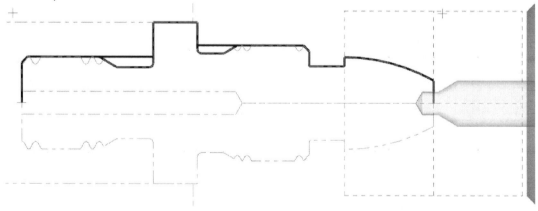

♦ Select the **OK** button to exit **Backplot**. ✓

24.2 Verify the toolpaths

◆ Verify operations 9, 10, 11, 12, 13, and 14 from the **Toolpaths Manager**.
◆ See **page 51** to review the procedure.

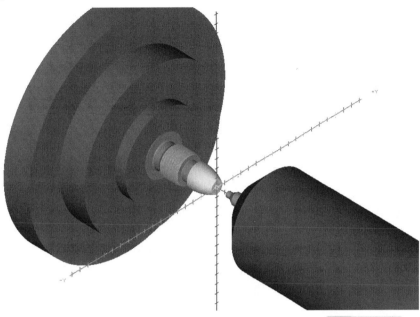

◆ To go back to the Mastercam window, minimize the **Mastercam Simulator** window as shown.

STEP 25: DRILL THE FLIPPED PART

In this step we will create another drilling operation to drill the part to size from the other side. The part will be drilled to just past half of its overall length.

Toolpath Preview:

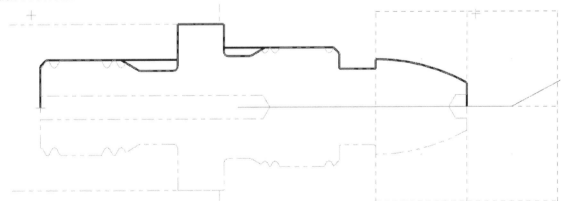

TURNING

• From the **General** group, select the **Drill** icon.

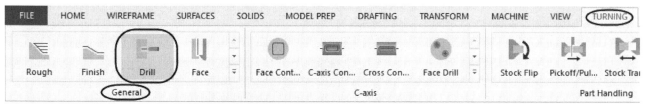

• Select the **0.125" Drill** from the tool list and enter the comment as shown.

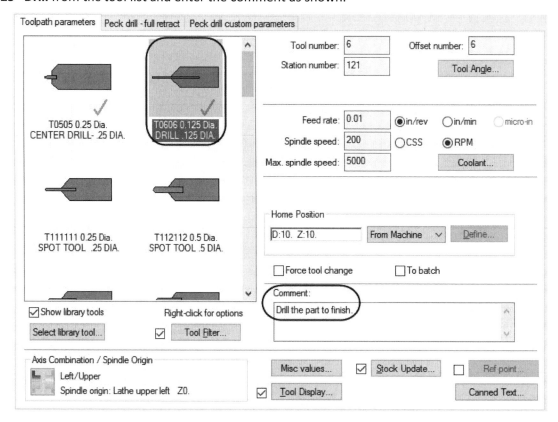

NOTE: The **Lathe Drill** dialog box will automatically open. No chaining is required because Mastercam drills along the center line to create the toolpath. The drill depths are specified within the dialog box.

• Select the **Simple drill - no peck** tab and make the changes as shown in the graphic below.

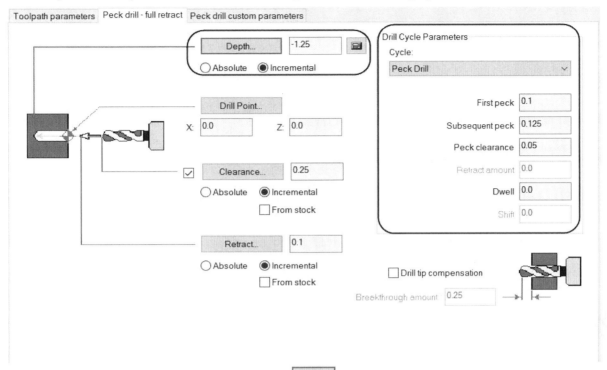

• Select the **OK** button to exit the **Lathe Drill** dialog box.

25.1 Backplot the toolpath

• Once the operation has been regenerated **Backplot** the toolpath.
• See **page 49** to review the procedure.

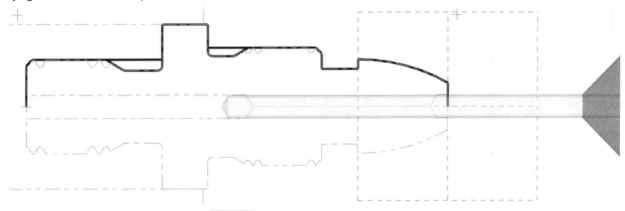

• Select the **OK** button to exit **Backplot**.

25.2 Verify the toolpaths

♦ Verify operations 9, 10, 11, 12, 13, 14, and 15 from the **Toolpaths Manager**.
♦ See **page 51** to review the procedure.

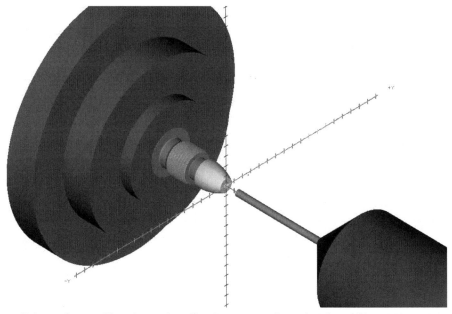

♦ To see a section through the part, click on the **Verify** tab. In the **Clipping** area select the drop down arrow on the **3/4** icon and select **3nd quadrant** as shown.

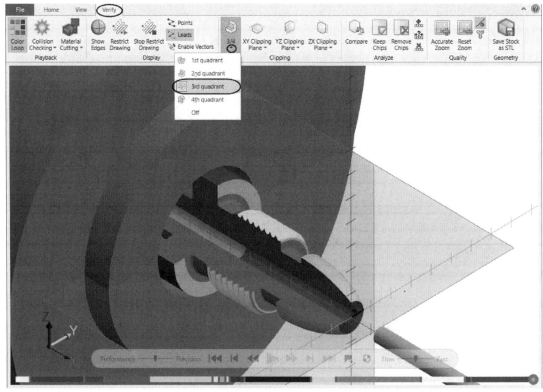

♦ To exit Mastercam Simulator click on the **Close** icon.

STEP 26: RUN THE POST PROCESSOR TO OBTAIN THE G-CODE FILE

Post Processing refers to the process by which the toolpaths in your Mastercam part files are converted to a format that can be understood by your machine tool's control. A special program reads your Mastercam file and writes the appropriate NC code.

- Make sure that all operations are selected, otherwise click on the **Select all operations** icon.
- Select the **Post selected operations** icon from the **Toolpaths Manager.**

- In the **Post processing** dialog box, make all of the necessary changes as shown.

NC File enabled allows you to keep the NC file and to assign the same name as the MCAM file.

Edit enabled allows you to automatically launch the default editor.

- Select the **OK** button to continue.
- Save the NC file.

• The **Mastercam Code Expert** window will be launched and the NC program will appear as shown.

```
1    %
2    O0005
3    (PROGRAM NAME - TUTORIAL #5 TOOLPATH)
4    (DATE=DD-MM-YY - 13-01-17 TIME=HH:MM - 10:51)
5    (MCX FILE - C:\USERS\GONG.ZHANG\DOCUMENTS\MASTERCAM\LATHE\TUTORIAL #5 TOOLPATH.MCAM)
6    (NC FILE - C:\USERS\GONG.ZHANG\DOCUMENTS\MASTERCAM\LATHE\TUTORIAL #5 TOOLPATH.NC)
7    (MATERIAL - STEEL INCH - 1030 - 200 BHN)
8    G20
9    (TOOL - 1 OFFSET - 1)
10   (OD ROUGH RIGHT - 80 DEG.  INSERT - CNMG-432)
11   ( FACE THE OD. )
12   G0 T0101
13   G18
14   G97 S711 M03
15   G0 G54 X1.075 Z.01 M8
16   G50 S3600
17   G96 S200
18   G99 G1 X-.0625 F.01
19   G0 Z.11
20   X1.075
21   Z0.
22   G1 X-.0625
23   G0 Z.1
24   ( ROUGH THE OD. )
25   X.7944
26   Z.21
27   G1 Z.11
28   Z-.74
29   X.8125
30   G18 G3 X.895 Z-.7813 K-.0413
31   G1 Z-1.115
32   X.975
```

• Select the **"X"** box at the upper right corner to exit the editor.

STEP 27: SAVE THE UPDATED MCAM FILE

REVIEW EXERCISE - STUDENT PRACTICE

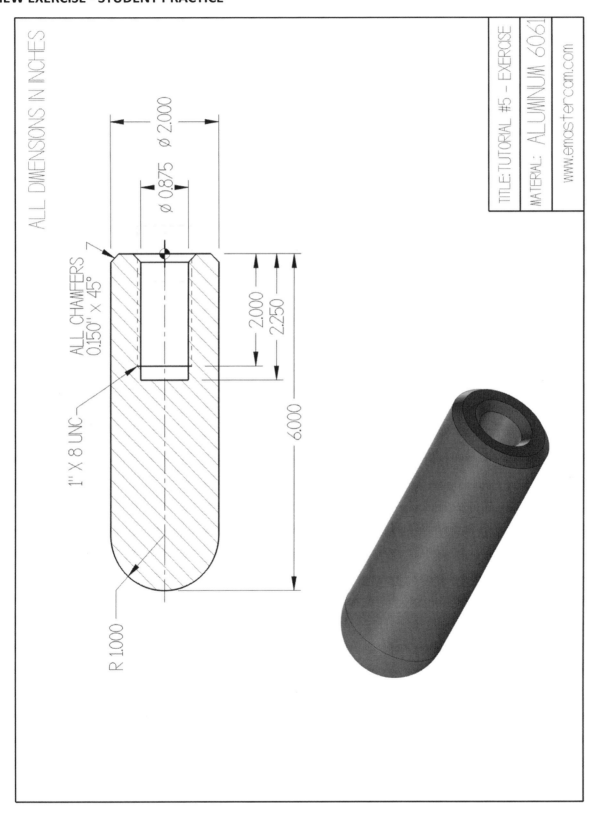

ALL DIMENSIONS IN INCHES

Ø 2.000

Ø 0.875

ALL CHAMFERS
0.150" x 45°

1" X 8 UNC

2.000

2.250

6.000

R 1.000

TITLE: TUTORIAL #5 - EXERCISE

MATERIAL: ALUMINUM 6061

www.emastercam.com

CREATE THE GEOMETRY FOR TUTORIAL #5 EXERCISE

Use these commands to create the top half of the geometry.
- Rectangle.
- Line Parallel.
- Chamfer.
- Arc Polar
- Trim Break Extend.

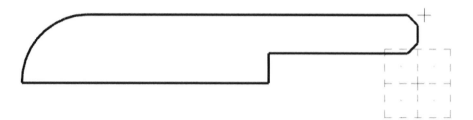

CREATE THE TOOLPATHS FOR TUTORIAL #5 EXERCISE

Create the Toolpaths for Tutorial #5 Exercise as per the instructions below.

Set the machine properties including the stock.
Face and Rough the chamfer on the OD.
The stock diameter is the same as the OD of the finished part.
The stock length is bigger on both sides.
- Use the stock setup to define the face operation.
- Use the OD Rough Right tool for the facing and roughing operations.

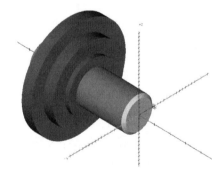

Spot Drill and Drill out the middle of the part.
- Use a large spot drill as your first operation.
- Use the depth calculator to spot drill to the appropriate depth.
- Use a large drill bit to drill out the bulk of the material from the center of the part.
- Select a suitable drill cycle for drilling.
- Also use a Flat Endmill with a final drilling operation to remove the material left by the drill tip from the center hole.

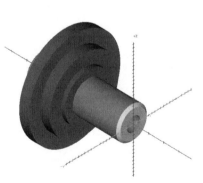

Machine the bottom chamfer and ID on the part with a boring bar.

◆ Chain the ID contour CCW.

◆ Use an ID Rough boring bar for the roughing toolpath to cut the interior to the correct size.

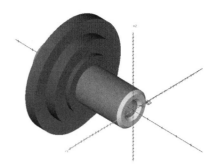

Thread the ID.

◆ Use an **ID THREAD - MIN 0.5 DIA** tool to thread the part.

◆ Use the Select from table option to find the **1" X 8 thread**.

◆ Select the appropriate starting position and ending position as dictated by the drawing. If the holder collides with the stock, select the tool from the **Toolpaths Manager** as shown.

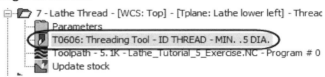

◆ In the **Define Tool** dialog box, click on the **Holders** tab and change the **Shank Cross Section** to circular as shown.

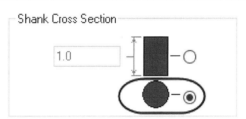

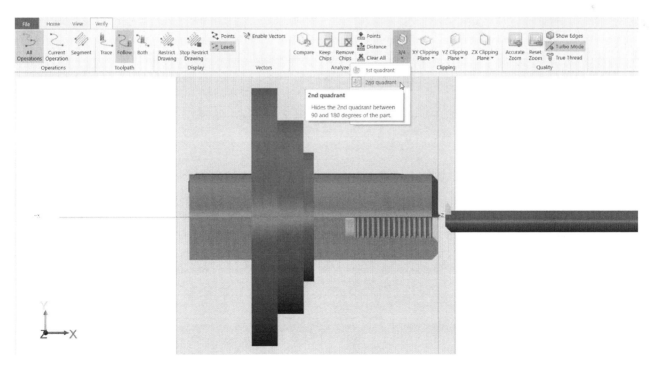

Flip the part.

- Select the geometry first. You may choose to offset the geometry to another level and blank the original geometry if you wish.
- Use the parameters shown below to help you establish the location of the stock flip.
- If you continue to have issues regenerating the Stock Flip try deleting the operation and beginning from scratch.

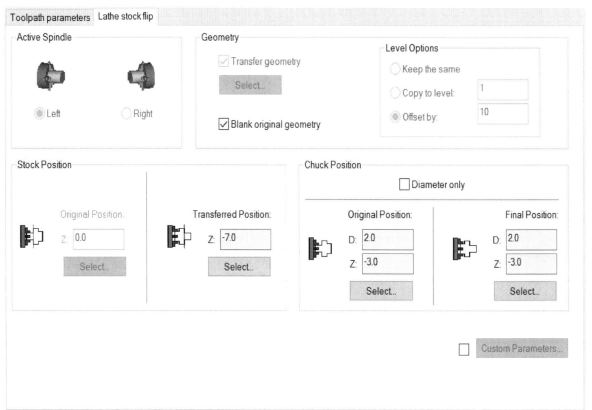

Rough and Finish the rounded face.

- Use the OD Rough Right tool to rough out the material.
- Use the OD Finish Right tool to finish the rounded face.
- Use Lead In/Out and extend the end of the contour for both toolpaths so that the tool machines past the geometry.

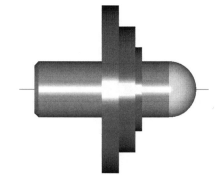

NOTES:

TUTORIAL #5 QUIZ

• What options does the Thread toolpath give you?

• Why would you flip the stock?

• What operation would you use to cut a chamfer on the inside of the part?

TUTORIAL #6

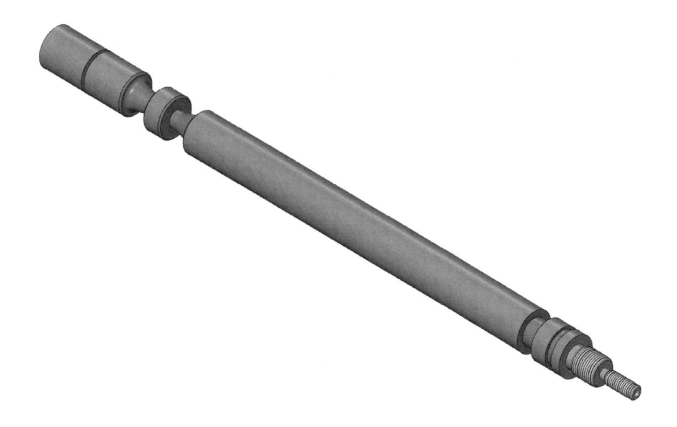

OVERVIEW OF STEPS TAKEN TO CREATE THE FINAL PART:

From drawing to CAD model:
* From the drawing we can gain an idea as to how to create the geometry in Mastercam.
* The student will need to create the geometry used to machine the OD of the part.
* The drawing should also include relief grooves for the threads.

Create the 2D CAD Model used to generate toolpaths from:
* The student will create the upper profile of the part. Only half of the geometry is needed to create the toolpaths necessary to machine the part.
* Create rectangle and create line will be used to make the outside profile of the part.

Create the necessary toolpaths to machine the part:
* The student will face, rough, finish, groove, thread and center drill the right hand side of the part with the stock only part way out of the chuck.
* A tailstock will be defined, and a tailstock operation will be created to advance the tailstock when needed.
* A stock advance operation will advance the stock in the chuck before the tail stock is advanced and the grooves will be machined.

Backplot and Verify the file:
* The Backplot will be used to simulate a step by step process of the tool's movements.
* The Verify will be used to watch a tool machine the part out of a solid model.

Post Process the file to generate the G-code:
* The student will then post process the file to obtain an NC file containing the necessary code for the machine.

 This tutorial takes approximately one hour to complete.

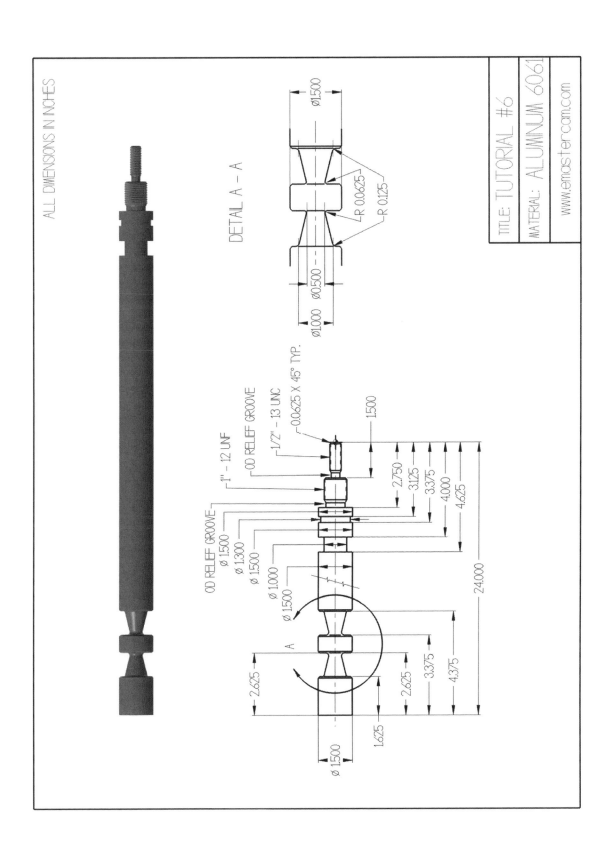

ALL DIMENSIONS IN INCHES

DETAIL A – A

Ø1.500

R 0.0625
R 0.125

Ø0.500
Ø1.000

TITLE: TUTORIAL #6
MATERIAL: ALUMINUM 6061
www.emastercam.com

1" – 12 UNF
OD RELIEF GROOVE
1/2" – 13 UNC
0.0625 X 45° TYP.

1500

2.750
3.125
3.375
4.000
4.625

OD RELIEF GROOVE
Ø 1.500
Ø 1.300
Ø 1.500
Ø 1.000
Ø 1.500

24.000

A

2.625

2.625
3.375
4.375

Ø 1.500

1.625

GEOMETRY CREATION

STEP 1: SETTING UP THE GRAPHIC USER INTERFACE

Please refer to the **Getting Started** section to set up the graphical user interface accordingly.

STEP 2: CREATE A RECTANGLE TO REPRESENT THE OUTSIDE PROFILE

In this step you will learn how to create a rectangle given the width, the height, and the anchor position.

Step Preview:

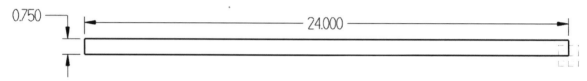

2.1 Create the 24.0" by 0.75" rectangle

WIREFRAME
* From the **Shapes** group, select **Rectangle.**

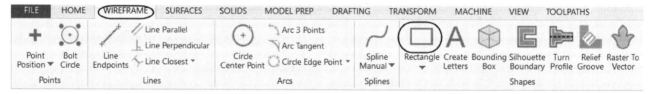

* Enter the **Width** and the **Height** as shown.
* Make sure **Anchor to center** and **Create surface** are not selected.

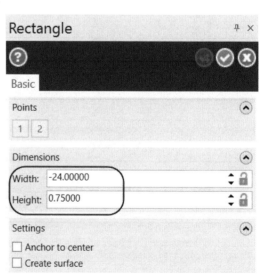

• To select the position of the base point, from the **General Selection** toolbar, click on the drop down arrow next to **AutoCursor** as shown.

• From the fly-out, menu select **Origin**.

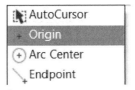

• To see the entire rectangle, right mouse click in the graphics window and select **Fit** as shown.

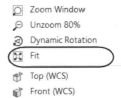

NOTE: To fit the geometry to the screen you can also press **Alt + F1**.

• A preview of the geometry should look as shown.

NOTE: The geometry should appear in a cyan blue color which is the color for live entities. While the rectangle is live you can adjust the dimensions or select a new base point.

• Select the **OK** button to exit the **Rectangle** command.

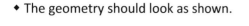
• The geometry should look as shown.

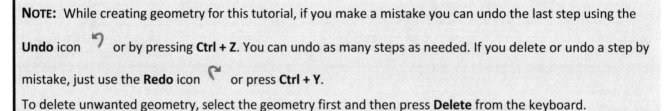

> **NOTE:** While creating geometry for this tutorial, if you make a mistake you can undo the last step using the
>
> **Undo** icon   🜋   or by pressing **Ctrl + Z**. You can undo as many steps as needed. If you delete or undo a step by
>
> mistake, just use the **Redo** icon   ↻   or press **Ctrl + Y**.
>
> To delete unwanted geometry, select the geometry first and then press **Delete** from the keyboard.
>
> To zoom or unzoom, move the cursor to the center of the geometry and scroll up or down on the mouse wheel.

STEP 3: CREATE PARALLEL LINES

In this step you will create parallel lines to serve as construction lines for the creation of the grooves on the left hand side of the part.

Step Preview:

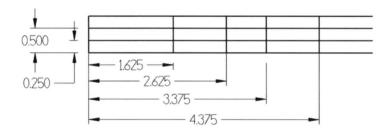

3.1 Create the vertical lines

• Move the cursor to the top left corner of the geometry and scroll the mouse wheel upwards to zoom in as shown.

WIREFRAME

• From the **Lines** group, select **Line Parallel**.

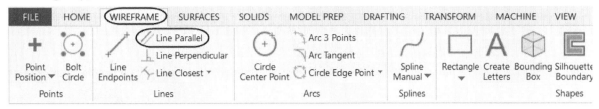

• [Select a line]: Select **Entity A** as shown in Figure: 3.1.1.
• [Select the point to place a parallel line through]: Click on a point to the right of **Entity A** as shown in Figure: 3.1.1.

Figure: 3.1.1

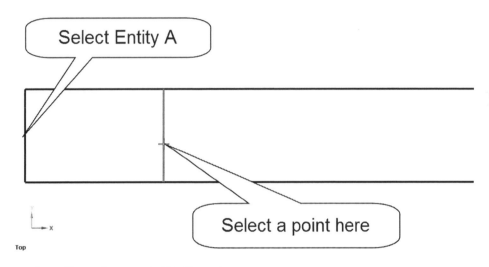

• In the **Line Parallel** panel, enter the **Offset Distance 1.625 (Enter)**.

♦ [Select a line]: Select **Entity A** again as shown in <u>Figure: 3.1.1</u>.
♦ [Select the point to place a parallel line through]: Click on a point to the right of **Entity A** as shown in <u>Figure: 3.1.1</u>.
♦ In the **Line Parallel** panel, enter the **Offset Distance 2.625** (**Enter**).

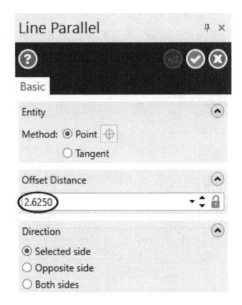

♦ [Select a line]: Select **Entity A** again as shown in <u>Figure: 3.1.1</u>.
♦ [Select the point to place a parallel line through]: Click on a point to the right of **Entity A** as shown in <u>Figure: 3.1.1</u>.
♦ In the **Line Parallel** panel, enter the **Offset Distance 3.375** (**Enter**).

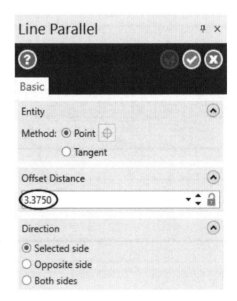

♦ [Select a line]: Select **Entity A** again as shown in <u>Figure: 3.1.1</u>.
♦ [Select the point to place a parallel line through]: Click on a point to the right of **Entity A** as shown in <u>Figure: 3.1.1</u>.

• In the **Line Parallel** panel, enter the **Offset Distance 4.375** (**Enter**).

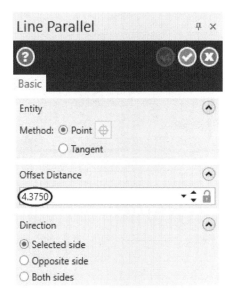

• Press enter to continue.
• The part should appear as shown in Figure: 3.1.2.

Figure: 3.1.2

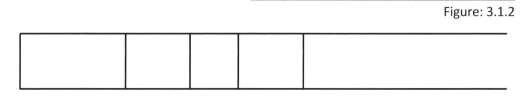

3.2 Create the horizontal lines

• [Select a line]: Select **Entity B** as shown in Figure: 3.2.1.
• [Select the point to place a parallel line through]: Click on a point above **Entity B** as shown in Figure: 3.2.1.

Figure: 3.2.1

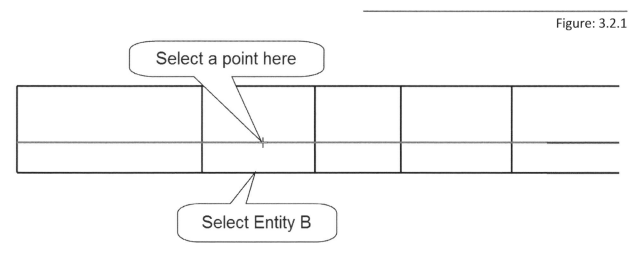

• Enter the **Offset Distance 0.25 (Enter)**.

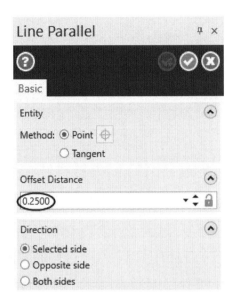

• [Select a line]: Select **Entity B** again as shown in <u>Figure: 3.2.1</u>.
• [Select the point to place a parallel line through]: Click on a point above **Entity B** as shown in <u>Figure: 3.2.1</u>.
• Enter the **Distance 0.5 (Enter)**.

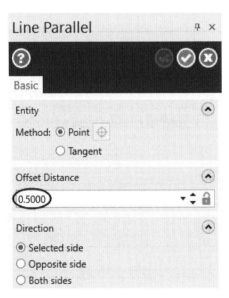

• Select the **OK** button to exit the command.

* The part should appear as shown in <u>Figure: 3.2.2</u>.

Figure: 3.2.2

STEP 4: CREATE ANGLED LINES GIVEN THEIR ENDPOINTS

In this step we will create two angled lines given their endpoints from the construction lines we created in the previous step.

Step Preview:

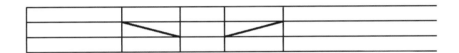

WIREFRAME

* From the **Lines** group, select **Line Endpoints**.

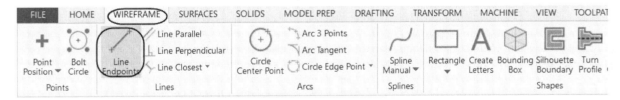

* [Specify the first endpoint]: Select **Intersection A** as shown.

Intersection A

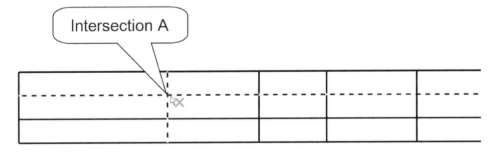

• [Specify the second endpoint]: Select **Intersection B** as shown.

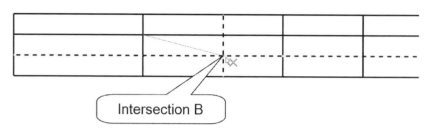

• Press **Enter** to stay within the command.
• [Specify the first endpoint]: Select **Intersection C** as shown.
• [Specify the second endpoint]: Select **Intersection D** as shown.

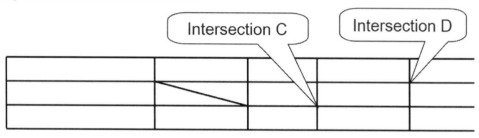

• Select the **OK** button to exit the command.
• The part should appear as shown in Figure: 4.0.1.

Figure: 4.0.1

STEP 5: DELETE THE EXTRA CONSTRUCTION LINES

In this step we will delete the extra construction lines.

Step Preview:

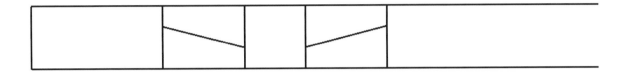

• Select **Entity A** and **Entity B** as shown.

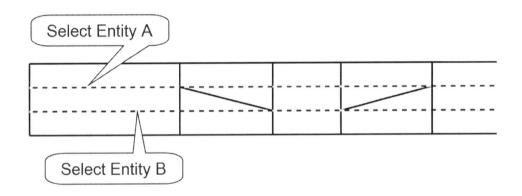

• Press the **Delete** key on the keyboard.

STEP 6: FILLET THE PART

In this step we will create the 4 fillets in the corners of the grooves while simultaneously trimming the geometry.

Step Preview:

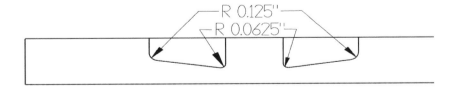

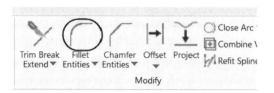

WIREFRAME
* From the **Modify** group, select **Fillet Entities**.

* Enter the **Radius**, set the style to **Normal** and ensure **Trim entities** is enabled as shown.

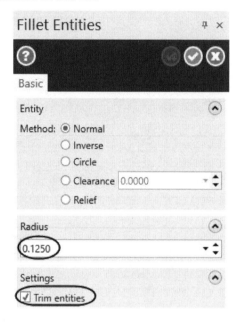

* [Fillet: Select an entity]: Select **Entity A** as shown in Figure: 6.0.1.
* [Fillet: Select another entity]: Select **Entity B** as shown in Figure: 6.0.1.

Figure: 6.0.1

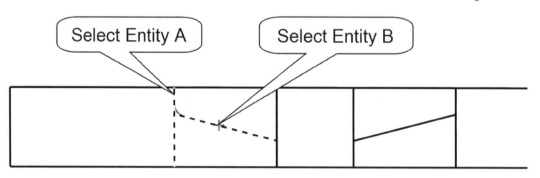

* Press **Enter** to continue.

♦ [Fillet: Select an entity]: Select **Entity C** as shown in <u>Figure: 6.0.2</u>.
♦ [Fillet: Select another entity]: Select **Entity D** as shown in <u>Figure: 6.0.2</u>.

Figure: 6.0.2

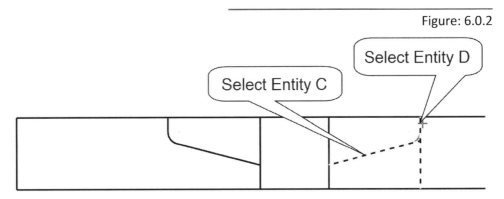

♦ Press **Enter** to finish the fillet and continue in the same command.
♦ Change the **Radius** as shown and press **Enter**.

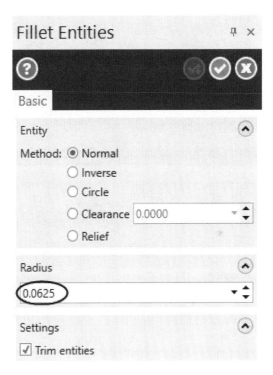

- [Fillet: Select an entity]: Select **Entity B** as shown in <u>Figure: 6.0.3</u>.
- [Fillet: Select another entity]: Select **Entity E** as shown in <u>Figure: 6.0.3</u>.
- Press **Enter** to continue.
- [Fillet: Select an entity]: Select **Entity C** as shown in <u>Figure: 6.0.3</u>.
- [Fillet: Select another entity]: Select **Entity F** as shown in <u>Figure: 6.0.3</u>.

Figure: 6.0.3

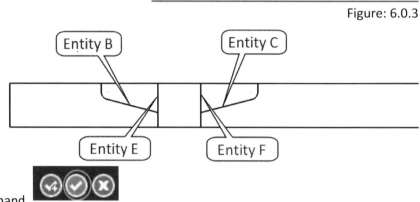

- Select the **OK** button to exit the command.
- Your part should appear as shown in <u>Figure: 6.0.4</u>.

Figure: 6.0.4

STEP 7: TRIM THE GROOVE

In this step we will use the Trim Break Extend command and enable the Divide/delete button to trim the grooves before creating the chamfers.

Step Preview:

WIREFRAME

- From the **Modify** group, select **Trim Break Extend**.

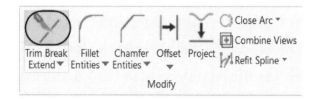

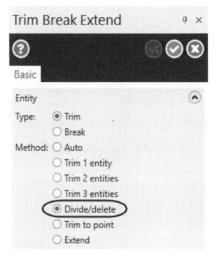

* Enable **Divide/delete**.

* [Select the curve to divide / delete]: Select the two portions of line as shown to delete them.

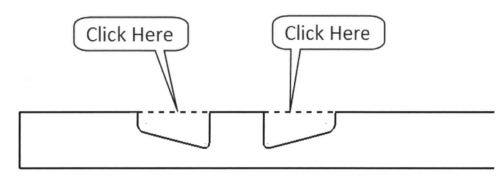

* Select the **OK** button to exit the command.

STEP 8: CHAMFER THE GROOVES

In this step we will chamfer the corners of the grooves.

Step Preview:

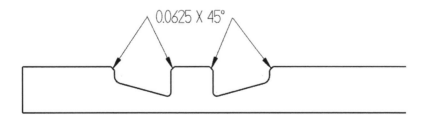

WIREFRAME

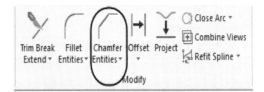

• From the **Modify** group, select **Chamfer Entities**.

• Change the **Distance** and make any other changes as shown.

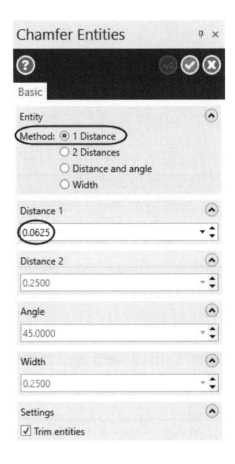

• [Select line or arc]: Select **Entity A** as shown in Figure: 8.0.1.
• [Select line or arc]: Select **Entity B** as shown in Figure: 8.0.1.

Figure: 8.0.1

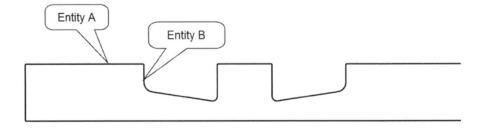

- [Select line or arc]: Select **Entity C** as shown in <u>Figure: 8.0.2</u>.
- [Select line or arc]: Select **Entity D** as shown in <u>Figure: 8.0.2</u>.

- [Select line or arc]: Select **Entity D** as shown in <u>Figure: 8.0.2</u>.
- [Select line or arc]: Select **Entity E** as shown in <u>Figure: 8.0.2</u>.

- [Select line or arc]: Select **Entity F** as shown in <u>Figure: 8.0.2</u>.
- [Select line or arc]: Select **Entity G** as shown in <u>Figure: 8.0.2</u>.

Figure: 8.0.2

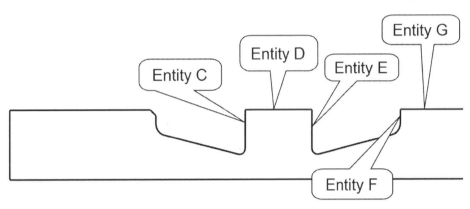

- Select the **OK** button to exit the command.
- The part should appear as shown in <u>Figure: 8.0.3</u>.

Figure: 8.0.3

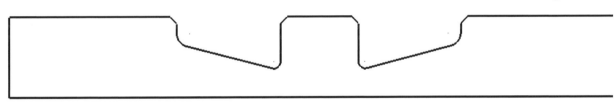

STEP 9: CREATE PARALLEL LINES

In this step we will create parallel lines to represent the geometry on the right side of the part.

Step Preview:

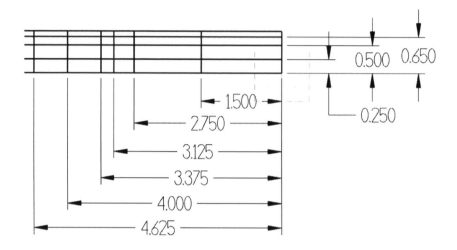

9.1 Zoom in to the right side of the part

• Press **Alt + F1** to fit the geometry in the graphics window.

• Move the cursor to the top right corner of the geometry and scroll the mouse wheel upwards to zoom in as shown.

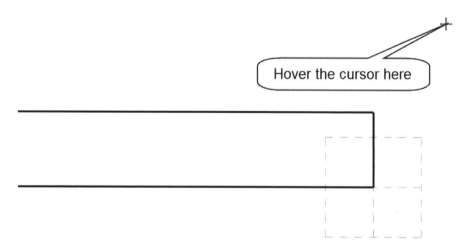

◆ The part should appear as shown.

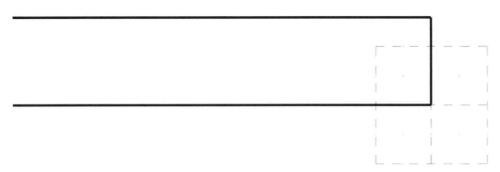

9.2 Create parallel lines

WIREFRAME

◆ From the **Lines** group, select **Line Parallel.**

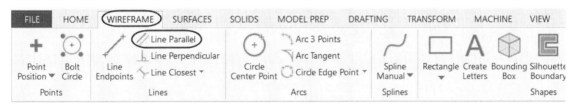

◆ [Select a line]: Select **Entity A** as shown in Figure: 9.2.1.

Figure: 9.2.1

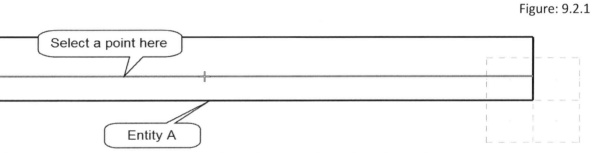

Select a point here

Entity A

◆ [Select the point to place a parallel line through]: Pick a point above the selected line.

• Enter the **Offset Distance 0.25** (press **Enter**).

• [Select a line]: Select **Entity A** again as shown in Figure: 9.2.1.
• [Select the point to place a parallel line through]: Pick a point above the selected line.
• Enter the **Offset Distance 0.5** (press **Enter**).

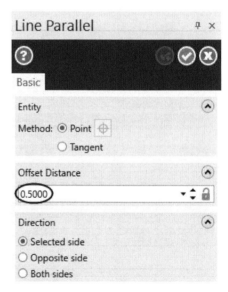

• [Select a line]: Select **Entity A** again as shown in Figure: 9.2.1.
• [Select the point to place a parallel line through]: Pick a point above the selected line.

- Enter the **Offset Distance 0.65** (press **Enter**).

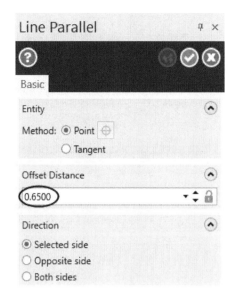

- Press **Enter** to continue.

- The part should appear as shown in Figure: 9.2.2.

Figure: 9.2.2

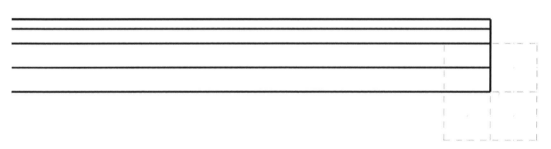

- [Select a line]: Select **Entity B** as shown in Figure: 9.2.3.

Figure: 9.2.3

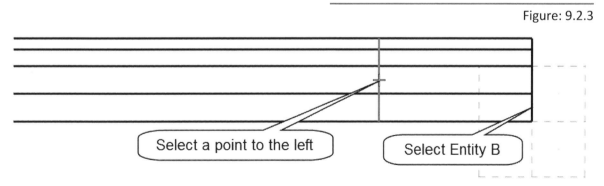

- [Select the point to place a parallel line through]: Pick a point to the left of the selected line.

♦ Enter the **Offset Distance 1.5** (press **Enter**).

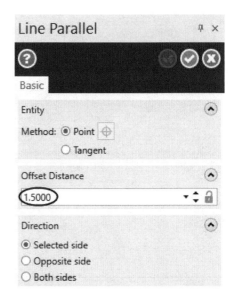

♦ [Select a line]: Select **Entity B** again as shown in <u>Figure: 9.2.3</u>.
♦ [Select the point to place a parallel line through]: Pick a point to the left of the selected line.
♦ Enter the **Offset Distance 2.75** (press **Enter**).

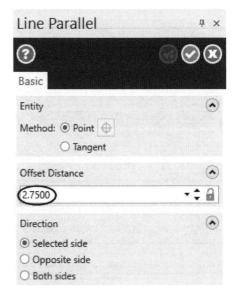

♦ [Select a line]: Select **Entity B** again as shown in <u>Figure: 9.2.3</u>.
♦ [Select the point to place a parallel line through]: Pick a point to the left of the selected line.

◆ Enter the **Offset Distance 3.125** (press **Enter**).

◆ [Select a line]: Select **Entity B** again as shown in <u>Figure: 9.2.3</u>.
◆ [Select the point to place a parallel line through]: Pick a point to the left of the selected line.
◆ Enter the **Offset Distance 3.375** (press **Enter**).

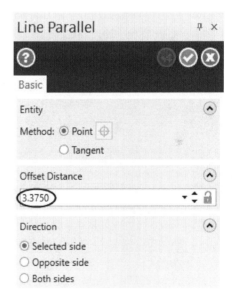

◆ Scroll down the mouse wheel to unzoom if needed.
◆ [Select a line]: Select **Entity B** again as shown in <u>Figure: 9.2.3</u>.
◆ [Select the point to place a parallel line through]: Pick a point to the left of the selected line.

• Enter the **Offset Distance 4.0** (press **Enter**).

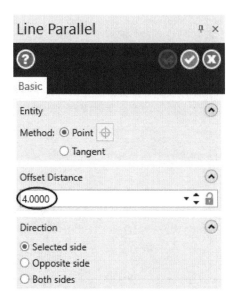

• [Select a line]: Select **Entity B** again as shown in <u>Figure: 9.2.3</u>.
• [Select the point to place a parallel line through]: Pick a point to the left of the selected line.
• Enter the **Offset Distance 4.625** (press **Enter**).

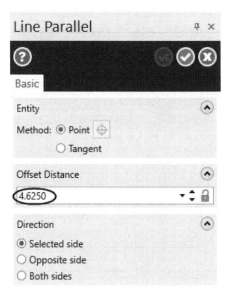

• Select the **OK** button to exit the command.

• The part should appear as shown in <u>Figure: 9.2.4</u>.

Figure: 9.2.4

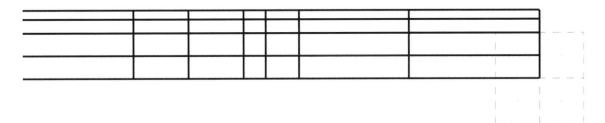

STEP 10: CHAMFER THE CORNERS AND TRIM SIMULTANEOUSLY

In this step we will create the final two chamfers on the end of the part and trim the geometry at the same time.

Step Preview:

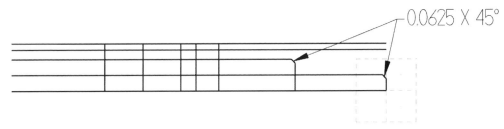

WIREFRAME

• From the **Modify** group, select **Chamfer Entities**.

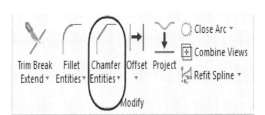

• Change the **Distance** and make any other changes as shown.

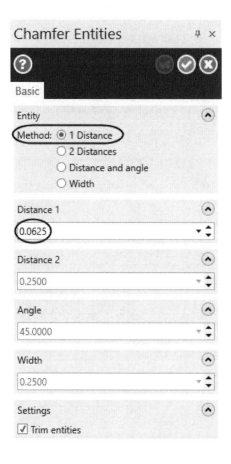

• [Select line or arc]: Select **Entity A** as shown in Figure: 10.0.1.

Figure: 10.0.1

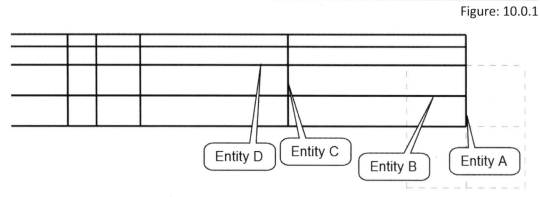

• [Select line or arc]: Select **Entity B** as shown in Figure: 10.0.1.
• Press **Enter** to continue.
• [Select line or arc]: Select **Entity C** as shown in Figure: 10.0.1.
• [Select line or arc]: Select **Entity D** as shown in Figure: 10.0.1.

• Select the **OK** button to exit the command.

• The part should appear as shown in <u>Figure: 10.0.2</u>.

Figure: 10.0.2

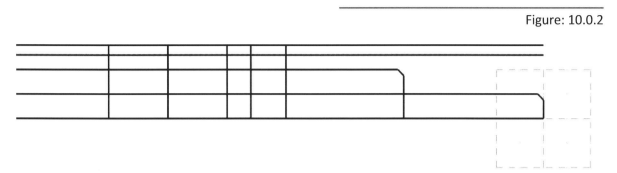

STEP 11: TRIM THE GEOMETRY

In this step we will use the **Divide/delete** command and the **Trim 2 entities** command to trim the geometry.

Step Preview:

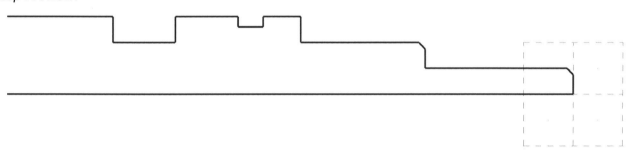

11.1 Use the Divide/delete command

WIREFRAME

• From the **Modify** group, select **Trim Break Extend.**

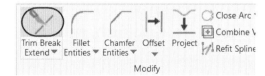

• Enable **Divide/delete.**

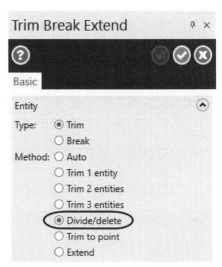

• [Select the curve to divide / delete]: Select the dashed lines as shown in <u>Figure: 11.1.1</u>.

Figure: 11.1.1

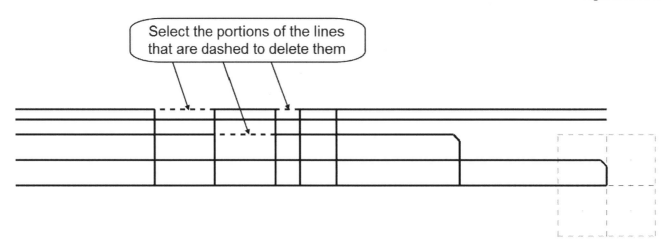

11.2 Use the Trim 2 entities command

* Enable the **Trim 2 entities** button.

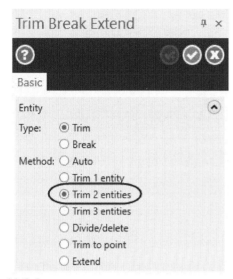

* [Select the entity to trim/extend]: Click on **Entity A** as shown in <u>Figure: 11.2.1</u>.
* [Select the entity to trim/extend to]: Click on **Entity B** as shown in <u>Figure: 11.2.1</u>.
* [Select the entity to trim/extend]: Click on **Entity C** as shown in <u>Figure: 11.2.1</u>.
* [Select the entity to trim/extend to]: Click on **Entity D** as shown in <u>Figure: 11.2.1</u>.
* [Select the entity to trim/extend]: Click on **Entity D** as shown in <u>Figure: 11.2.1</u>.
* [Select the entity to trim/extend to]: Click on **Entity E** as shown in <u>Figure: 11.2.1</u>.

Figure: 11.2.1

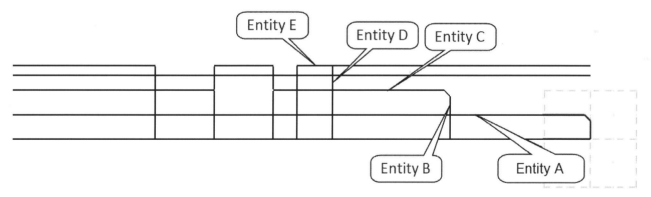

- [Select the entity to trim/extend]: Click on **Entity F** as shown in Figure: 11.2.2.
- [Select the entity to trim/extend to]: Click on **Entity G** as shown in Figure: 11.2.2.
- [Select the entity to trim/extend]: Click on **Entity G** as shown in Figure: 11.2.2.
- [Select the entity to trim/extend to]: Click on **Entity H** as shown in Figure: 11.2.2.
- [Select the entity to trim/extend]: Click on **Entity I** as shown in Figure: 11.2.2.
- [Select the entity to trim/extend to]: Click on **Entity J** as shown in Figure: 11.2.2.
- [Select the entity to trim/extend]: Click on **Entity J** as shown in Figure: 11.2.2.
- [Select the entity to trim/extend to]: Click on **Entity K** as shown in Figure: 11.2.2.

Figure: 11.2.2

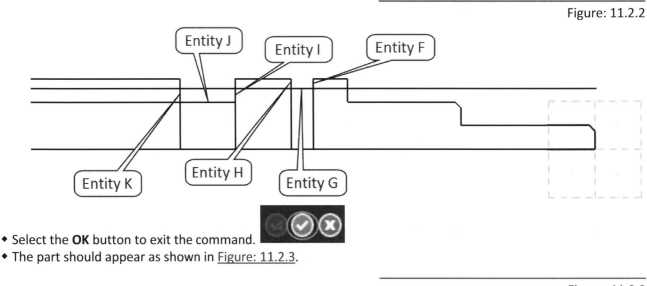

- Select the **OK** button to exit the command.
- The part should appear as shown in Figure: 11.2.3.

Figure: 11.2.3

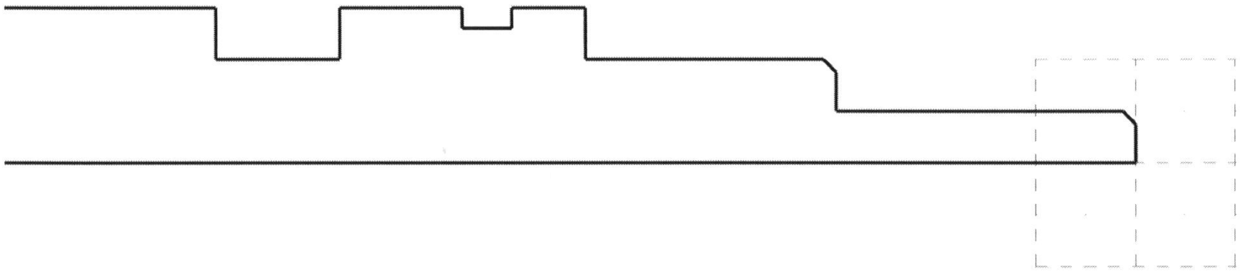

STEP 12: CREATE RELIEF GROOVES

The **Relief Groove** command will create geometry based on the thread size and orientation information you provide the command. Thread relief grooves provide clearance for threading tools to retract at the end of the cut and relieve stress concentrations at the end of the part to make the part stronger.

Step Preview:

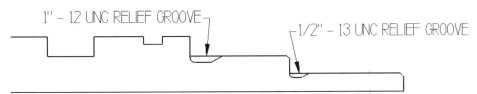

12.1 Create the 1/2" - 13 UNC Relief Groove

WIREFRAME

• From the **Shapes** group, select **Relief Groove**.

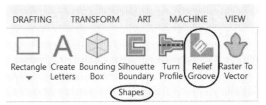

• The **DIN Relief Groove Parameters** dialog box will appear. Enable **OD thread** and select the **Select From Table** button as shown below.

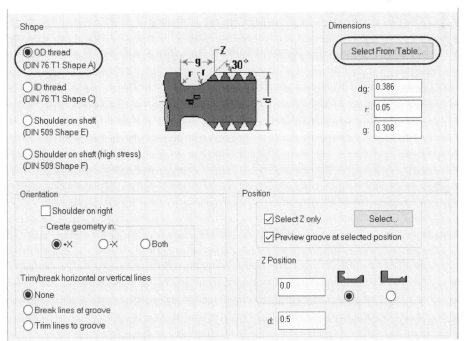

◆ Scroll through the list and select the **1/2" - 13 UNC** thread.

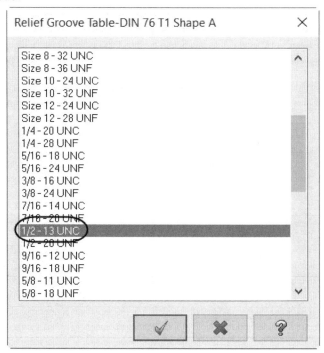

Relief Groove Table-DIN 76 T1 Shape A   ✕

Size 8 - 32 UNC
Size 8 - 36 UNF
Size 10 - 24 UNC
Size 10 - 32 UNF
Size 12 - 24 UNC
Size 12 - 28 UNF
1/4 - 20 UNC
1/4 - 28 UNF
5/16 - 18 UNC
5/16 - 24 UNF
3/8 - 16 UNC
3/8 - 24 UNF
7/16 - 14 UNC
7/16 - 20 UNF
1/2 - 13 UNC
1/2 - 20 UNF
9/16 - 12 UNC
9/16 - 18 UNF
5/8 - 11 UNC
5/8 - 18 UNF

◆ Select the **OK** button to exit the dialog box.

• Change the **Orientation, Trim/break horizontal or vertical lines** and **Position** values as shown.

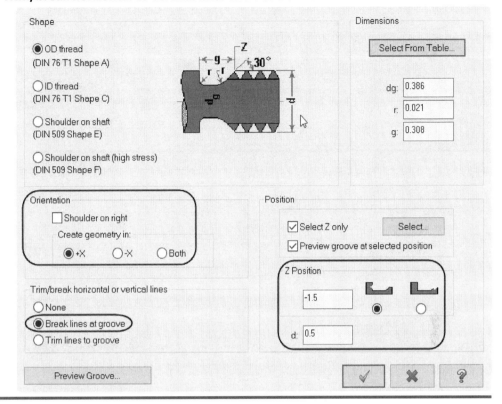

Shape determines what type of relief groove you would like to create. You can select **OD** or **ID thread** relief grooves or **Shoulder on shaft** types.

Orientation establishes where on the **X axis** you would like to create the geometry, or the direction the geometry is created in.

Trim/Break horizontal or vertical lines - use this option to either trim or break the geometry the groove is created with, or you can select **None** to make no trimming or breaking changes.

Position tells Mastercam where the relief groove will be created. You can also specify the Z Position of the front of the relief groove or the back by selecting one of the geometry entities.

• Select the **OK** button to create the relief groove.

* The part should appear as shown in <u>Figure: 12.1.1</u>.

Figure: 12.1.1

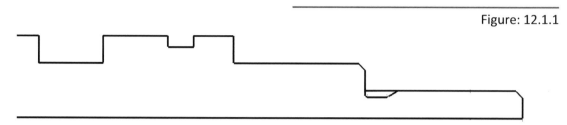

12.2 Create the 1" - 12 UNF Relief Groove

WIREFRAME

* From the **Shapes** group, select **Relief Groove**.

* Ensure **OD thread** is enabled and click on the **Select From Table** button as shown.

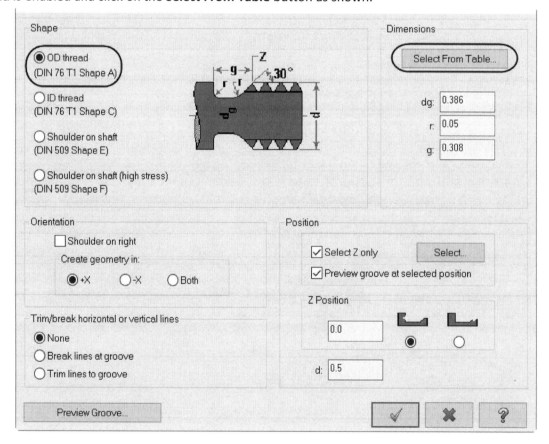

- Scroll through the list and select the **1" - 12 UNF** thread.

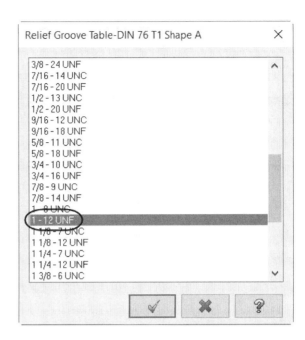

Relief Groove Table-DIN 76 T1 Shape A

```
3/8 - 24 UNF
7/16 - 14 UNC
7/16 - 20 UNF
1/2 - 13 UNC
1/2 - 20 UNF
9/16 - 12 UNC
9/16 - 18 UNF
5/8 - 11 UNC
5/8 - 18 UNF
3/4 - 10 UNC
3/4 - 16 UNF
7/8 - 9 UNC
7/8 - 14 UNF
1 - 8 UNC
1 - 12 UNF
1 1/8 - 7 UNC
1 1/8 - 12 UNF
1 1/4 - 7 UNC
1 1/4 - 12 UNF
1 3/8 - 6 UNC
```

- Select the **OK** button to exit the dialog box.
- Change the **Orientation, Trim/break horizontal or vertical lines** and **Position** values as shown.

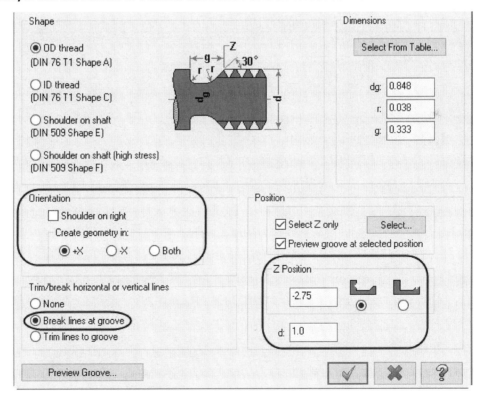

- Select the **OK** button to create the relief groove.

• The part should appear as shown in <u>Figure: 12.2.1</u>.

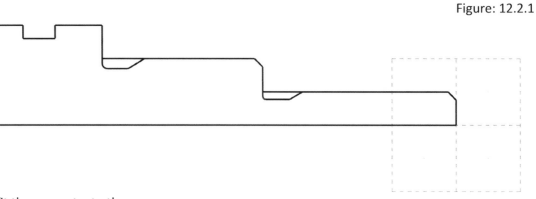

Figure: 12.2.1

• Press **Alt + F1** to fit the geometry to the screen.
• The finished part should appear as shown in <u>Figure: 12.2.2</u>.

Figure: 12.2.2

STEP 13: SAVE THE FILE

FILE
• **Save As.**

• Click on the **Browse** icon as shown.
• Find a location on the computer to save your file.
• File name: "Your Name_6".

TOOLPATH CREATION

PART SETUP 1:

PART SETUP 2:

SETUP SHEET 1:

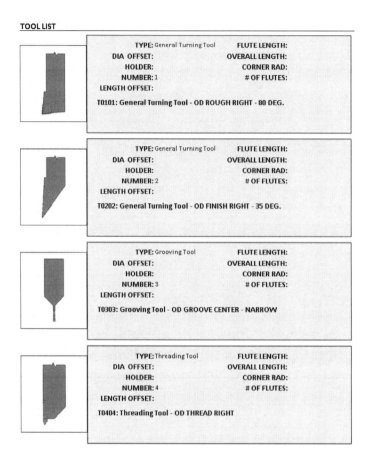

SETUP SHEET 2:

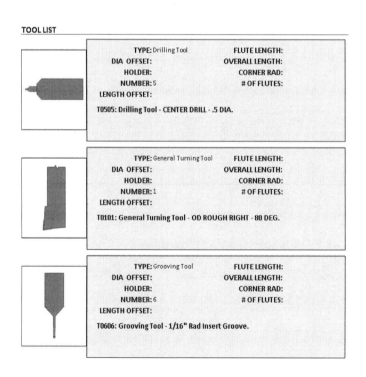

STEP 14: SET UP THE TOOL SETTINGS AND THE STOCK

In this step you will learn how to assign tool numbers, tool offset numbers, and default values for feeds, speeds, and other toolpath parameters. You will also learn how to define the stock and chuck jaws using the lathe machine groups.

- Press **Alt + F1** to fit the drawing to the screen.
- To display the **Toolpaths Manager** panel select the **Toolpaths** tab as shown.

NOTE: If the **Lathe Machine Group** is not displayed in the **Toolpaths Manager**, see **Tutorial 2 page 78**. If another machine is already selected, to remove it see **Tutorial 2 page 102**.

- Select the plus sign in front of **Properties** in the **Toolpaths Manager** to expand the **Toolpaths Group Properties.**

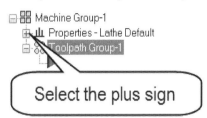

- Select **Tool settings** to set the tool parameters.

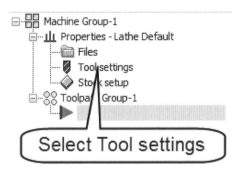

- Change the parameters to match the screenshot in Figure: 14.0.1.

Figure: 14.0.1

Default program number is used to enter a number if your machine requires a number for a program name.

Assign tool numbers sequentially allows you to overwrite the tool number from the library with the next available tool number.

Warn of duplicate tool numbers allows you to get a warning if you enter two tools with the same number.

Override defaults with modal values enables the system to keep the values that you enter.

Feed Calculation set to **From tool** uses the feed rate, plunge rate, retract rate and spindle speed from the tool definition.

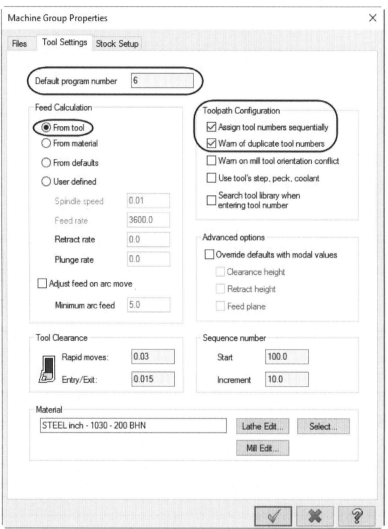

- Select the **Stock Setup** tab.

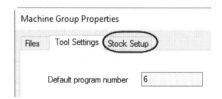

- Choose the **Properties** button to set up the stock for the **Left Spindle**.

◆ Define the stock by setting the stock geometry to **Cylinder** and entering the stock dimensions.
◆ Ensure you enable **Use Margins** and enter the values as shown in <u>Figure: 14.0.2</u>.

Figure: 14.0.2

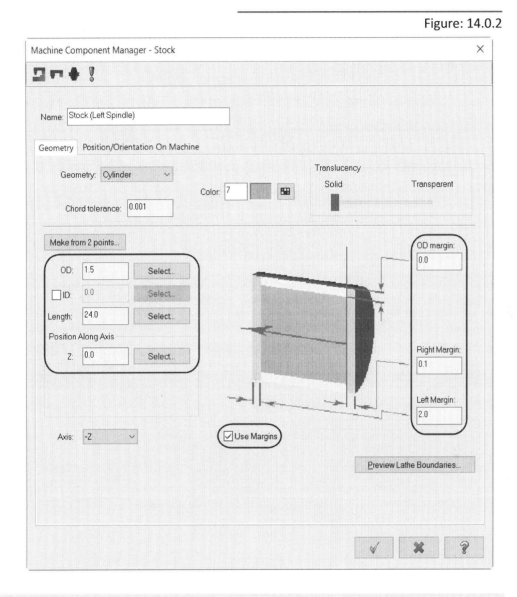

NOTE: The **stock** model that you create can be displayed with the part geometry when viewing the file or the toolpaths, during backplot, or while verifying toolpaths. You can create stock on the left or right spindle.

◆ Select the **OK** button to exit the **Machine Component Manager - Stock** dialog box.
◆ Ensure that **Left Spindle** is selected and then select the **Properties** button in the **Chuck Jaws** area as shown.

• Make the necessary changes to define the chuck size, the clamping method and the stock position. Ensure that you choose the clamping method **OD #1** as shown in the graphic below.

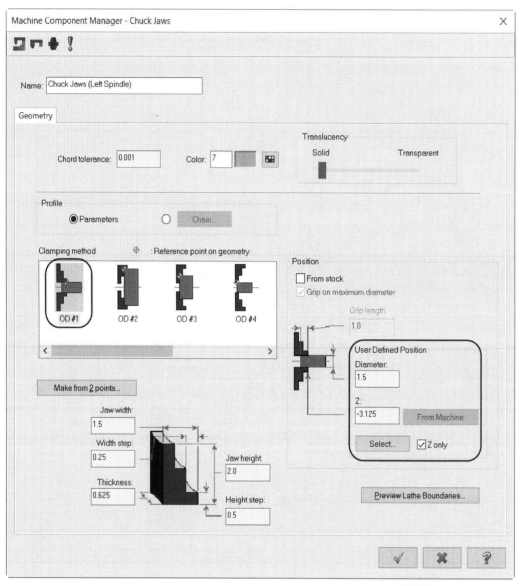

• Select the **OK** button to exit the **Machine Component Manager - Chuck Jaws** dialog box.
• In the **Tailstock Center** area click on the **Properties** button.

♦ Define the tailstock we will be using by matching the parameters shown below.

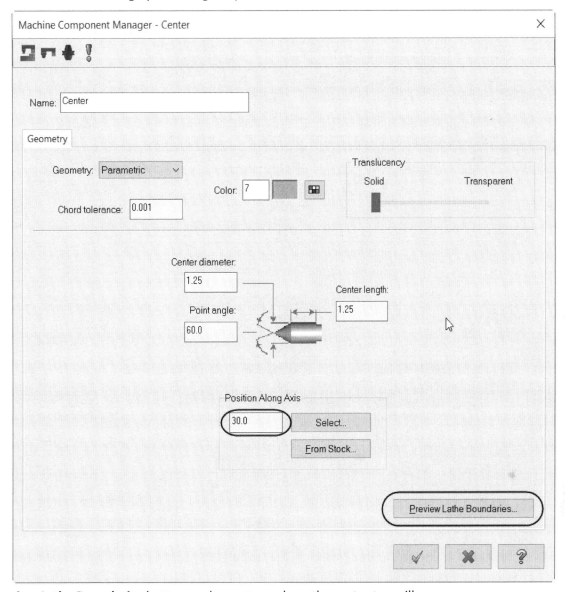

♦ Select the **Preview Lathe Boundaries** button as shown to see how the part setup will appear.

♦ Press **Enter** to continue.

♦ Select the **OK** button to exit the **Machine Component Manager - Center** dialog box.

♦ Select the **OK** button to exit the **Machine Group Properties** dialog box.

♦ Press **Alt + F1** to fit the geometry to the screen.

STEP 15: FACE THE PART

NOTE: To create the **Facing** toolpath, follow the instructions in **Step 9** in **Tutorial 1** on **page 46**. Make sure that the **Finish Z value** is set to **0.0**.

Toolpath Preview:

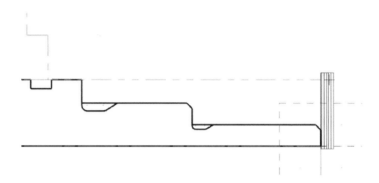

STEP 16: ROUGH THE OD

Rough Toolpaths quickly remove large amounts of stock in preparation for a finish pass. Roughing passes are typically straight cuts parallel to the **Z axis**.

Toolpath Preview:

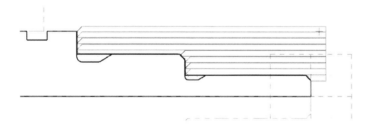

TURNING
* From the **General** group, select the **Rough** icon.

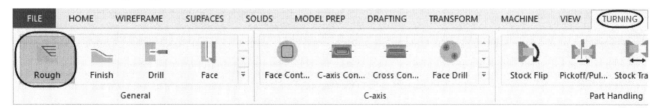

♦ Leave the default settings in the **Chaining** dialog box.

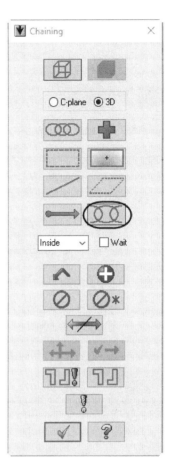

NOTE: The chaining mode is **Partial** by default. You will have to select the first entity and the last entity of the contour.

♦ [Select the entry point or chain the inner boundary]: Select **Entity A**.

> **NOTE:** Zoom in by scrolling up on the mouse wheel. Hold down the **Shift** key and with the mouse wheel held down center the part. Make sure that the chaining direction is **CCW**, otherwise select the **Reverse** button in the **Chaining** dialog box.

♦ [Select the last entity]: Select **Entity B**.

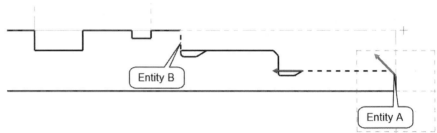

♦ [Branch point reached. Select next branch]: Select **Branch A**.

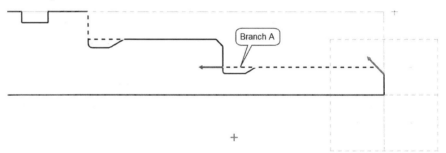

♦ [Branch point reached. Select next branch]: Select **Branch B**.

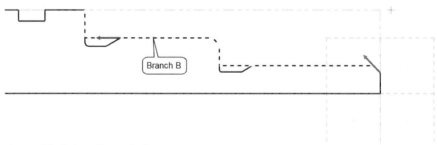

♦ [Branch point reached. Select next branch]: Select **Branch C**.

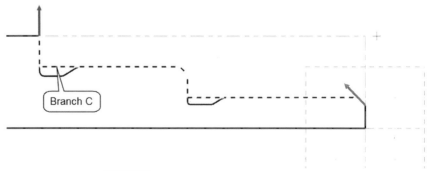

♦ Select the **OK** button to exit the **Chaining** dialog box.

• In the **Toolpath parameters** tab, select the same tool that we used in the facing operation and make all of the necessary changes as shown in the screenshot.

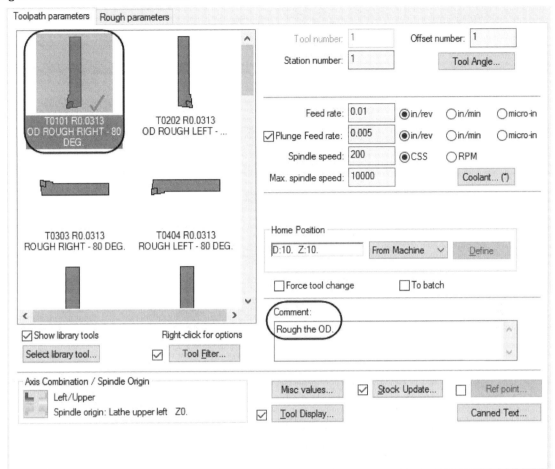

• Select the **Rough parameters** tab and make any changes as shown.

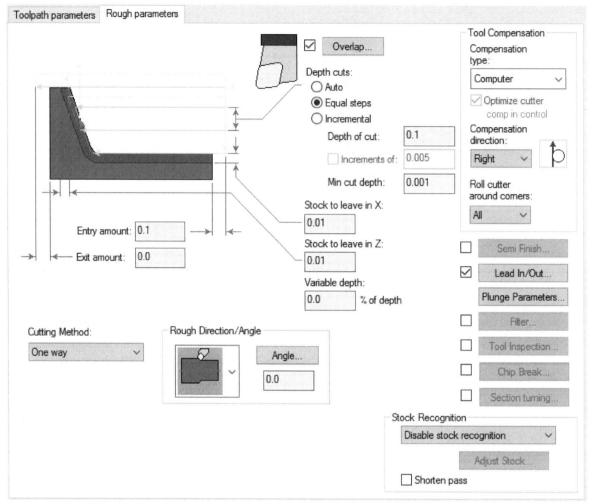

• Select the **OK** button to exit the **Lathe Rough** dialog box.

STEP 17: BACKPLOT AND VERIFY THE TOOLPATHS

17.1 Backplot the toolpaths

♦ Make sure that both toolpaths are selected (signified by the green check mark on the folder icon). If the operations are not selected choose the **Select all operations** icon.

♦ Select the **Backplot selected operations** icon.

♦ See to review the procedure.

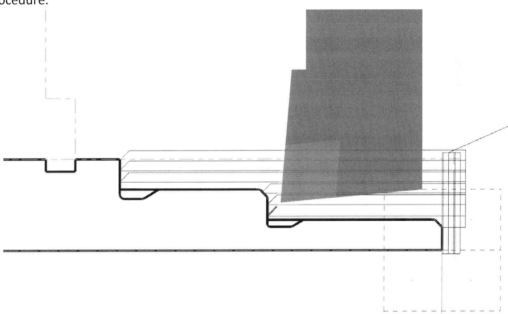

♦ Select the **OK** button to exit **Backplot**.

17.2 Verify the toolpaths

♦ To verify all toolpaths, from the **Toolpaths Manager**, choose the **Select all operations** icon. ►ₖ
♦ Select the **Verify selected operations** icon.

♦ See **page 51** to review the procedure.

+ The part should look as shown in <u>Figure: 17.2.1</u>.

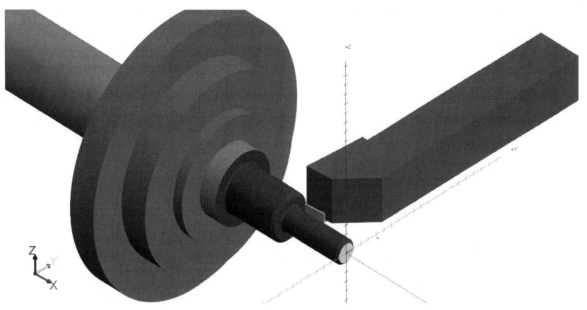

NOTE: To rotate the part, move the cursor to the center of the part and click and hold the mouse wheel and slowly move it in one direction.
To zoom in or out scroll up or down as needed.

+ To go back to the Mastercam window, minimize the **Mastercam Simulator** window as shown.

STEP 18: FINISH THE OD WITH DOWN CUTTING

Finish Toolpaths follow the contour of the chained geometry. Typically a finish toolpath follows a roughing toolpath. We will also enable **Down Cutting**. **Down Cutting** allows Mastercam to machine walls downward after roughing flat areas. There are five different cutting strategies to choose from.

Toolpath Preview:

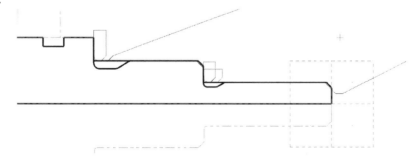

TURNING

- From the **General** group, select the **Finish** icon.

- Select the **Last** button in the **Chaining** dialog box to select the chain we selected in the roughing operation.

- Select the **OK** button to exit the **Chaining** dialog box.
- Select the **OD Finish Right -35 Degree** tool and enter the comment as shown.

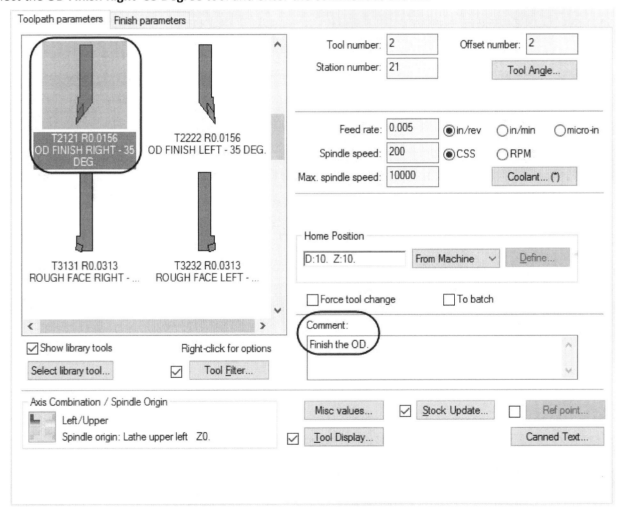

• Select the **Finish parameters** tab and enable **Down cutting**.

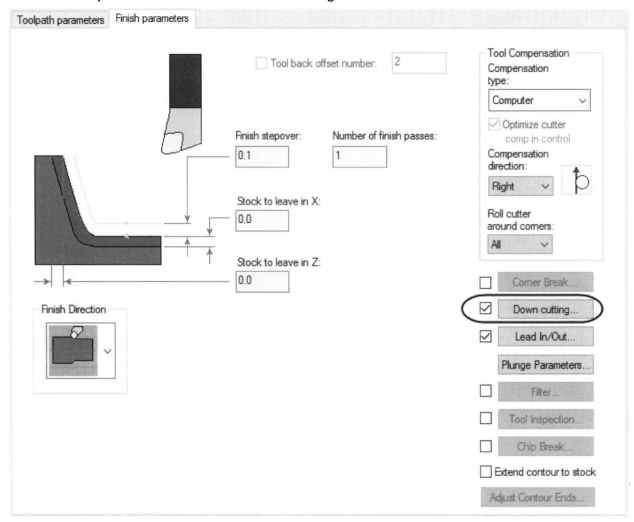

• Click on the **Down cutting** button to modify its parameters. [Down cutting...]

• Make any changes as shown in the **Down Cutting Parameters** dialog box.

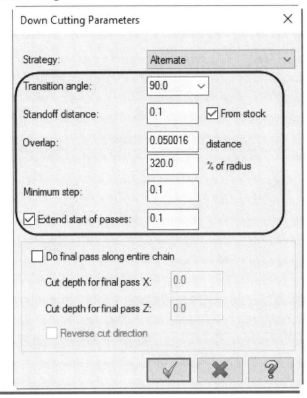

Strategy allows you to choose from a list of different cutting strategies.

Transition angle determines which regions are considered walls or flats.

Standoff distance lets you enter a distance to determine where the tool stops before retracting at the end of the part. The distance is measured back from the transition point.

Overlap sets the overlap amount for the wall and flat cuts.

Minimum step sets how high the wall must be to be considered a wall instead of part of a flat. This can prevent unnecessary down cutting on very short steps.

Extend start of passes extends the start of each pass along the wall and flat. This is useful for starting the pass off of the part.

Do final pass along entire chain adds an extra pass after all of the passes along the walls and flats. The extra pass cuts in a single direction along the entire chain.

NOTE: This option allows you to cut the vertical walls in a downward direction and the flats in a horizontal direction.

• Select the **OK** button to exit the **Down Cutting Parameters** dialog box.

• Select the **OK** button to exit the **Lathe Finish** dialog box.

18.1 Backplot the toolpath

- Once the operation has been regenerated **Backplot** the toolpath.
- See **page 49** to review the procedure.

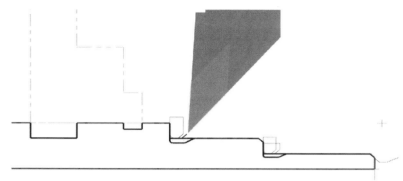

- Select the **OK** button to exit **Backplot**.

18.2 Verify the toolpaths

- To verify all toolpaths, from the **Toolpaths Manager**, choose the **Select all operations** icon.
- Select the **Verify selected operations** icon.

- See **page 51** to review the procedure.

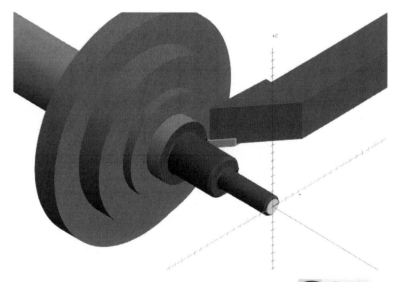

- To go back to the Mastercam window, minimize the **Mastercam Simulator** window as shown.
- Press **Alt + T** to remove the toolpath display.

STEP 19: MACHINE THE 1" - 12 UNF AND 1/2" - 13 UNC RELIEF GROOVES

In this step we will create a groove toolpath to machine the grooves behind the area we will thread.

Toolpath Preview:

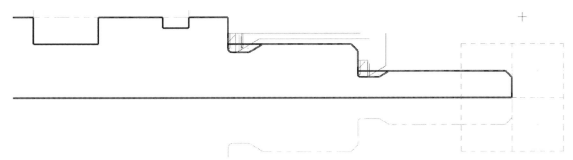

TURNING

◆ From the **General** group, click on the **Expand gallery** arrow key.

◆ Select **Groove**.

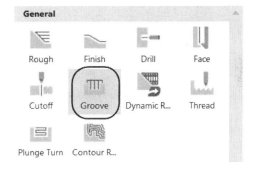

◆ When the **Grooving Options** dialog box appears choose **Multiple chains** as shown.

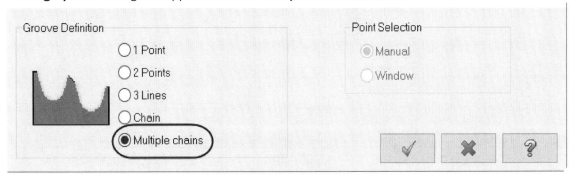

◆ Select the **OK** button to exit the **Grooving Options** dialog box.

- ◆ [Select the entry point or chain the inner boundary]: Select **Entity A** (the small angled line) as shown.
- ◆ [Select the last entity]: Select **Entity B** (the small vertical line) as shown.

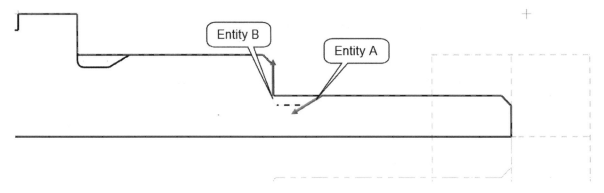

- ◆ [Select the inner boundary or select the retraction point or select done]: Select **Entity C** (the small angled line) as shown.
- ◆ [Select the last entity]: Select **Entity D** (the small vertical line) as shown.

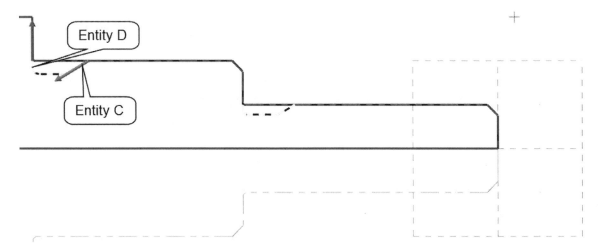

- ◆ Select the **OK** button to exit the **Chaining** dialog box.

♦ Select the **OD Groove Center - Narrow** tool from the tool list and enter the comment as shown.

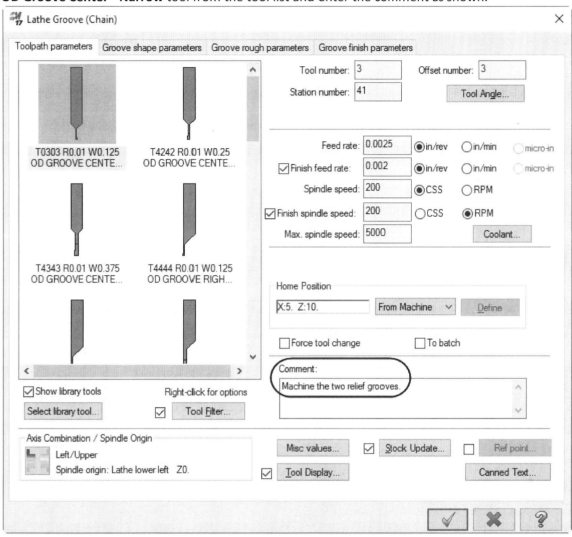

♦ Select the **Groove shape parameters** tab and enable **Use stock for outer boundary.**

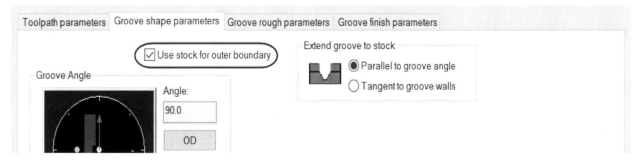

♦ Select the **Groove rough parameters** tab and ensure the parameters match the screenshot below.

Toolpath parameters | Groove shape parameters | Groove rough parameters | Groove finish parameters

☑ Rough

☐ Finish each groove before roughing next

Cut Direction:

Bi-Directional, Alternating ▼

Retraction Moves

◉ Rapid

○ Feed rate 0.01 ◉ in/rev ○ in/min

Stock clearance: 0.1

Stock amount: 0.0

First Plunge Feed Rate

☑ Plunge 0.002 ◉ in/rev ○ in/min

☐ Retract 0.01 ◉ in/rev ○ in/min

Rough step:

Percent of tool width ▼

75.0

Stock to leave in X: 0.005

Dwell Time

◉ None

1.0 ○ Seconds

○ Revolutions

Backoff %: 20.0

Stock to leave in Z: 0.005

Groove Walls

◉ Steps

○ Smooth

Parameters

Face Groove

Maximum start diameter: 200.0

Minimum start diameter: 0.0

☐ Peck Groove...

☐ Depth Cuts...

☐ Filter...

☐ Tool Inspection...

• Select the **Groove finish parameters** tab and make any changes as shown.

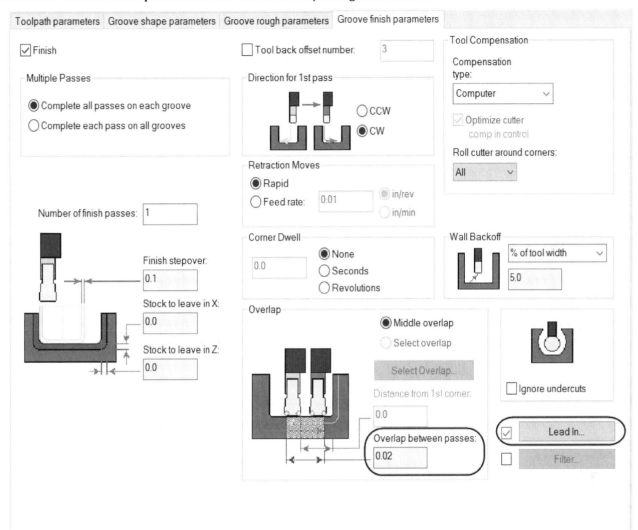

• Select the **Lead In** button and ensure the **First pass lead in** entry vector is set to **Tangent** as shown.

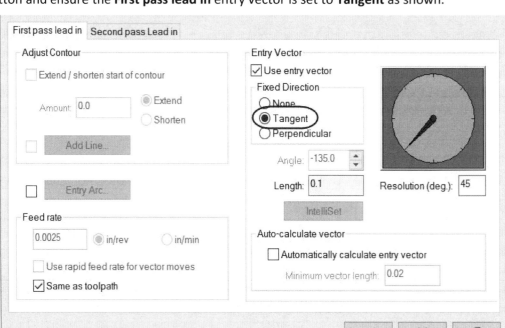

• Select the **Second pass Lead in** tab and ensure the entry vector is the same as shown.

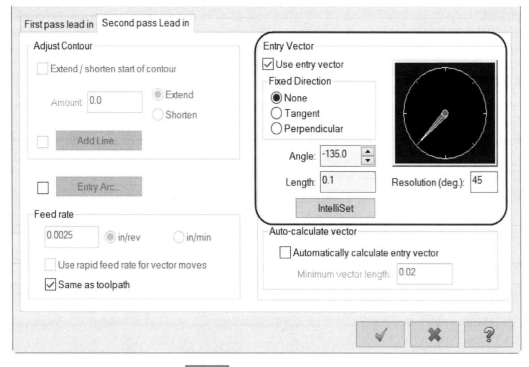

• Select the **OK** button to exit the **Lead In** dialog box.

• Select the **OK** button to exit the **Lathe Groove (Chain)** dialog box.

19.1 Backplot the toolpath

◆ Once the operation has been regenerated **Backplot** the toolpath.
◆ See **page 49** to review the procedure.

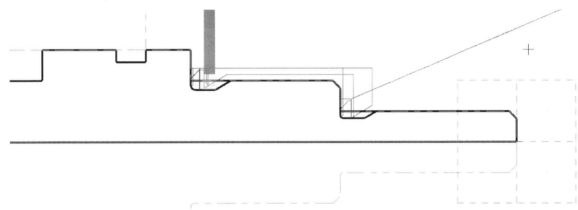

◆ Select the **OK** button to exit **Backplot**.

19.2 Verify the toolpaths

◆ To verify all toolpaths, from the **Toolpaths Manager**, choose the **Select all operations** icon.
◆ See **page 51** to review the procedure.

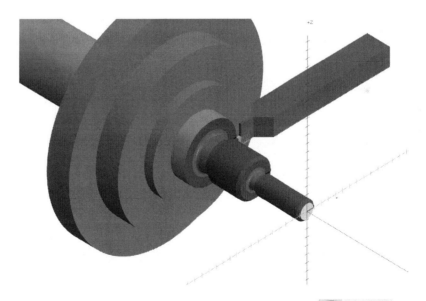

◆ To go back to the Mastercam window, minimize the **Mastercam Simulator** window as shown.
◆ If needed, press **Alt + T** to remove the toolpath display.

STEP 20: MACHINE THE 1/2" - 13 UNC THREAD

Thread Toolpaths give you the option to create a screw, bolt or nut. You can program straight threads on the outside, inside, or face of the part. You can also program multiple lead threads.

Toolpath Preview:

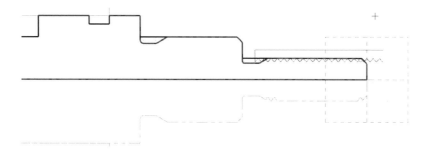

TURNING

♦ From the **General** group, select **Thread**.

NOTE: The toolpath dialog box will open automatically.

• Select the **OD Thread Right Medium** tool from the tool list and enter the comment as shown.

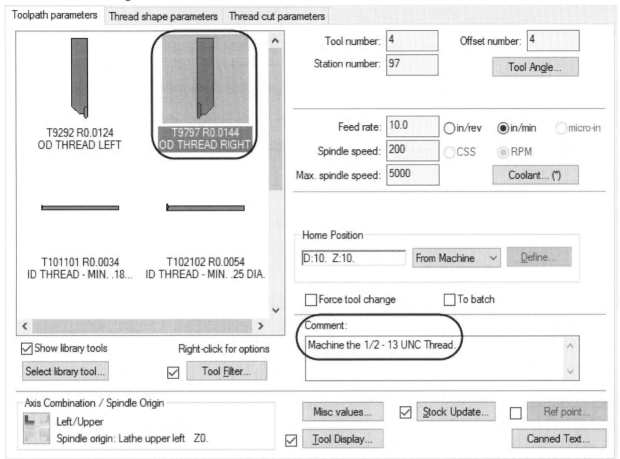

• Select the **Thread shape parameters** tab and from the **Thread Form** area click on the **Select from table** button.

Select from table...

♦ Change the **Thread form** if necessary and select the proper thread from the list as shown.

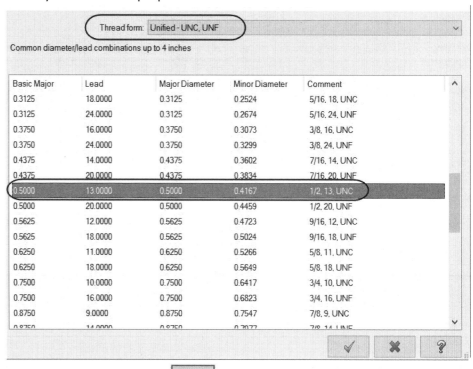

Basic Major	Lead	Major Diameter	Minor Diameter	Comment
0.3125	18.0000	0.3125	0.2524	5/16, 18, UNC
0.3125	24.0000	0.3125	0.2674	5/16, 24, UNF
0.3750	16.0000	0.3750	0.3073	3/8, 16, UNC
0.3750	24.0000	0.3750	0.3299	3/8, 24, UNF
0.4375	14.0000	0.4375	0.3602	7/16, 14, UNC
0.4375	20.0000	0.4375	0.3834	7/16, 20, UNF
0.5000	13.0000	0.5000	0.4167	1/2, 13, UNC
0.5000	20.0000	0.5000	0.4459	1/2, 20, UNF
0.5625	12.0000	0.5625	0.4723	9/16, 12, UNC
0.5625	18.0000	0.5625	0.5024	9/16, 18, UNF
0.6250	11.0000	0.6250	0.5266	5/8, 11, UNC
0.6250	18.0000	0.6250	0.5649	5/8, 18, UNF
0.7500	10.0000	0.7500	0.6417	3/4, 10, UNC
0.7500	16.0000	0.7500	0.6823	3/4, 16, UNF
0.8750	9.0000	0.8750	0.7547	7/8, 9, UNC
0.8750	14.0000	0.8750	0.7977	7/8, 14, UNF

♦ Select the **OK** button to exit the **Thread Table** dialog box.

♦ Ensure that your parameters match the screenshot below.

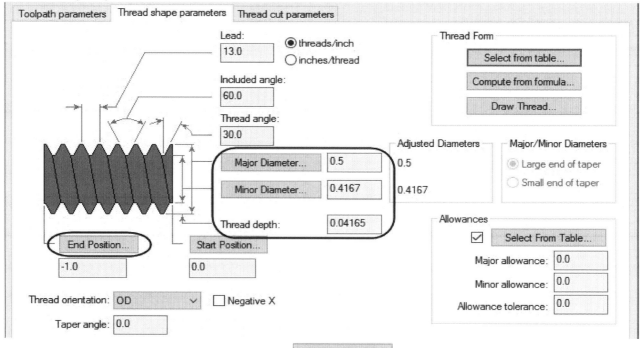

♦ Select the **End Position** button as outlined above.

• Mastercam will return you to the graphic user interface. Select the **Midpoint** as shown.

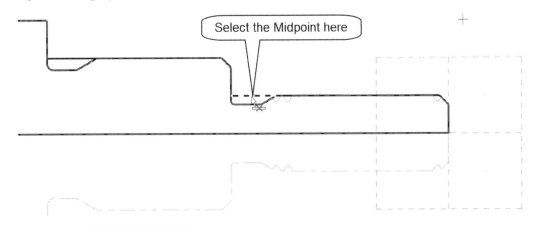

Select the Midpoint here

• Select the **Start Position** button. Start Position...

• Mastercam will return you to the graphic user interface. Select the **Endpoint** as shown.

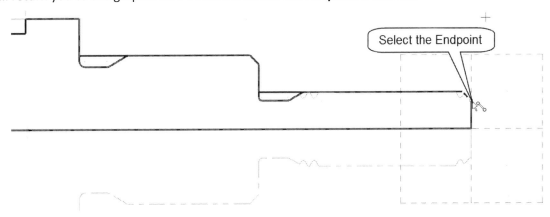

Select the Endpoint

• The **End Position** and **Start Position** should appear as shown.

End Position... | Start Position...
-1.346 | 0.0

- Select the **Thread cut parameters** tab and make the necessary changes to match the screenshot below.

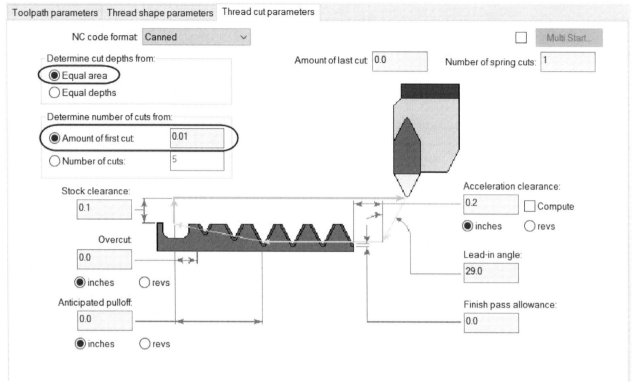

- Select the **OK** button to exit the **Lathe Thread** dialog box.

20.1 Verify the toolpaths

- To verify all toolpaths, from the **Toolpaths Manager**, choose the **Select all operations** icon.
- See **page 51** to review the procedure.

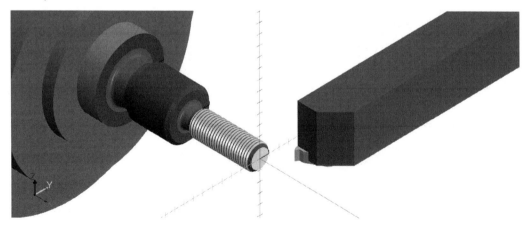

- To go back to the Mastercam window, minimize the **Mastercam Simulator** window as shown.

STEP 21: MACHINE THE 1" - 12 UNF THREAD

Thread Toolpaths give you the option to create a screw, bolt or nut. You can program straight threads on the outside, inside, or face of the part. You can also program multiple lead threads.

Toolpath Preview:

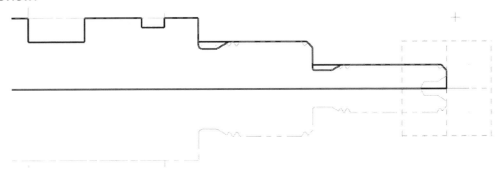

TURNING

* From the **General** group, select **Thread**.

> **NOTE:** The toolpath dialog box will open automatically.

• Select the same **OD Thread Right Medium** tool from the tool list and enter the comment as shown.

| Toolpath parameters | Thread shape parameters | Thread cut parameters |

T0404 R0.0144
OD THREAD RIGHT

T9292 R0.0124
OD THREAD LEFT

T101101 R0.0034
ID THREAD - MIN. .18...

T102102 R0.0054
ID THREAD - MIN. .25 DIA.

☑ Show library tools   Right-click for options

Select library tool...   ☑ Tool Filter...

Tool number: 4   Offset number: 4

Station number: 97   Tool Angle...

Feed rate: 15.384615   ○ in/rev ● in/min ○ micro-in

Spindle speed: 200   ○ CSS ● RPM

Max. spindle speed: 5000   Coolant... (*)

Home Position

D:10. Z:10.   From Machine ∨   Define...

☐ Force tool change   ☐ To batch

Comment:

Machine the 1" - 12 UNF Thread.

Axis Combination / Spindle Origin

Left/Upper
Spindle origin: Lathe upper left Z0.

Misc values...   ☑ Stock Update...   ☐ Ref point...

☑ Tool Display...   Canned Text...

♦ Select the **Thread shape parameters** tab and from the **Thread Form** area click on the **Select from table** button.

> Select from table...

♦ Change the **Thread form** if necessary and select the proper thread from the list as shown.

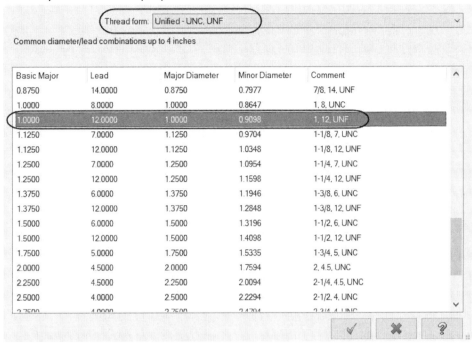

♦ Select the **OK** button to exit the **Thread Table** dialog box.
♦ Ensure that your parameters match the screenshot below.

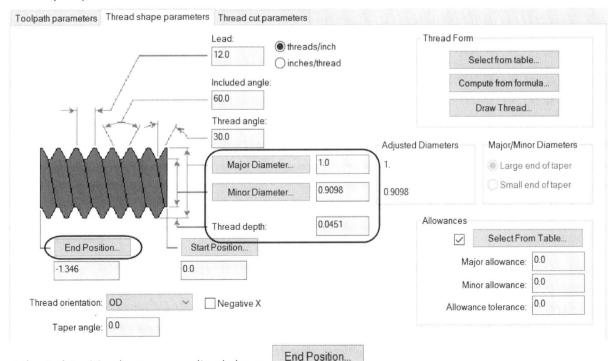

♦ Select the **End Position** button as outlined above.

• Mastercam will return you to the graphic user interface. Select the **Midpoint** as shown.

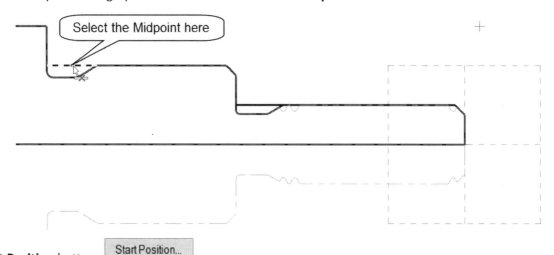

• Select the **Start Position** button.
• Mastercam will return you to the graphic user interface. Select the **Endpoint** as shown.

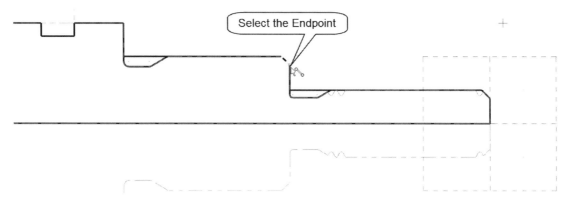

• The **End Position** and **Start Position** should appear as shown.

• Select the **Thread cut parameters** tab and make any changes to match the screenshot below.

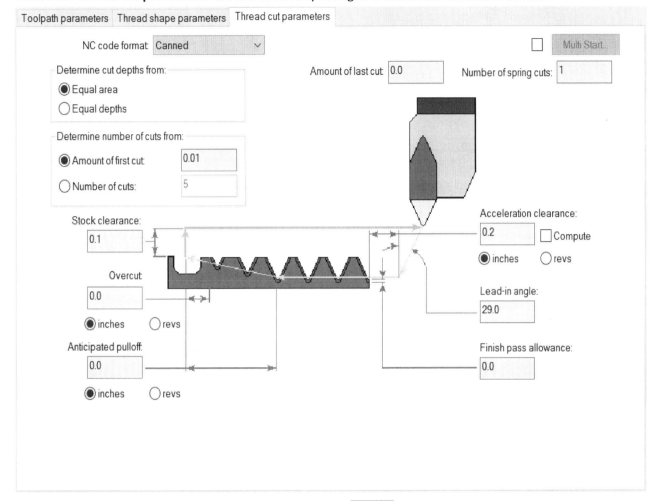

• Select the **OK** button to exit the **Lathe Thread** dialog box.

21.1 Verify the toolpaths

- To verify all toolpaths, from the **Toolpaths Manager**, choose the **Select all operations** icon.
- See **page 51** to review the procedure.

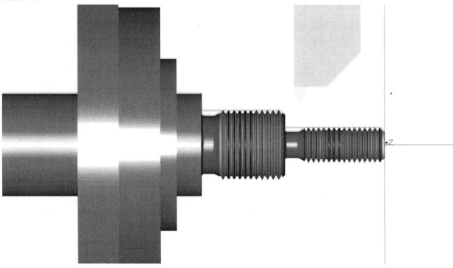

- To go back to the Mastercam window, minimize the **Mastercam Simulator** window as shown.

STEP 22: CENTER DRILL THE PART

Drill Toolpaths create a drilling toolpath on the face of the part along the center line. In this step we will center drill the face before drilling the part.

Toolpath Preview:

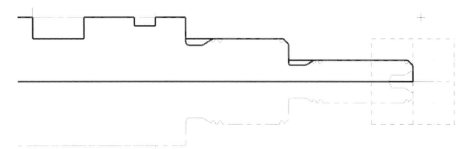

TURNING
- From the **General** group, click on the **Expand gallery** arrow key.

• Select the **Drill** icon.

> **NOTE:** The **Lathe Drill** dialog box will automatically open. No chaining is required because Mastercam drills along the center line to create the toolpath. The drill depths are specified within the dialog box.

• Select the **0.5" Diameter Center Drill** from the tool list and enter the comment as shown.

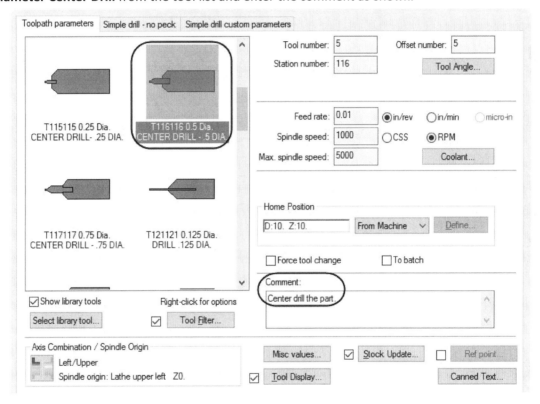

- Select the **Simple drill - no peck** tab and change the parameters to match the screenshot below.

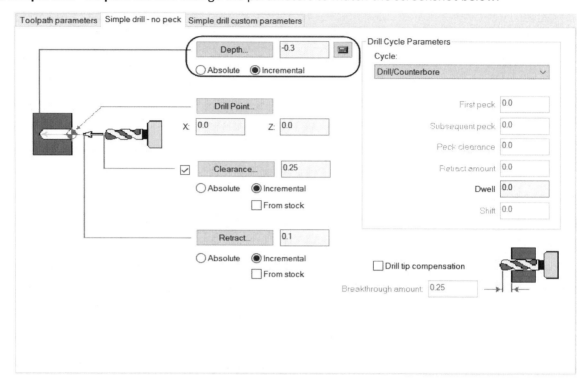

- Select the **OK** button to exit the **Lathe Drill** dialog box.

22.1 Backplot the toolpath

- Once the operation has been generated **Backplot** the toolpath.
- See **page 49** to review the procedure.

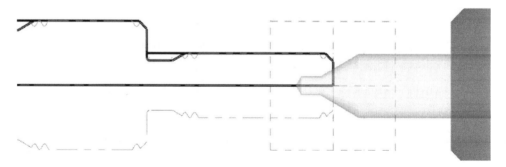

- Select the **OK** button to exit **Backplot**.

22.2 Verify the toolpaths

- To verify all toolpaths, from the **Toolpaths Manager**, choose the **Select all operations** icon.
- See **page 51** to review the procedure.

Lathe Training Tutorial *Mastercam* 2018

- To see a section through the part, select the **Verify** tab. Click on the drop down arrow below the **3/4** icon and enable **2nd quadrant** as shown.

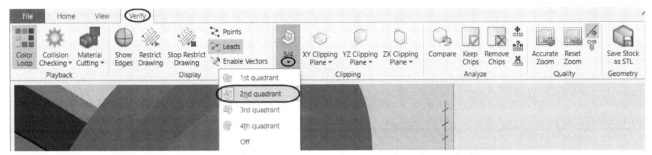

- Rotate and zoom in on the part to see the operation as shown in the picture below.

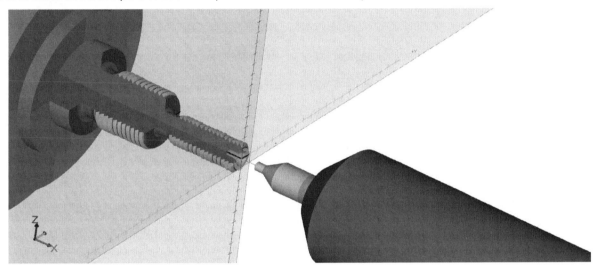

- Click again on the section options and turn it **Off**.

- To go back to the Mastercam window, minimize the **Mastercam Simulator** window as shown.

STEP 23: ADVANCE THE STOCK

Stock Advance uses a bar feeder to advance the stock through a spindle. This allows for an increase in productivity because you don't have to stop the machine to place stock in the chuck.

Toolpath Preview:

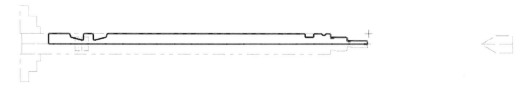

TURNING

• From the **Part Handling** group, click on the **Expand gallery** arrow key.

• Select **Stock Advance**.

• The **Lathe Stock Advance** dialog box will appear. Click on the **Select** button as shown.

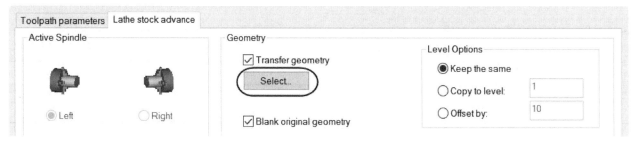

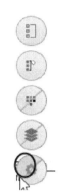

• [Select entities to transfer]: Click the **Select all advanced** button.

• Click on the **All Entities** button in the dialog box.

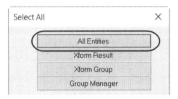

• Press **Enter**.

• The **Lathe Stock Advance** dialog box will re-appear. Change the **Transferred Position** to the location shown.

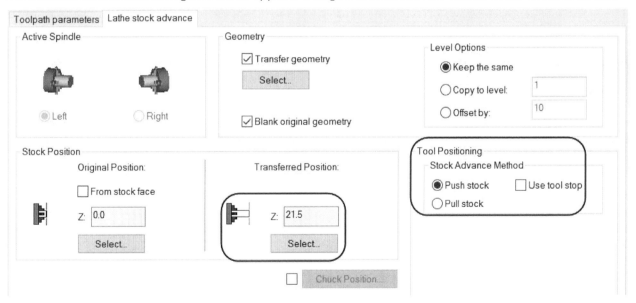

> **NOTE:** The **Z** value is based on how much you want the part to stick out.

• Select the **OK** button to exit the **Lathe Stock Advance** dialog box.
• Press **Alt + F1** to see the entire part.

• The part should look as shown in <u>Figure: 23.0.1</u>.

Figure: 23.0.1

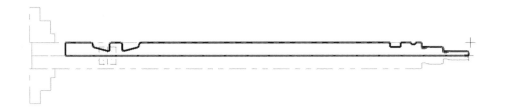

STEP 24: ADVANCE THE TAILSTOCK

Advance Tailstock allows the user to machine long work pieces near their centers.

Toolpath Preview:

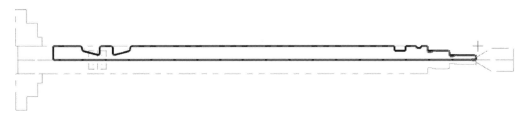

TURNING

• From the **Part Handling** group, select the **Tailstock** icon.

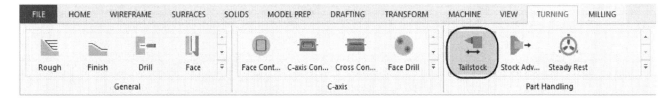

♦ The **Lathe Tailstock** dialog box will open automatically. Make any changes as shown.

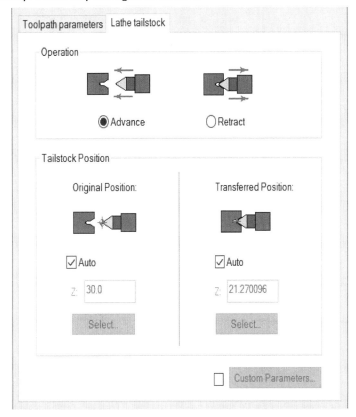

NOTE: When the **Operation** is set to **Advance**, Mastercam automatically advances the quill. You need to have first defined a tailstock in the **Stock Setup**.

♦ Select the **OK** button to exit the **Lathe Tailstock** dialog box.
♦ The **Tailstock Advance** should appear as shown.

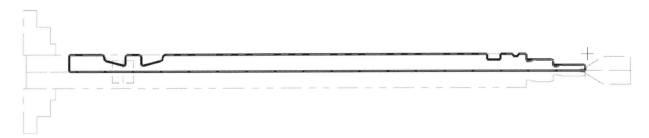

STEP 25: MACHINE THE GROOVES

In this step we will create a grooving operation with multiple chains to machine the remaining grooves in the same toolpath.

Toolpath Preview:

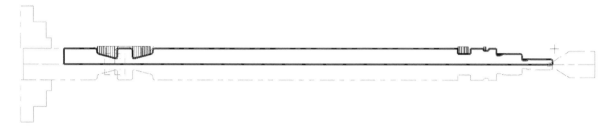

TURNING

• From the **General** group, click on the **Expand gallery** arrow key.

• Select **Groove**.

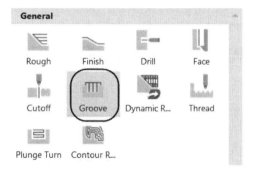

• When the **Grooving Options** dialog box appears choose **Multiple chains** as shown.

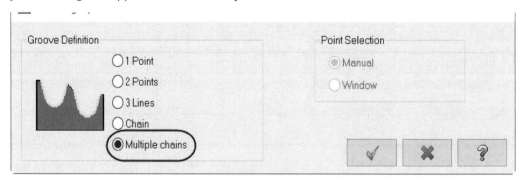

• Select the **OK** button to exit the **Grooving Options** dialog box.

◆ Move the cursor to where the groove is located and scroll up the mouse wheel to zoom in.
◆ [Select the entry point or chain the inner boundary]: Select **Entity A** as shown.

NOTE: Make sure the direction of chaining is as shown. Otherwise, click on the **Reverse** button in the **Chaining** dialog box.

◆ [Select the last entity]: Select **Entity B** as shown.

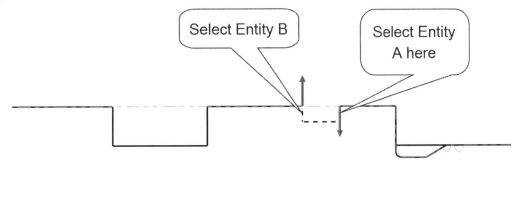

◆ [Select the inner boundary or select the retraction point or select done]: Select **Entity C** as shown.
◆ [Select the last entity]: Select **Entity D** as shown.

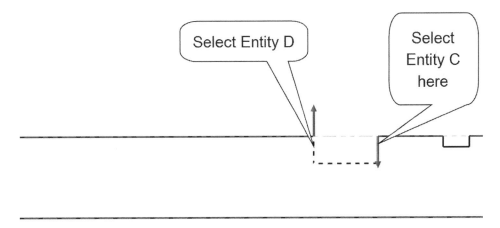

◆ Press **Alt + F1** to fit the geometry to the screen.

- Use the mouse wheel to zoom in on the left side of the part.
- [Select the inner boundary or select the retraction point or select done]: Select **Entity E** (the chamfer line) as shown.
- [Select the last entity]: Select **Entity F** (the chamfer line) as shown.

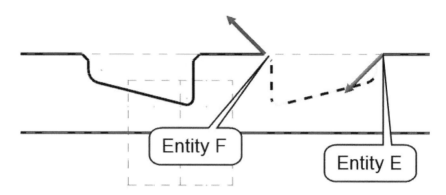

- [Select the inner boundary or select the retraction point or select done]: Select **Entity G** (the chamfer line) as shown.
- [Select the last entity]: Select **Entity H** (the chamfer line) as shown.

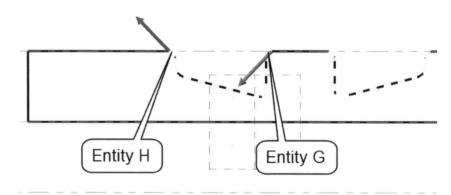

- Select the **OK** button to exit the **Chaining** dialog box.
- Select the **OD Groove Center - Medium** tool from the tool list as shown to use the existing groove sizes.

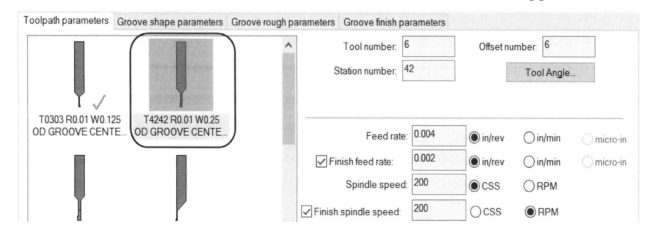

● Right mouse click in the tool list window and select **Create new tool** to make a round insert groove that will cleanup the 0.0625" fillets at the bottom of the grooves.

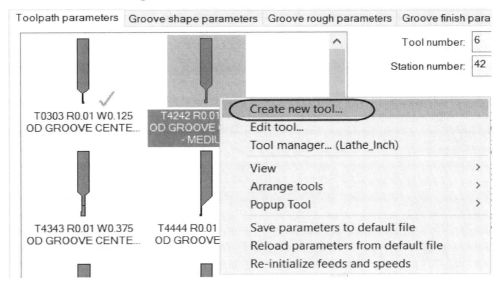

● Select the **Inserts** tab and enable **Single End (round)** and change first the **B** value and then the **A** value as shown.

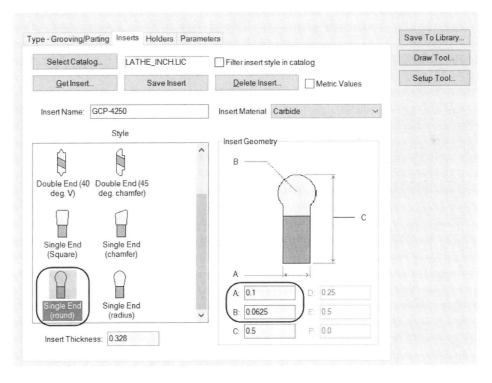

| **NOTE:** You have to enter **B** value first in order to set 0.1 as the **A** value.

• Select the **Holders** tab and make the changes as shown.

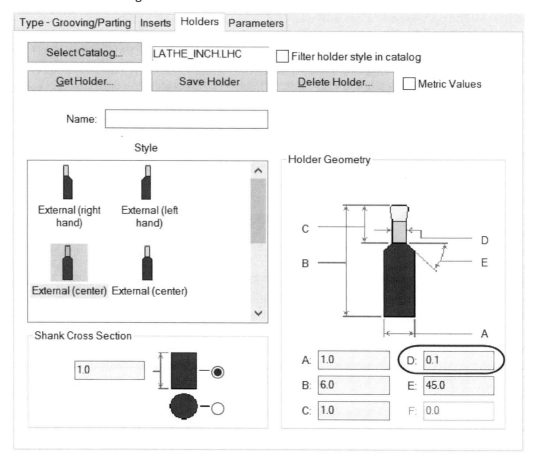

• Select the **Parameters** tab and enter the **Tool name** as shown.

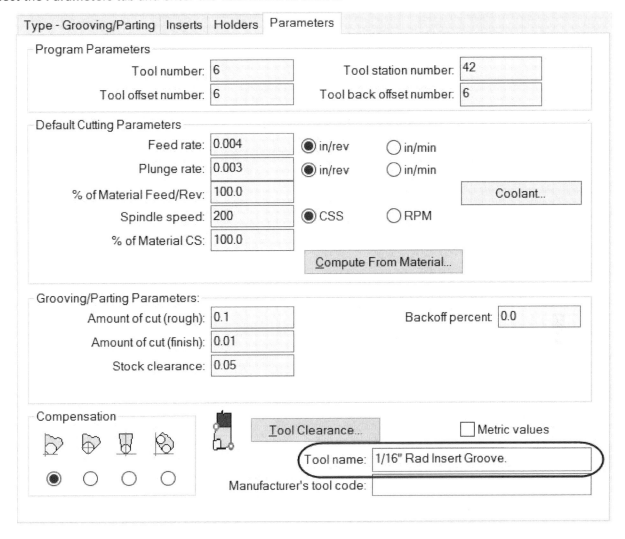

| Type - Grooving/Parting | Inserts | Holders | Parameters |

Program Parameters

Tool number: 6   Tool station number: 42

Tool offset number: 6   Tool back offset number: 6

Default Cutting Parameters

Feed rate: 0.004   ● in/rev   ○ in/min

Plunge rate: 0.003   ● in/rev   ○ in/min

% of Material Feed/Rev: 100.0   Coolant...

Spindle speed: 200   ● CSS   ○ RPM

% of Material CS: 100.0

Compute From Material...

Grooving/Parting Parameters:

Amount of cut (rough): 0.1   Backoff percent: 0.0

Amount of cut (finish): 0.01

Stock clearance: 0.05

Compensation

Tool Clearance...   ☐ Metric values

Tool name: 1/16" Rad Insert Groove.

Manufacturer's tool code:

• Select the **OK** button to exit the **Define Tool** dialog box.

♦ Enter the comment in the **Comment** area. The **Toolpath parameters** page should look as shown.

Toolpath parameters	Groove shape parameters	Groove rough parameters	Groove finish parameters

T0303 R0.01 W0.125
OD GROOVE CENTE...

T0606 R0.0625 W0.125
1/16" Rad Insert Groove

T4242 R0.01 W0.25
OD GROOVE CENTE...

T4343 R0.01 W0.375
OD GROOVE CENTE...

☑ Show library tools

Right-click for options

Select library tool...

☑ Tool Filter...

Axis Combination / Spindle Origin
Left/Upper
Spindle origin: Lathe upper left Z0.

Tool number: 6   Offset number: 6
Station number: 42   Tool Angle...

Feed rate: 0.004   ◉ in/rev ○ in/min ○ micro-in
☑ Finish feed rate: 0.002   ◉ in/rev ○ in/min ○ micro-in
Spindle speed: 200   ◉ CSS ○ RPM
☑ Finish spindle speed: 200   ○ CSS ◉ RPM
Max. spindle speed: 5000   Coolant... (*)

Home Position
D:10. Z:10.   From Machine ∨   Define

☐ Force tool change   ☐ To batch

Comment:
Machine the grooves.

Misc values...   ☑ Stock Update...   ☐ Ref point...
☑ Tool Display...   Canned Text...

♦ Select the **Groove shape parameters** tab and enable **Use stock for outer boundary.**

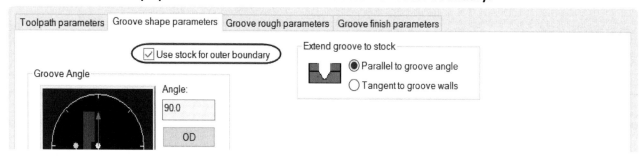

Toolpath parameters	Groove shape parameters	Groove rough parameters	Groove finish parameters

☑ Use stock for outer boundary

Extend groove to stock
◉ Parallel to groove angle
○ Tangent to groove walls

Groove Angle
Angle:
90.0
OD

◆ Select the **Groove rough parameters** tab and make any changes to match the screenshot below.

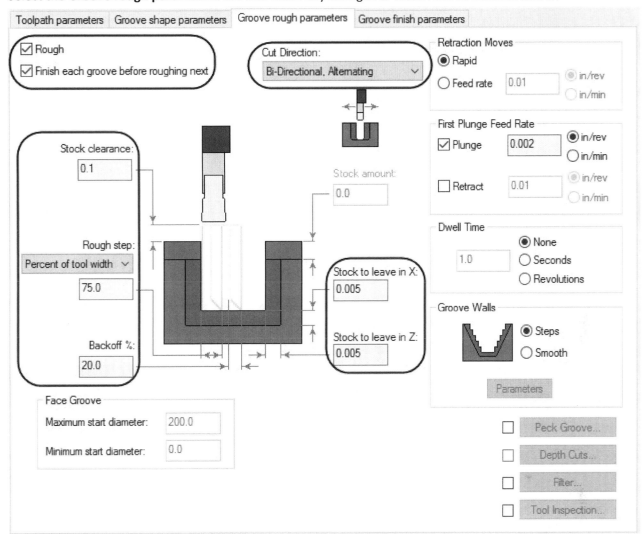

• Select the **Groove finish parameters** tab and make any changes as shown.

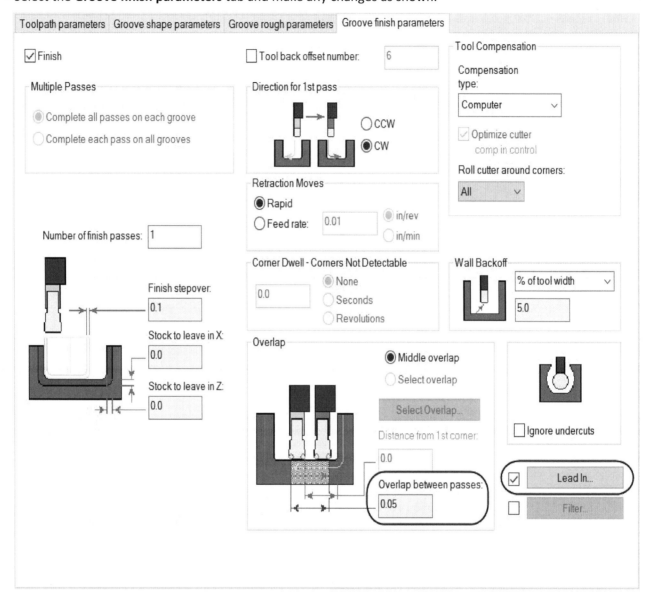

• Select the **Lead In** button and in the **First pass lead in** tab change the **Entry Vector** to **Tangent** as shown.

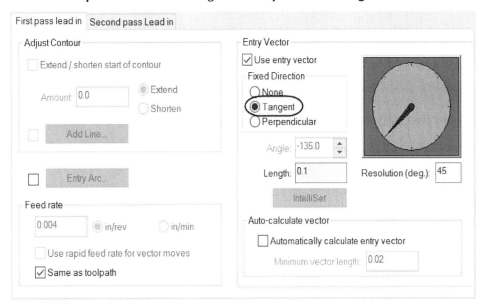

• In the **Second pass Lead in** tab change the **Entry Vector** to **Tangent** as well.

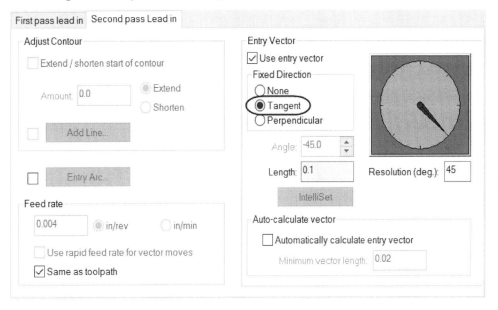

• Select the **OK** button to exit the **Lead In** dialog box.

• Select the **OK** button to exit the **Lathe Groove (Chain)** dialog box.

25.1 Backplot the toolpath

• Once the operation has been regenerated **Backplot** the toolpath.
• See **page 49** to review the procedure.

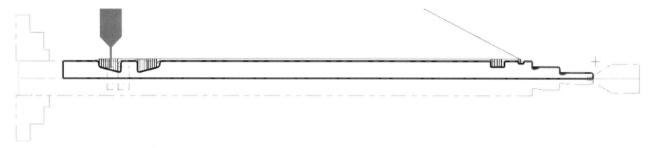

• Select the **OK** button to exit **Backplot**.

25.2 Verify the toolpaths

• To verify all toolpaths, from the **Toolpaths Manager**, choose the **Select all operations** icon.
• See **page 51** to review the procedure.

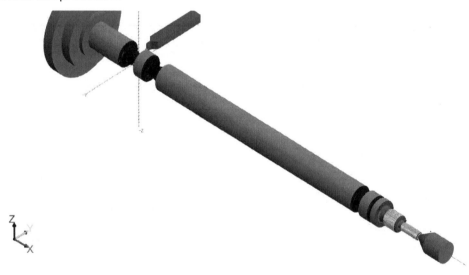

• To exit the Mastercam Simulator click on the **Close** icon.

STEP 26: CUTOFF THE PART

NOTE: To create the **Cutoff** toolpath, follow **Step 14** in **Tutorial 3** on **page 227**.

Toolpath Preview:

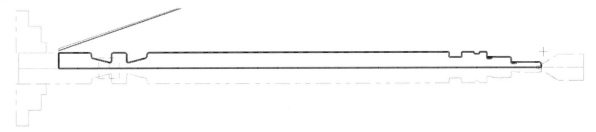

STEP 27: RUN THE POST PROCESSOR TO OBTAIN THE G-CODE FILE

Post Processing refers to the process by which the toolpaths in your Mastercam part files are converted to a format that can be understood by your machine tool's control. A special program reads your Mastercam file and writes the appropriate NC code.

- Make sure that all operations are selected, otherwise click on the **Select all operations** icon. ▸◂
- Select the **Post selected operations** icon from the **Toolpaths Manager.**

• In the **Post processing** dialog box make all of the necessary changes as shown.

NC File enabled allows you to keep the NC file and to assign the same name as the MCAM file.

Edit enabled allows you to automatically launch the default editor.

• Select the **OK** button to continue.
• Save the NC file.

• The **Mastercam Code Expert** window will be launched and the NC program will appear as shown.

```
1    %
2    O0006
3    (PROGRAM NAME - TUTORIAL #6)
4    (DATE=DD-MM-YY - 13-01-17 TIME=HH:MM - 15:37)
5    (MCX FILE - C:\USERS\GONG.ZHANG\DOCUMENTS\MASTERCAM\LATHE\TUTORIAL #6 TOOLPATH.MCAM)
6    (NC FILE - C:\USERS\GONG.ZHANG\DOCUMENTS\MASTERCAM\LATHE\TUTORIAL #6.NC)
7    (MATERIAL - STEEL INCH - 1030 - 200 BHN)
8    G20
9    (TOOL - 1 OFFSET - 1)
10   (OD ROUGH RIGHT - 80 DEG.  INSERT - CNMG-432)
11   ( FACE THE PART. )
12   G0 T0101
13   G18
14   G97 S477 M03
15   G0 G54 X1.6 Z.055 M8
16   G50 S3600
17   G96 S200
18   G99 G1 X-.0625 F.01
19   G0 Z.155
20   X1.6
21   Z.01
22   G1 X-.0625
23   G0 Z.11
24   X1.6
25   Z0.
26   G1 X-.0625
27   G0 Z.1
28   ( ROUGH THE OD. )
29   X1.3118
30   Z.2
31   G1 Z.1
32   Z-2.74
```

• Select the **"X"** box at the upper right corner to exit the editor.

STEP 28: SAVE THE UPDATED MCAM FILE

REVIEW EXERCISE - STUDENT PRACTICE

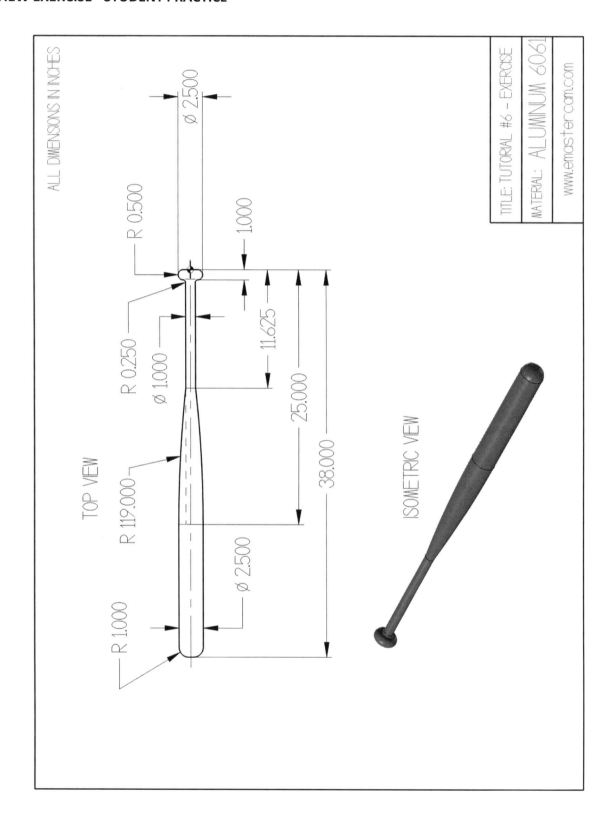

CREATE THE GEOMETRY FOR TUTORIAL #6 EXERCISE

Use these commands to create the top half of the geometry.
- Rectangle.
- Line Parallel.
- Arc Tangent.
- Fillet Entities.
- Trim Break Extend.

CREATE THE TOOLPATHS FOR TUTORIAL #6 EXERCISE

Create the Toolpaths for Tutorial #6 Exercise as per the instructions below.

NOTE: This part uses a rounded insert that is aimed towards cutting this baseball bat out of wood.

Set the machine properties including the stock.
- Set the Stock size to **OD = 2.75"** and **Length = 41"**.
- Set the initial Chuck position to grip on maximum diameter and **grip length = 36"**.
- Set the Tailstock position to **38"** and use the default size settings.

NOTE: For the next step you will need to break the **0.5"** radius in half.

Rough and Finish half of the round profile.
- Partial chain the right side of the **0.5"** radius CCW.
- Choose an appropriate tool for roughing.
- Use **Lead In/Out** to guide the tool to safe locations.
- Select the same geometry for the finishing operation.

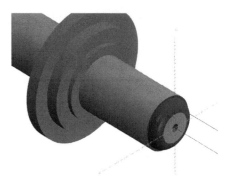

Center Drill the part.

- Use the **3/4"** center drill.
- Drill to a depth of **-0.5"**.

Advance the Stock and the Tailstock.

- Use a **Stock Advance** operation and enter in the transferred position to be **34.5"**.
- Select all of the geometry from the graphics screen.
- Enable **Blank original geometry**.
- Create a **Tailstock advance** operation, and set the position for Original Position and for Transferred Position to auto.

Rough and Finish the OD of the part using a custom tool.

- Chain the OD contour CCW. Make the partial chain start at the left half of the **0.5"** radius and stop just before the start of the **1.0"** radius so that Mastercam does not create a toolpath cutting through the entire part.
- Follow the steps beginning on **page 515** to create a custom grooving tool with a round insert of radius **0.25"**.
- From the **Rough parameters** page open the **Lead In/Out** dialog box and extend the **Lead out** by **1.5"**.
- Select the **Plunge Parameters** button and enable **Allow plunging in relief** as shown.

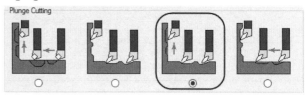

- Ensure the **Stock Recognition** is set to **Use stock for outer boundary**.

◆ Use the same tool and chain to finish the OD contour.

Rough and Finish the left curve.
◆ Use the single entity chaining mode to select only the **1.0"** radius.
◆ Use the same custom tool with the **0.25"** insert radius. Leave the plunge parameters the same as above.
◆ In the **Lead out** tab of the **Lead In/Out** dialog box, select the **Add Line** button and add a **0.5"** line at an angle of **180 degrees**.
◆ Disable **Stock Recognition**.
◆ Use all the same parameters for the finishing operation.

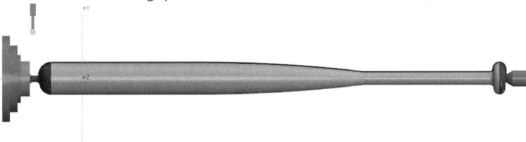

Cutoff the part.

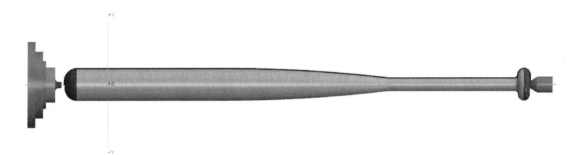

NOTES:

TUTORIAL #6 QUIZ

* What is a center drill used for?

* Why would you use a stock advance toolpath?

* Why would you advance a tailstock?

TUTORIAL #7

OVERVIEW OF STEPS TAKEN TO CREATE THE FINAL PART:

From SolidWorks file to CAD Model:
* The student will open a SolidWorks file in Mastercam.
* The student will need to create the geometry used to machine the part from the supplied solid model.

Create the 2D CAD Model used to generate toolpaths from:
* The student will create the lower profile of the part in the Top view on its own level.
* The profile of the part will be created using the Turn Profile command.
* The part will be properly orientated when we select the VTL CNC machine.

Create the necessary toolpaths to machine the part:
* The student will set up the stock and chuck jaws as it would appear on the VTL.
* The student will create facing, roughing, finishing, and threading toolpaths on the OD.
* The student will create drilling, finishing, and grooving toolpaths on the ID.
* A chain will be flipped to reverse the direction of a finish pass.

Backplot and Verify the file:
* The Backplot will be used to simulate a step by step process of the tool's movements.
* The Verify will be used to watch a tool machine the part out of a solid model.

Post Process the file to generate the G-code:
* The student will then post process the file to obtain an NC file containing the necessary code for the machine.

 This tutorial takes approximately one hour to complete.

GEOMETRY CREATION

STEP 1: SETTING UP THE GRAPHIC USER INTERFACE

Please refer to the **Getting Started** section to set up the graphical user interface accordingly.

STEP 2: DOWNLOAD THE FILE LATHE TRAINING TUTORIAL

You will require an internet connection to download this file.

RESOURCES: - Download the file from www.emastercam.com/trainingfiles.
* Save the file on the desktop.

STEP 3: REMOVING ANY MACHINE FROM THE TOOLPATHS MANAGER

In this step you have to clear any machine that might exist in the **Toolpaths Manager**. The only Mastercam product that does not require any machine is Design.

> **NOTE:** This tutorial covers machining a part in a VTL machine. We will bring in a part from SolidWorks and manipulate the geometry appropriately. It is important to make sure that in the **Toolpaths Manager** no machine is selected.

* To unhide and lock the manager panels, see **Tutorial 1 page 40**.

MACHINE
* If another machine is already selected, from the **Machine ribbon** in the **Machine Type** group select **Design**.
* From the **Toolpaths Manager**, click on the **Delete all operations, groups and tools** icon as shown.

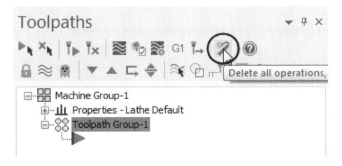

* This warning message will appear on the screen.

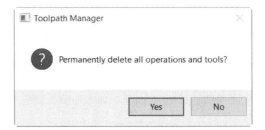

* Select the **Yes** button to continue.
* In the **Toolpaths Manager** you should have no **Machine Group** as shown.

STEP 4: OPEN THE SOLIDWORKS FILE IN MASTERCAM

In this step we will open the SLDPRT file in Mastercam.

* From the **Quick Access Toolbar** located at the upper left corner of the screen, select the **Open** icon as shown.

* Ensure the **Files type** is set to **SOLIDWORKS Files (*.sldprt; *.sldasm, *.slddrw)**. This will show all the SolidWorks files you have on your desktop.

* Locate the file in the location it was saved i.e. the desktop.

- Select the file **TUTORIAL #7.SLDPRT** as shown in <u>Figure: 4.0.1</u>.

Figure: 4.0.1

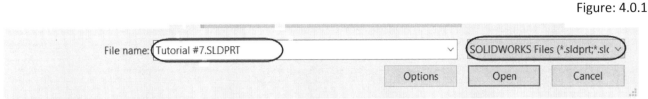

- Open the file.
- Right mouse click in the graphics window and select the **Isometric** view.

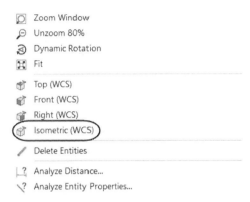

- Press **Alt + F1** to fit the geometry into the graphics window.
- Press **Alt + S** to see the part in the shaded mode.

NOTE: Currently you have a solid. Unlike wireframe models, which are a collection of curves, and surface models, which are a collection of surfaces, a solid model is a single entity.
Any time you want to see the solid in a shaded or unshaded mode press **Alt + S**.

- The part should appear as shown in <u>Figure: 4.0.2</u>.

Figure: 4.0.2

STEP 5: CHANGE THE MAIN LEVEL TO 2

In this step we will change the main level to 2 to differentiate the geometry that will be created from the solid model.

* From the bottom of the **Toolpaths Manager**, select the **Levels** tab as shown.

* Click in the **Name** area in the **Levels Manager** and highlight the existing name and enter **"Solid"** as shown.
* Press **Enter** once complete.

◆ Click in the **Number** area and enter in the level number **2** and type in the name **"Turn Profile Geometry"** as shown.

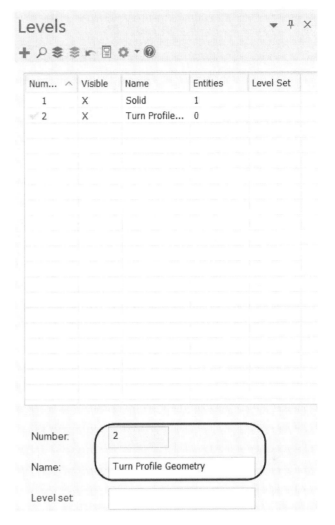

◆ Press **Enter** once complete.

STEP 6: CREATE A TURN PROFILE OF THE PART

In this step we will use the solid we imported from SolidWorks and create geometry from it. **Turn Profile** will create a 2D profile from an existing solid, solid face or surface. The profile will be created in the top view of the active WCS by either spinning the solid about the **X axis** or creating a cross section (slice) through the selected solid in the XY plane.

Step Preview:

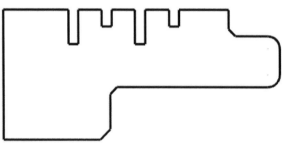

WIREFRAME

- From the **Shapes** group, select **Turn Profile** as shown.

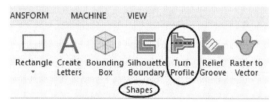

- To select the **Top** view, right mouse click in the graphics window and select **Top (WCS)** as shown

- Scroll down on the mouse wheel to unzoom the geometry.

♦ [Select solid bodies, solid faces or surfaces]: Select the solid on the graphic user interface.

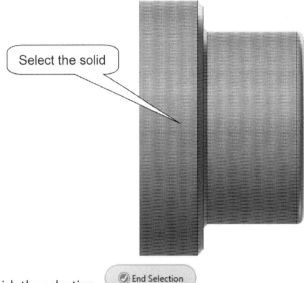

Select the solid

♦ Click on the **End Selection** button or press **Enter** to finish the selection. End Selection
♦ The **Turn Profile** panel will appear. Set the **Computation Method** to **Spin** and the **Profile** to **Lower Profile** as shown.

Spin is used to create a profile by spinning the solid about the WCS **X axis**.

Slice is used to create the profile from a slice through the middle of the solid in the WCS XY plane.

Tesselation Tolerance sets the maximum allowed deviation of a given triangular facet from the selected surfaces.

Profile controls whether the upper, lower or both halves of the profile (Full Profile) are created.

• Select the **OK** button to generate the geometry.

> **NOTE:** This may take a minute depending on the processing speed of your computer.

• In the **Levels** panel, click in the **Visible** column next to **Level 1** to remove the **X** and make it invisible as shown.

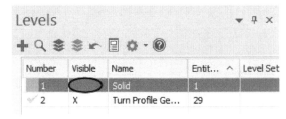

• The geometry should appear as shown in <u>Figure: 6.0.1</u>.

Figure: 6.0.1

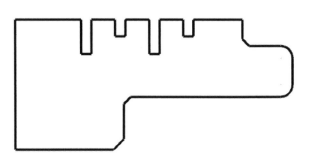

> **NOTE:** Observe how the part is orientated, as if we were programming a standard lathe toolpath. When we select the VTL machine definition, the geometry will be rotated 90 degrees automatically for us. VTL stands for "Vertical Turret Lathe." A VTL works with the same concept as a horizontal lathe, except the turret is mounted on the "floor" and the part is machined vertically.

STEP 7: SAVE THE FILE

FILE
• **Save As.**

• Click on the **Browse** icon as shown.
• Find a location on the computer to save your file.
• File name: "Your Name_7".

TOOLPATH CREATION

PART SETUP:

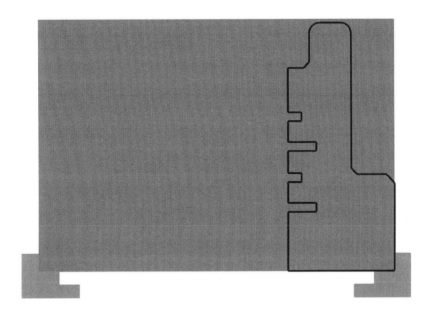

SETUP SHEET:

TOOL LIST

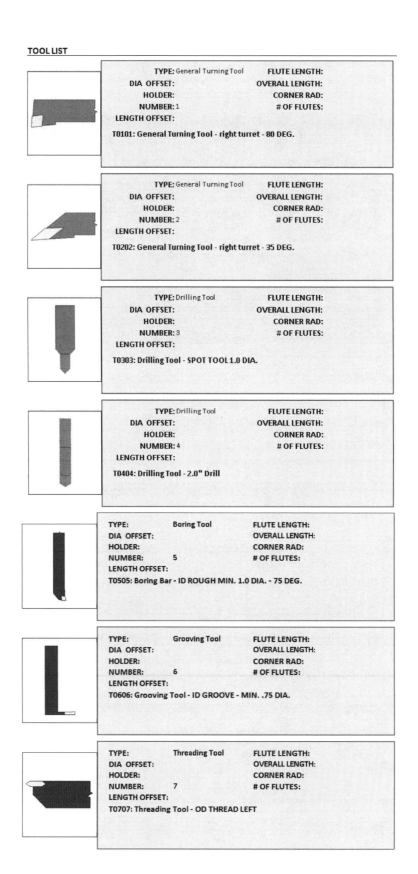

TYPE: General Turning Tool	**FLUTE LENGTH:**
DIA OFFSET:	**OVERALL LENGTH:**
HOLDER:	**CORNER RAD:**
NUMBER: 1	**# OF FLUTES:**
LENGTH OFFSET:	

T0101: General Turning Tool - right turret - 80 DEG.

TYPE: General Turning Tool	**FLUTE LENGTH:**
DIA OFFSET:	**OVERALL LENGTH:**
HOLDER:	**CORNER RAD:**
NUMBER: 2	**# OF FLUTES:**
LENGTH OFFSET:	

T0202: General Turning Tool - right turret - 35 DEG.

TYPE: Drilling Tool	**FLUTE LENGTH:**
DIA OFFSET:	**OVERALL LENGTH:**
HOLDER:	**CORNER RAD:**
NUMBER: 3	**# OF FLUTES:**
LENGTH OFFSET:	

T0303: Drilling Tool - SPOT TOOL 1.0 DIA.

TYPE: Drilling Tool	**FLUTE LENGTH:**
DIA OFFSET:	**OVERALL LENGTH:**
HOLDER:	**CORNER RAD:**
NUMBER: 4	**# OF FLUTES:**
LENGTH OFFSET:	

T0404: Drilling Tool - 2.0" Drill

TYPE: Boring Tool	**FLUTE LENGTH:**
DIA OFFSET:	**OVERALL LENGTH:**
HOLDER:	**CORNER RAD:**
NUMBER: 5	**# OF FLUTES:**
LENGTH OFFSET:	

T0505: Boring Bar - ID ROUGH MIN. 1.0 DIA. - 75 DEG.

TYPE: Grooving Tool	**FLUTE LENGTH:**
DIA OFFSET:	**OVERALL LENGTH:**
HOLDER:	**CORNER RAD:**
NUMBER: 6	**# OF FLUTES:**
LENGTH OFFSET:	

T0606: Grooving Tool - ID GROOVE - MIN. .75 DIA.

TYPE: Threading Tool	**FLUTE LENGTH:**
DIA OFFSET:	**OVERALL LENGTH:**
HOLDER:	**CORNER RAD:**
NUMBER: 7	**# OF FLUTES:**
LENGTH OFFSET:	

T0707: Threading Tool - OD THREAD LEFT

STEP 8: SELECT THE MACHINE AND SET UP THE STOCK

In Mastercam, you select a **Machine Definition** before creating any toolpaths. The **Machine Definition** is a model of your machine's capabilities and features and acts like a template for setting up machining jobs. The machine definition ties together three main components: the schematic model of your machine's components, the control definition that models your control unit's capabilities and the post processor that will generate the required machine code (G-code). For this exercise we will select the VTL RIGHT machine definition. Selecting this machine will automatically change the orientation of the part by rotating the geometry 90 degrees CCW and allow us to set up the stock appropriately for a VTL.

> **NOTE:** For the purpose of this tutorial, we will be using the VTL Right machine.

8.1 Download the files and save them to an appropriate location

You will require an internet connection to download this file.

RESOURCES - DOWNLOAD VTL MACHINE ZIP FILES FROM WWW.EMASTERCAM.COM/TRAININGFILES/.
- Save the file in an appropriate location.
- Extract the files from the zip file into a folder.
- Copy and paste the post files (.pst and .psb if applicable) into the Lathe Posts folder in your shared directories. Use the following link in your computer directory to find the folder.

C:\Users\Public\Documents\shared Mcam2018\lathe\Posts

- Copy and paste the machine definition (.mcam-lmd) and control definition (.mcam-control) into the "CNC_MACHINES" folder of the Mastercam shared folder.

C:\Users\Public\Documents\shared Mcam2018\CNC_MACHINES

- Save and close the file you are working on and then reopen the file.
- Select **Open** icon in the **Quick Access Toolbar** and open file "Your Name_7".

MACHINE
- Select the drop down arrow below **Lathe** and select **Manage List** as shown.

• Select **VTL RIGHT TURRET.MCAM-LMD** then click on the **Add** button as shown.

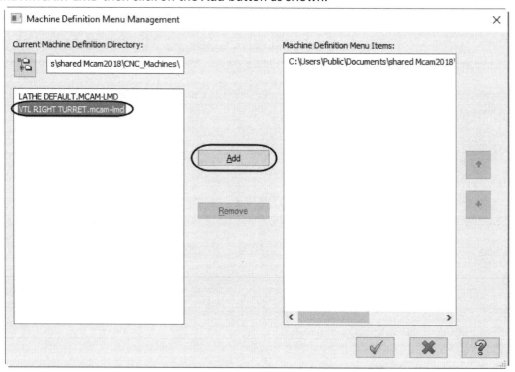

• Select the **OK** button to exit the **Machine Definition Menu Management** dialog box.

MACHINE
• Click on the drop down arrow below **Lathe** and select **VTL RIGHT TURRET.MCAM-LMD** as shown.

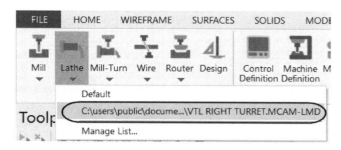

◆ The geometry should be automatically rotated as shown.

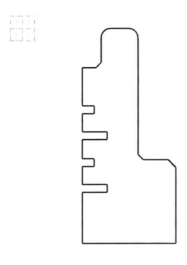

◆ Also note in the lower corner of the graphics screen that the construction plane is set to **Top-Lathe VTL** and the coordinates are **D Z**.

◆ To open the **Toolpaths Manager** panel, click on the **Toolpaths** tab located at the bottom of the **Levels** panel as shown.

◆ Select the plus sign in front of **Properties** in the **Toolpaths Manager** to expand the **Toolpaths Group Properties.**

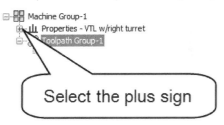

◆ Select **Files** as shown.

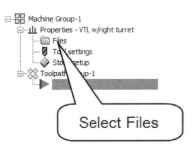

◆ The machine should be displayed as shown. Note that the **Control** and **Post** files will change as well.

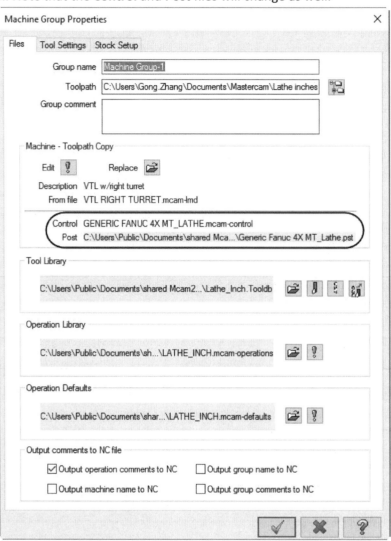

◆ Select the **Open** button in the **Tool Library** area as shown.

◆ Select the tool library **VTL_TOOLS_INCH.tooldb** as shown.

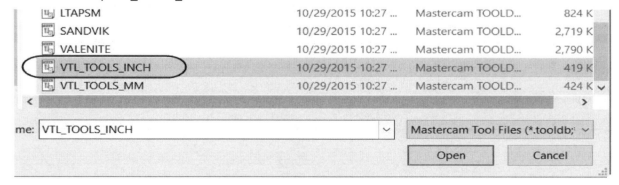

- After you have selected the library, click on **Open**.
- Select the **Tool Settings** tab.
- Change the parameters to match the screenshot as shown in <u>Figure: 8.1.1</u>.

Figure: 8.1.1

Default program number is used to enter a number if your machine requires a number for a program name.

Assign tool numbers sequentially allows you to overwrite the tool number from the library with the next available tool number.

Warn of duplicate tool numbers allows you to get a warning if you enter two tools with the same number.

Override defaults with modal values enables the system to keep the values that you enter.

Feed Calculation set to **From tool** uses the feed rate, plunge rate, retract rate and spindle speed from the tool definition.

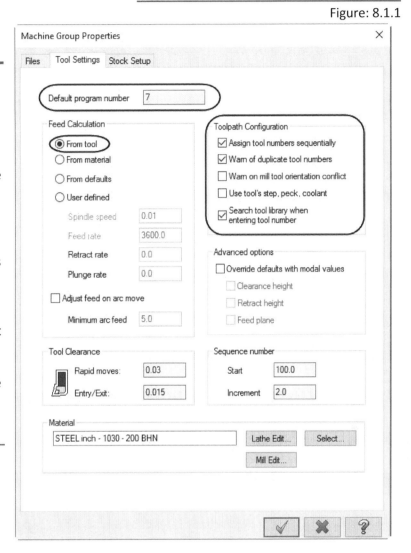

- Select the **Stock Setup** tab.
- Make sure that in the **Stock Plane**, you have **Top** as shown.

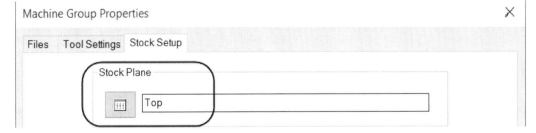

♦ Choose the **Properties** button to set up the stock for the **Lower Spindle**.

♦ Define the stock by setting the **Geometry** to **Cylinder** and match the settings as shown.

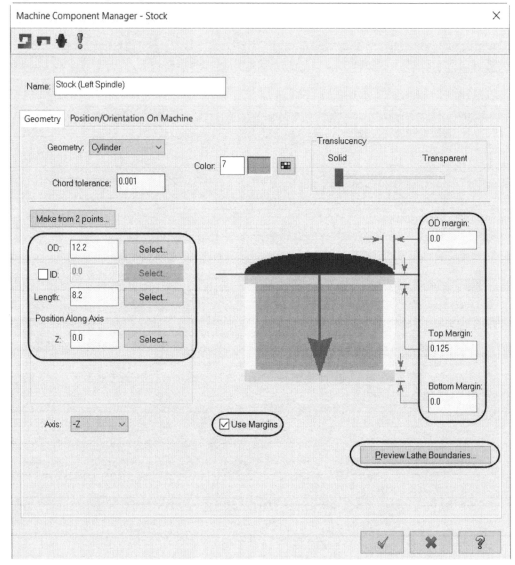

◆ Select the **Preview Lathe Boundaries** button and the part should appear as shown in <u>Figure: 8.1.2</u>.

Figure: 8.1.2

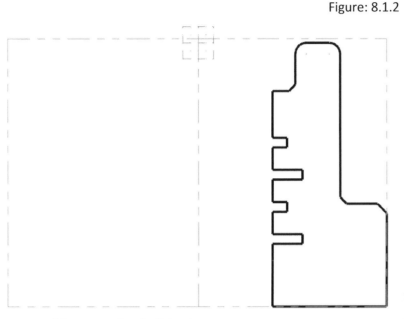

◆ Press **Enter** to return to the **Machine Component Manager - Stock** dialog box.

◆ Select the **OK** button to exit the **Machine Component Manager - Stock** dialog box.

◆ Ensure that **Lower Spindle** is selected and then select the **Properties** button in the **Chuck Jaws** area as shown.

- Make the necessary changes to define the chuck size, the clamping method and the stock position. Ensure that you choose the clamping method **OD#2** as shown in the graphic below.

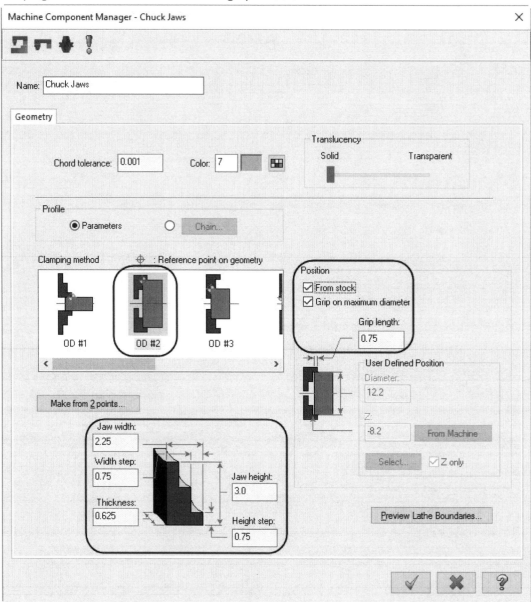

- Select the **OK** button to exit the **Machine Component Manager - Chuck Jaws** dialog box.
- Enable **Fit screen to boundaries** in the **Display Options** area.

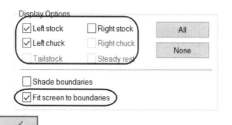

- Select the **OK** button to exit the **Machine Group Properties** dialog box.

• Press **Alt + F1** to fit the geometry to the screen.
• The part should appear as shown in <u>Figure: 8.1.3</u>.

Figure: 8.1.3

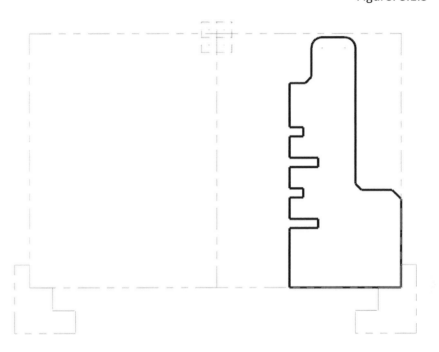

STEP 9: FACE THE PART

In this step we will create a **Face** toolpath to remove the material from the top of the part that was added in the stock setup page.

Toolpath Preview:

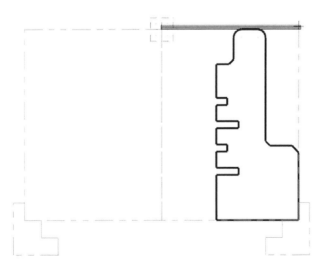

TURNING

• From the **General** group, select the **Face** icon.

• Select the **Right turret - 80 Deg** tool from the tool list and enter the comment as shown.

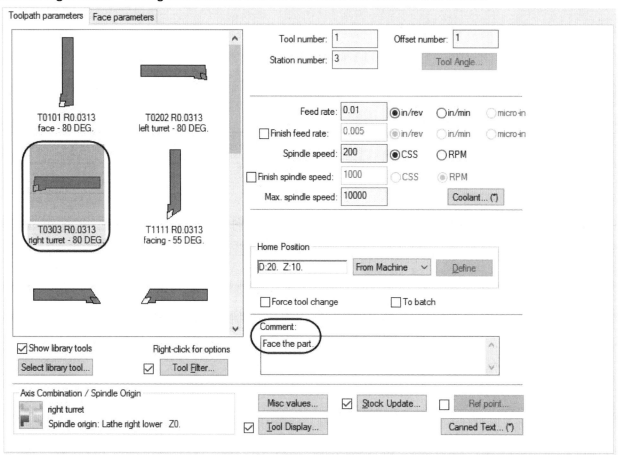

- Select the **Face parameters** tab and make any necessary changes to match the screenshot below.

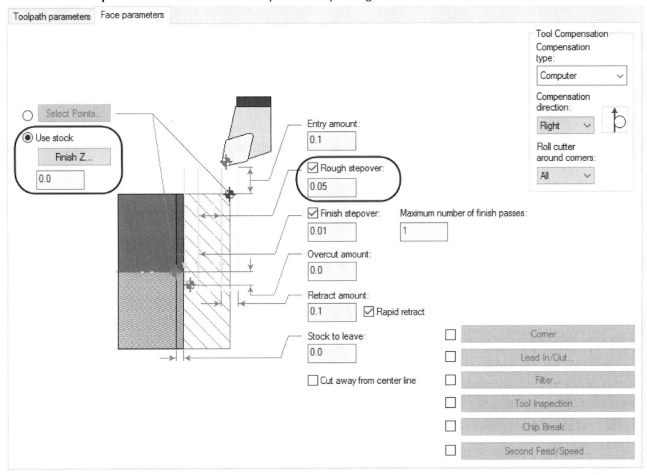

- Select the **OK** button to exit the **Lathe Face** dialog box.

STEP 10: BACKPLOT THE TOOLPATHS

Backplotting shows the path the tools take to cut the part. This display lets you spot errors in the program before you machine the part. As you backplot toolpaths, Mastercam displays additional information such as the X, Y, and Z coordinates, the path length, the minimum and maximum coordinates and the cycle time. It also shows any collisions between the workpiece and the tool.

10.1 Backplot the toolpaths

* Make sure that the toolpath is selected (signified by the green check mark on the folder icon). If the operation is not selected choose the **Select all operations** icon.

* Select the **Backplot selected operations** icon.

* See **page 49** to review the procedure.

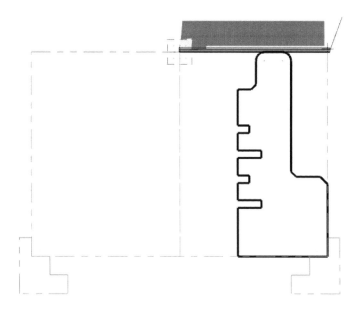

> **NOTE:** The holder of the tool needs to be longer. Alternatively you can rough out the OD first and then face the part.

* Select the **OK** button to exit **Backplot**.

10.2 Verify the toolpaths

• To verify all toolpaths, from the **Toolpaths Manager**, choose the **Select all operations** icon.

• Select the **Verify selected operations** icon.

• See **page 51** to review the procedure.

> **NOTE:** To rotate the part, move the cursor to the center of the part and click and hold the mouse wheel and slowly move it in one direction.
> To zoom in or out scroll up or down on the mouse wheel as needed.

• The part should look as shown in Figure: 10.2.1.

Figure: 10.2.1

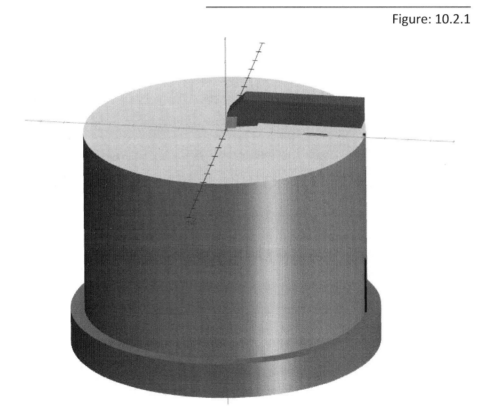

• To go back to the Mastercam window, minimize the **Mastercam Simulator** window as shown.

• If needed, press **Alt + T** to remove the toolpath display.

STEP 11: ROUGH THE OD OF THE PART

In this step we will create a roughing toolpath to remove the bulk of the material on the OD of the part.

Toolpath Preview:

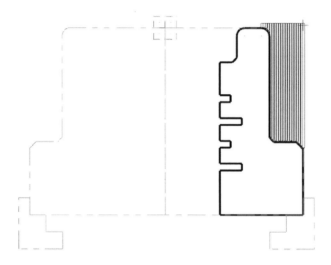

TURNING

♦ From the **General** group, select the **Rough** icon.

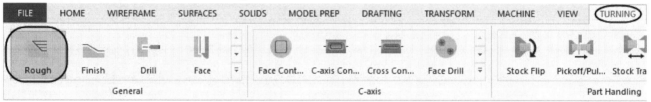

♦ Leave the default settings in the **Chaining** dialog box.

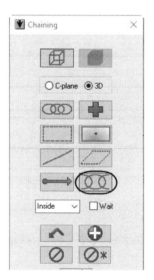

NOTE: The chaining mode is **Partial** by default. You will have to select the first entity and the last entity of the contour.

- [Select the entry point or chain the inner boundary]: Select **Entity A** (the fillet) then **Entity B** as shown. Ensure the chaining direction is Clockwise.

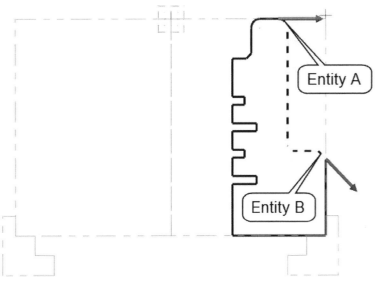

- Select the **OK** button to exit the **Chaining** dialog box.
- The **Lathe Rough** dialog box will appear. Select the same tool that was used in the previous operation and enter the comment as shown.

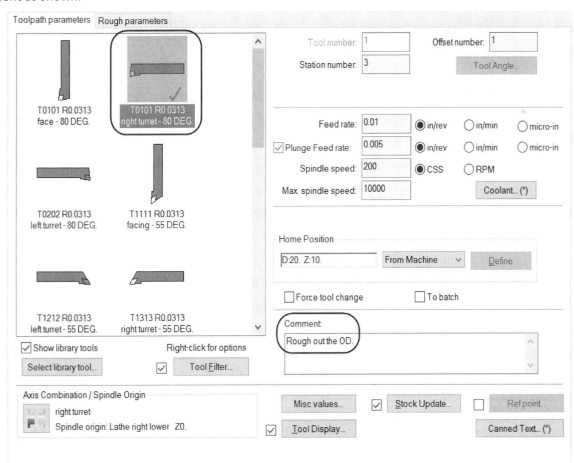

- Select the **Rough parameters** tab and change the **Rough Direction**, the **Depth cuts** settings, and enable **Use stock for outer boundary** as shown.

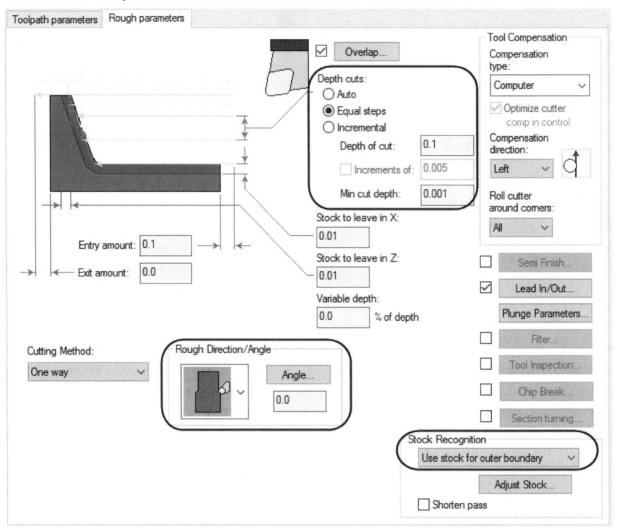

- Select the **OK** button to exit the **Lathe Rough** dialog box to generate the toolpath.

11.1 Backplot the toolpath

- Once the operation has been regenerated, **Backplot** the toolpath.
- See **page 49** to review the procedure.

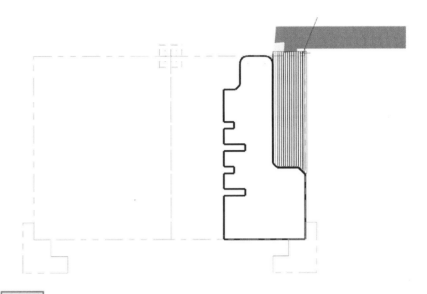

- Select the **OK** button to exit **Backplot**.

11.2 Verify the toolpaths

- To verify all toolpaths, from the **Toolpaths Manager**, choose the **Select all operations** icon.
- See **page 51** to review the procedure.

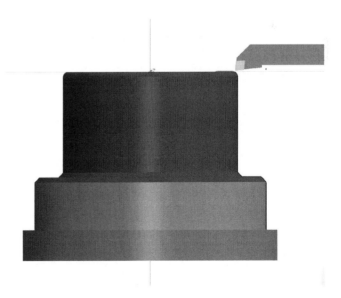

- To go back to the Mastercam window, minimize the **Mastercam Simulator** window as shown.

STEP 12: FINISH THE OD

In this step we will finish the OD and remove the leftover material from the previous operation.

Toolpath Preview:

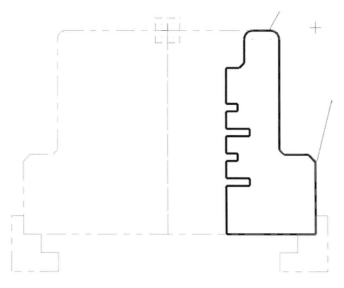

TURNING

* From the **General** group, select the **Finish** icon.

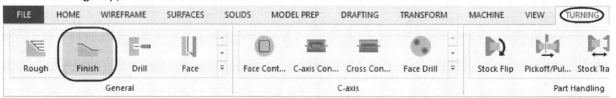

* Select the **Last** button in the **Chaining** dialog box as shown.

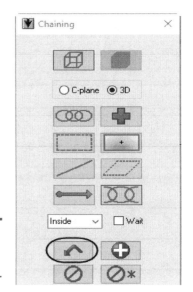

The **Last** button will automatically select the last chain that we used in the roughing toolpath.

* Select the **OK** button to exit the **Chaining** dialog box.

◆ Select the **Right turret - 35 Deg** tool from the tool list and enter the comment as shown.

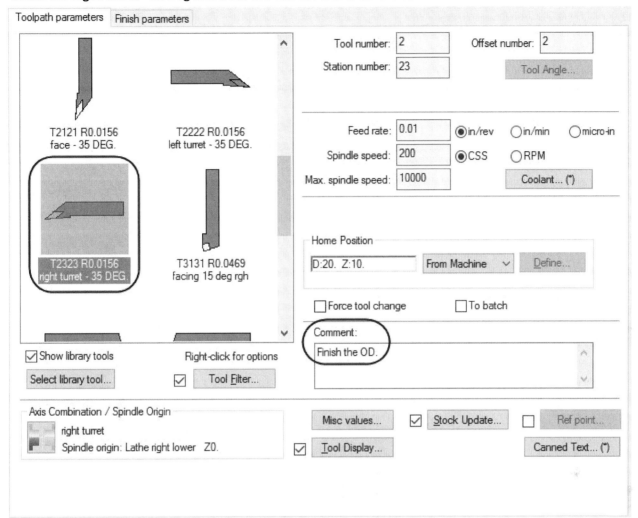

NOTE: If the tool is not found in the list above, click on **Select library tool** for more options.

• Select the **Finish parameters** tab and make sure the compensation direction is **Left.**

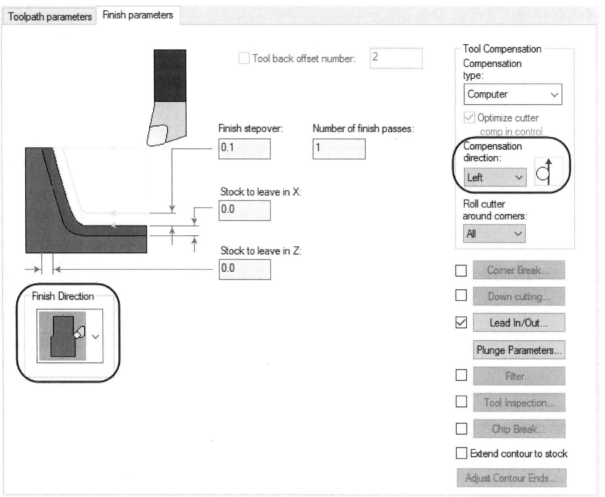

• Select the **OK** button to exit the **Lathe Finish** dialog box.

12.1 Backplot the toolpath

- Once the operation has been regenerated **Backplot** the toolpath.
- See **page 49** to review the procedure.

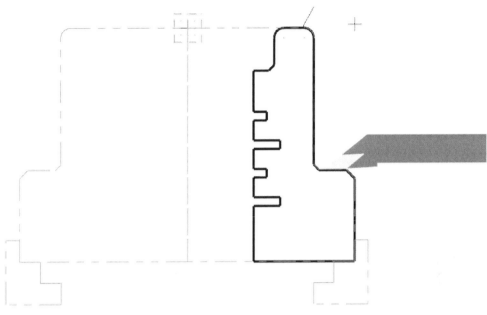

- Select the **OK** button to exit **Backplot**.

12.2 Verify the toolpaths

- To verify all toolpaths, from the **Toolpaths Manager**, choose the **Select all operations** icon.
- See **page 51** to review the procedure.

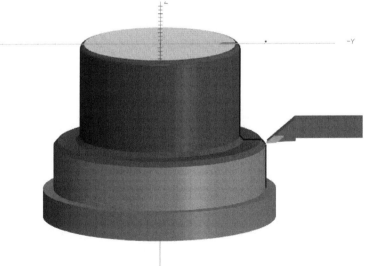

- To go back to the Mastercam window, minimize the **Mastercam Simulator** window as shown.

STEP 13: SPOT DRILL THE CENTER OF THE PART

In this step we will spot drill the center of the part before we drill the part to remove the bulk of the material.

Toolpath Preview:

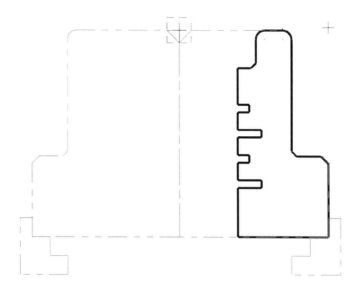

TURNING

♦ From the **General** group, select the **Drill** icon.

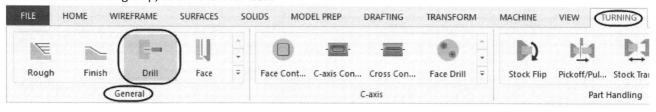

NOTE: The **Lathe Drill** dialog box will automatically open. No chaining is required because Mastercam drills along the center line to create the toolpath. The drill depths are specified within the dialog box.

◆ Select the **Select library tool** button when the toolpath dialog box appears.

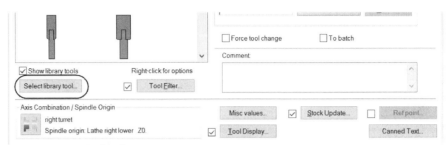

◆ Click on the **Open** button in the **Tool Selection** dialog box.

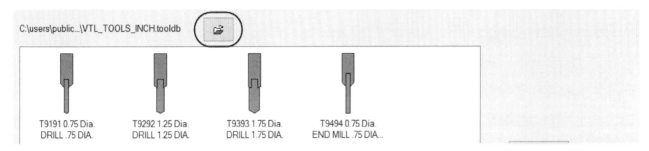

◆ Select the **lathe_inch.tooldb** library and select the open button as outlined below.

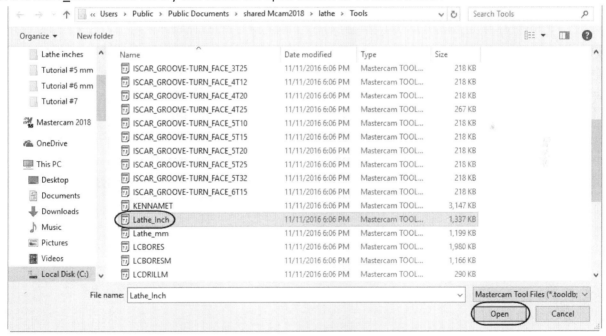

◆ Select the **OK** button to exit the **Tool Selection** dialog box.

• Disable the **Tool Filter** button and select the **SPOT TOOL 1.0 DIA** from the tool list then enter the comment as shown.

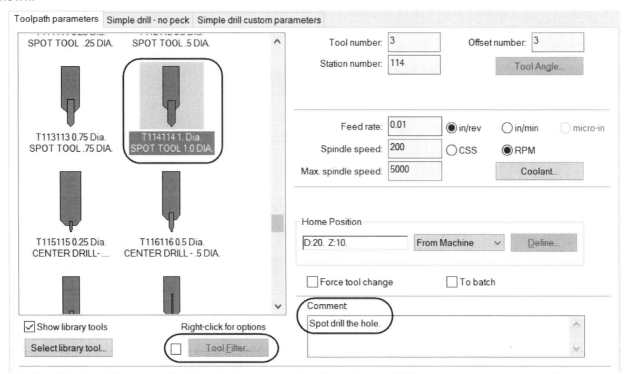

• Select the **Simple drill - no peck** tab and change the **Depth** as shown. Make any other necessary changes.

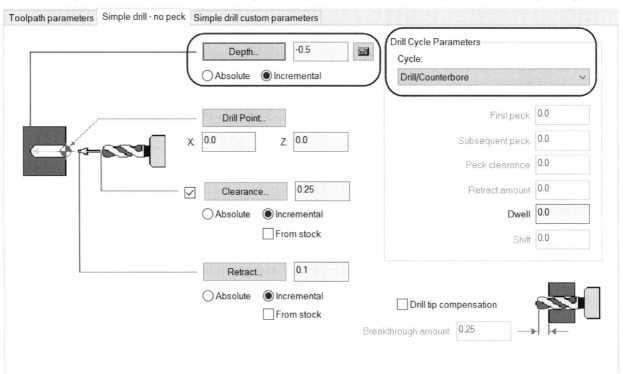

• Select the **OK** button to exit the **Lathe Drill** dialog box.

13.1 Verify the toolpaths

- To verify all toolpaths, from the **Toolpaths Manager**, choose the **Select all operations** icon.
- See **page 51** to review the procedure.

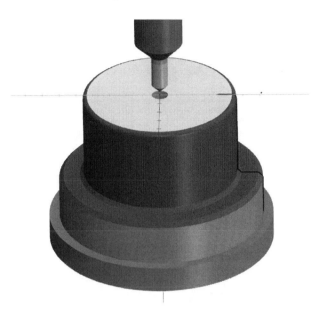

- To go back to the Mastercam window, minimize the **Mastercam Simulator** window as shown.

STEP 14: DRILL THE PART WITH A LARGE DRILL

In this step we will use a 2.0" Drill to remove a large amount of material from the center of the part.

Toolpath Preview:

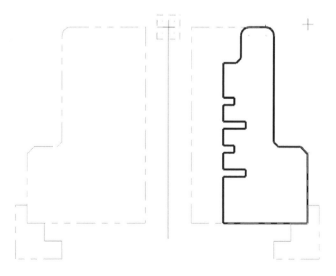

TURNING

♦ From the **General** group, select the **Drill** icon.

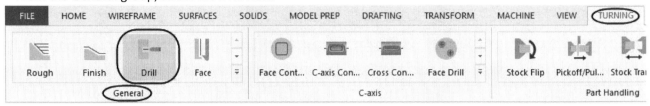

♦ Right mouse click in the tool list window and choose **Create new tool**.

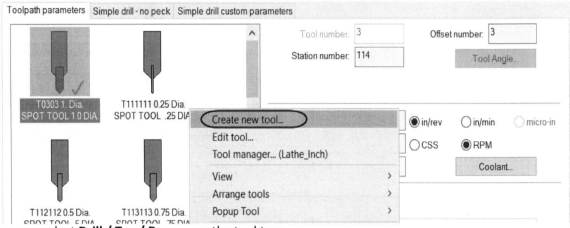

♦ In the **Type** area select **Drill / Tap / Reamer** as the tool type.

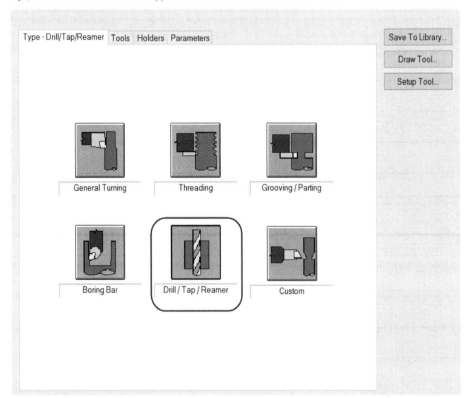

♦ Make any necessary changes to the tool size as shown. Ensure the **Diameter** is equal to **2.0"**.

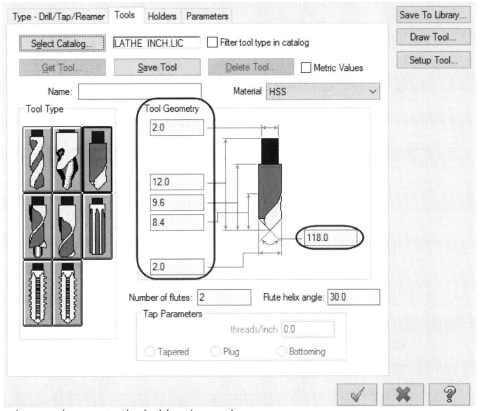

♦ Select the **Holders** tab and make any changes to the holder size as shown.

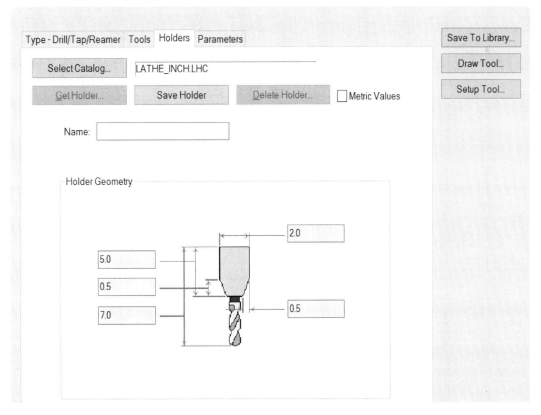

• Select the **Parameters** tab and change the **Tool name** as outlined below.

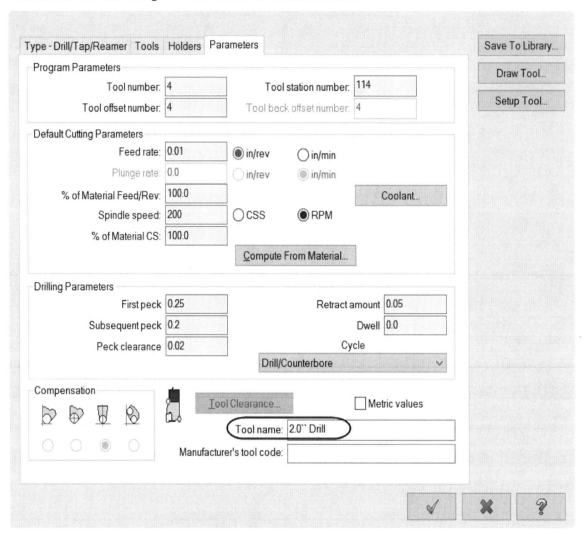

• Select the **OK** button to exit the **Define Tool** dialog box.

◆ The new tool we just created should show up in the tool list. Enter the comment as shown.

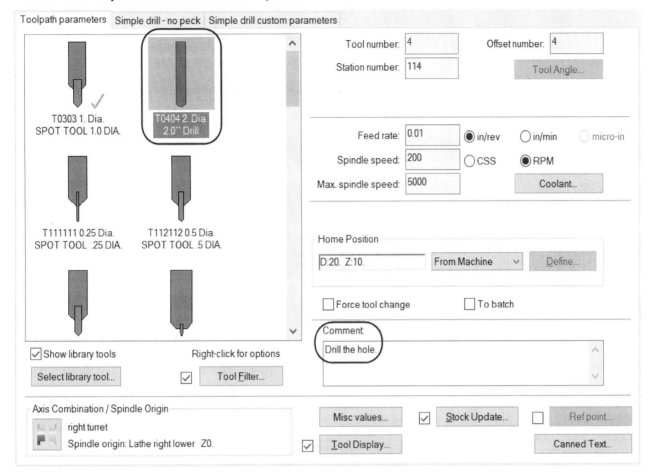

• Select the **Simple drill - no peck** tab and make any changes as shown.

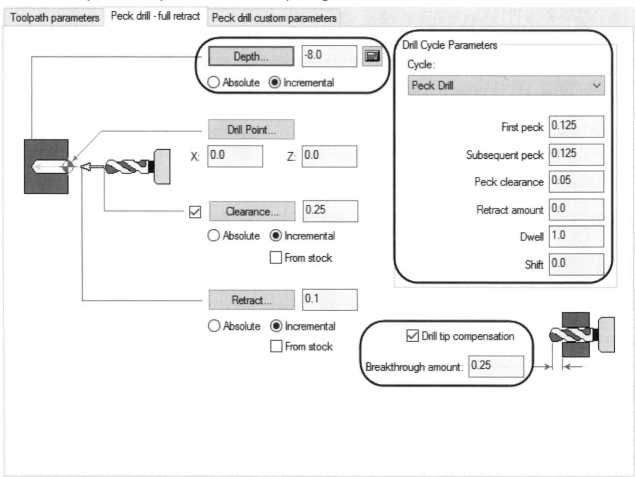

• Select the **OK** button to create the drill toolpath.

14.1 Verify the toolpaths

• To verify all toolpaths, from the **Toolpaths Manager**, choose the **Select all operations** icon.

• See **page 51** to review the procedure.

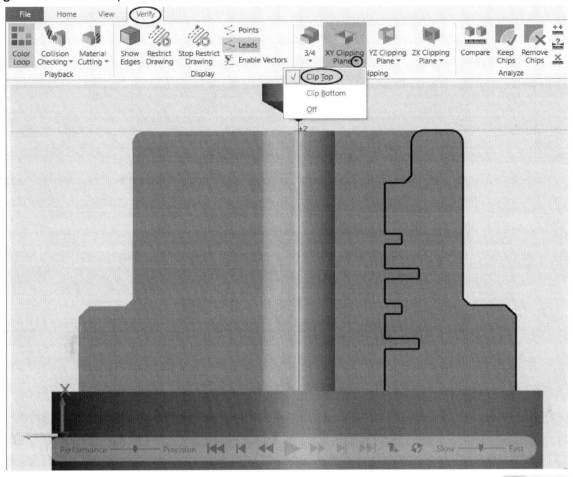

• To go back to the Mastercam window, minimize the **Mastercam Simulator** window as shown.

STEP 15: ROUGH AND FINISH THE INSIDE DIAMETER OF THE PART

In this step we will create a **Rough** toolpath to machine the inside diameter of the part to its finished size.

Toolpath Preview:

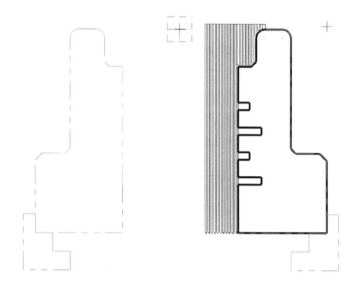

TURNING

♦ From the **General** group, select the **Rough** icon.

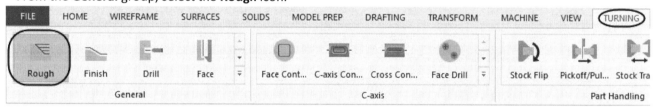

• Leave the default settings in the **Chaining** dialog box.

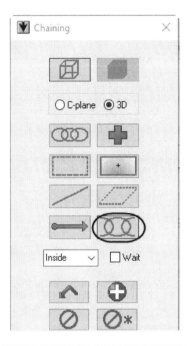

> **NOTE:** The chaining mode is **Partial** by default. You will have to select the first entity and the last entity of the contour.

• [Select the entry point or chain the inner boundary]: Select **Entity A,** then **Entity B** as shown. Ensure the chaining direction is as shown.

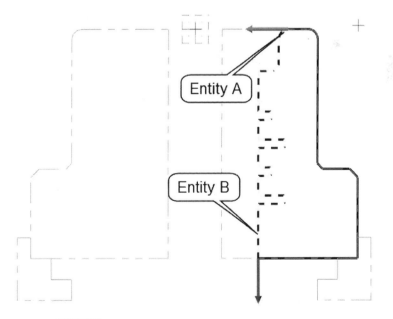

• Select the **OK** button to exit the **Chaining** dialog box.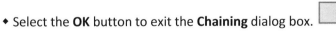

• Find the **ID Rough Min 1.0 Dia - 75 Deg** and right click on the tool and select **Edit Tool.**

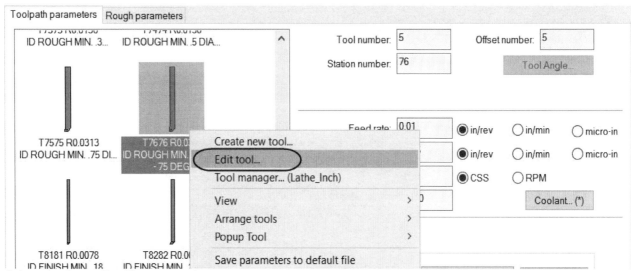

• Select the **Setup Tool** button as shown.

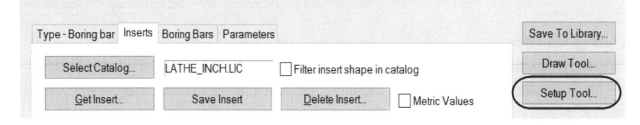

• Change the Turret to **Right** as shown.

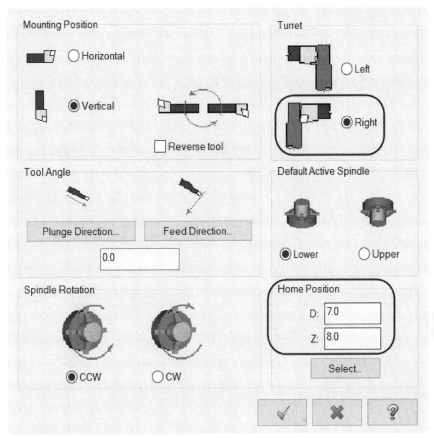

• Select the **OK** button to exit the **Lathe Tool Setup (VTL)** dialog box.

• Select the **OK** button to exit the **Define Tool** dialog box.

♦ The new tool should be selected. Enter the comment as shown.

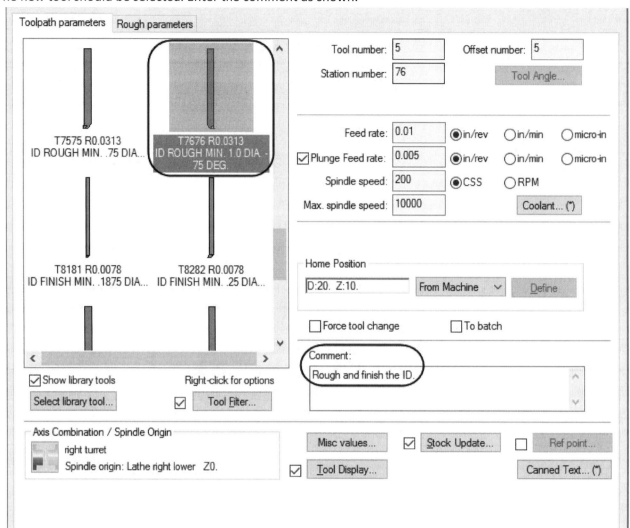

- Select the **Rough parameters** tab and make any changes as shown.
- Select **Use stock for outer boundary** as outlined below.
- Enable **Semi Finish** and click on the button to open the dialog box.

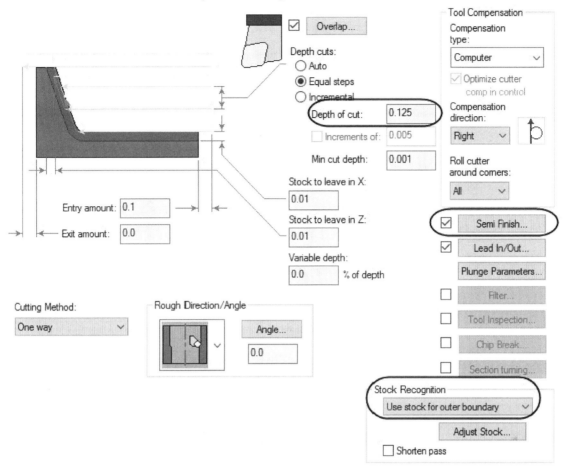

- In the **Semi Finish Parameters** dialog box, change the parameters as shown to make one finish pass.

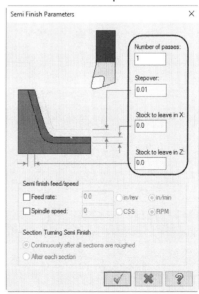

- Select **OK** to exit the **Semi Finish Parameters** dialog box.

- Select the **OK** button to exit the **Lathe Rough** dialog box.

15.1 Backplot the toolpath

- Once the operation has been regenerated **Backplot** the toolpath.
- See **page 49** to review the procedure.

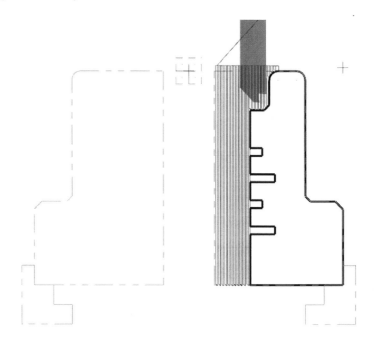

- Select the **OK** button to exit **Backplot**.

15.2 Verify the toolpaths

- To verify all toolpaths, from the **Toolpaths Manager**, choose the **Select all operations** icon.

* See **page 51** to review the procedure.

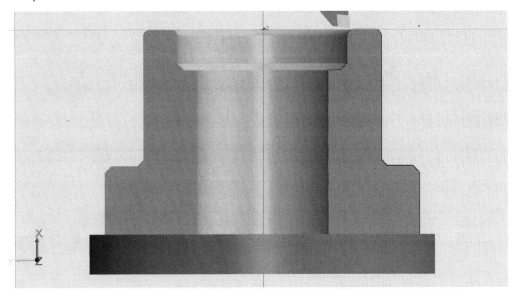

* To go back to the Mastercam window, minimize the **Mastercam Simulator** window as shown.

STEP 16: MACHINE THE GROOVES ON THE ID OF THE PART

In this step we will create a grooving toolpath to rough and finish the 4 grooves in one step using a custom tool.

Toolpath Preview:

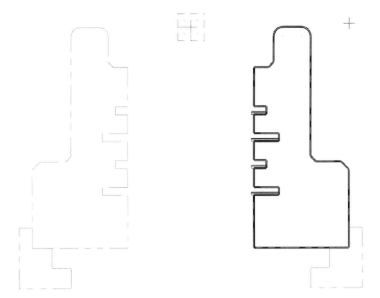

TURNING

* From the **General** group, click on the **Expand gallery** arrow key.

* Select **Groove**.

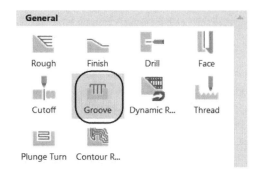

* When the **Grooving Options** dialog box appears choose **Multiple chains** as shown.

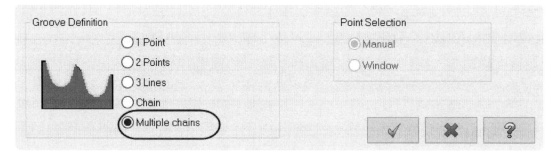

* Select the **OK** button to exit the **Grooving Options** dialog box.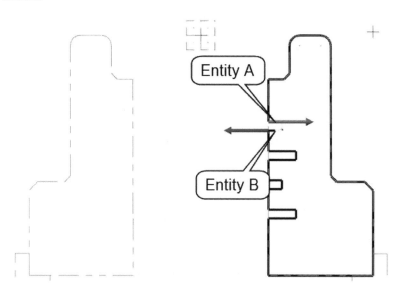
* [Select the entry point or chain the inner boundary]: Select **Entity A** as shown.
* [Select the last entity]: Select **Entity B** as shown.

- [Select the inner boundary or select the retraction point or select done]: Select **Entity C** as shown.
- [Select the last entity]: Select **Entity D** as shown.

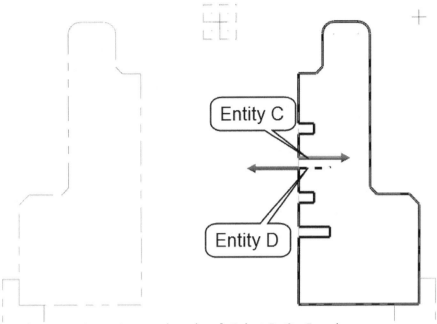

- [Select the inner boundary or select the retraction point or select done]: Select **Entity E** as shown.
- [Select the last entity]: Select **Entity F** to complete the chain as shown.

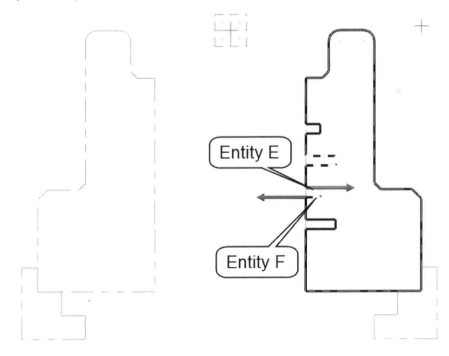

- [Select the inner boundary or select the retraction point or select done]: Select **Entity G** as shown.
- [Select the last entity]: Select **Entity H** to complete the chain as shown.

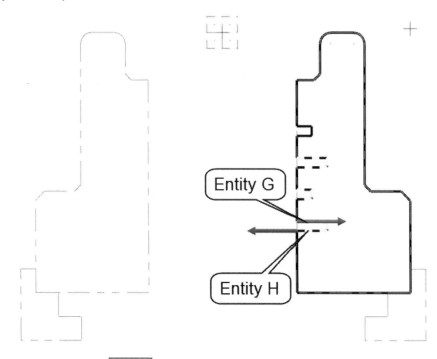

- Select the **OK** button to exit the **Chaining** dialog box.
- Right click on the **ID Groove Min. 0.75 Dia.** tool from the tool list and select **Edit tool** as shown.

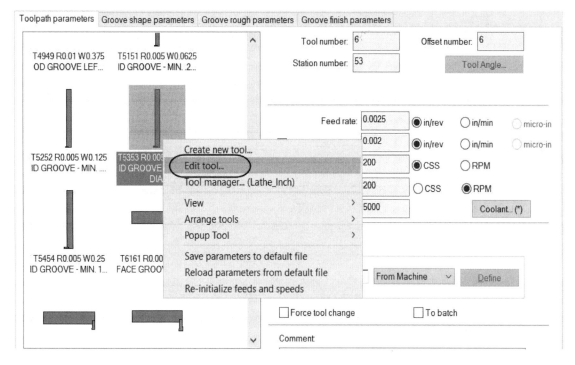

◆ When the **Define Tool** dialog box appears, select the **Setup Tool** button.

◆ Change the **Turret** to **Right** as shown. Make any other changes as shown.

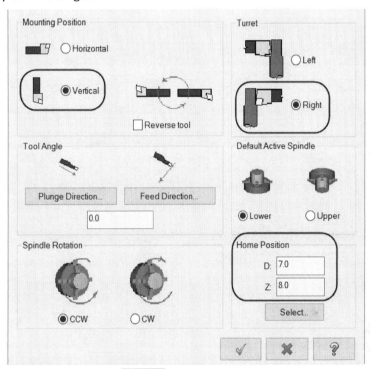

◆ Select the **OK** button to exit the **Lathe Tool Setup (VTL)** dialog box.

• Select the **Holders** tab and make the changes to the holder size as shown.

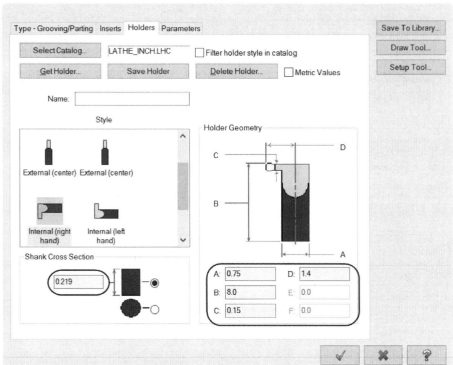

• Select the **OK** button to exit the **Define Tool** dialog box.

• The new tool should be selected. Enter the comment as shown.

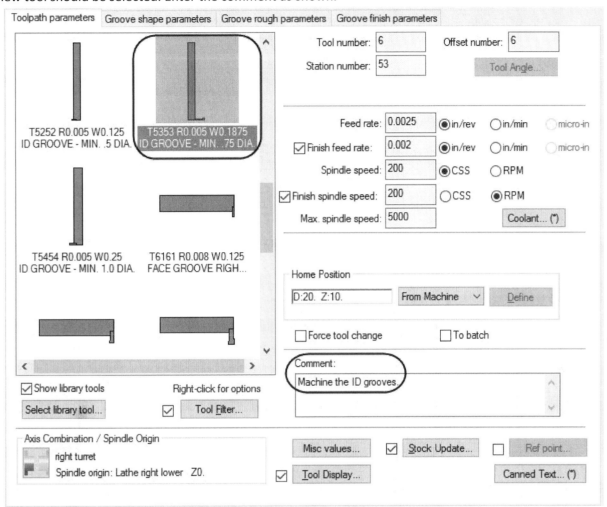

• Select the **Groove shape parameters** tab and enable **Use stock for outer boundary**.

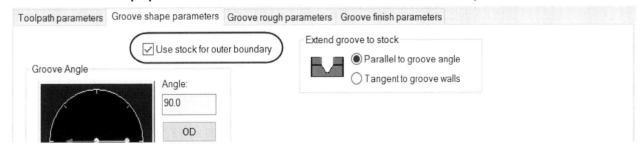

♦ Select the **Groove rough parameters** tab and make any changes as shown.

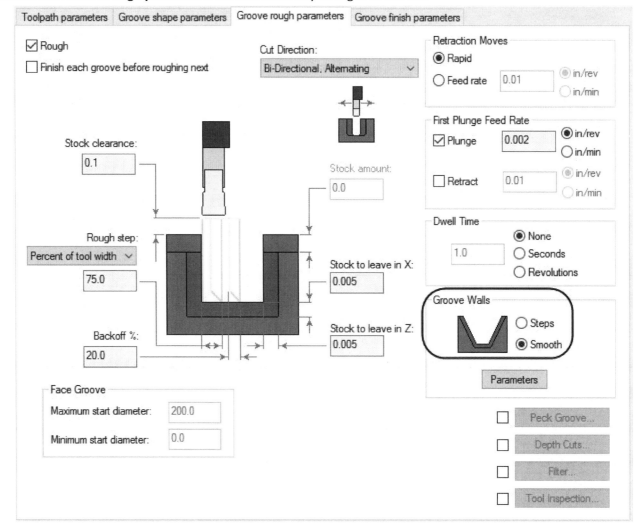

Toolpath parameters   Groove shape parameters   Groove rough parameters   Groove finish parameters

☑ Rough
☐ Finish each groove before roughing next

Cut Direction:
Bi-Directional, Alternating

Retraction Moves
● Rapid
○ Feed rate   0.01   ● in/rev ○ in/min

First Plunge Feed Rate
☑ Plunge   0.002   ● in/rev ○ in/min
☐ Retract   0.01   ● in/rev ○ in/min

Stock clearance:
0.1

Stock amount:
0.0

Dwell Time
1.0
● None
○ Seconds
○ Revolutions

Rough step:
Percent of tool width
75.0

Stock to leave in X:
0.005

Backoff %:
20.0

Stock to leave in Z:
0.005

Groove Walls
○ Steps
● Smooth
Parameters

Face Groove
Maximum start diameter: 200.0
Minimum start diameter: 0.0

☐ Peck Groove...
☐ Depth Cuts...
☐ Filter...
☐ Tool Inspection...

• Select the **Groove finish parameters** tab and make any changes as shown.

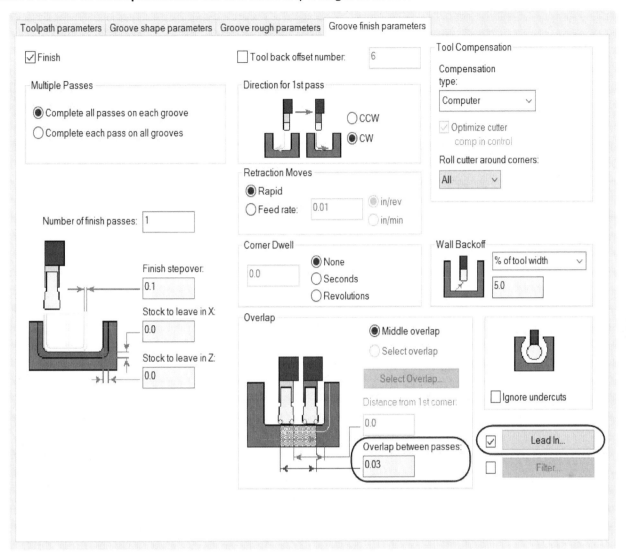

• Select the **Lead In** button.

• Change the **First pass lead in Entry Vector** to **-90** degrees as shown.

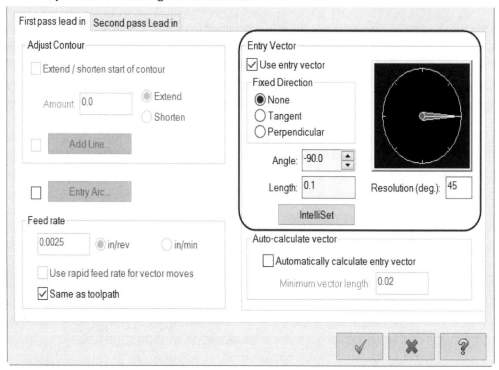

• Set the **Second pass Lead in Entry Vector** to **-90** degrees as well.

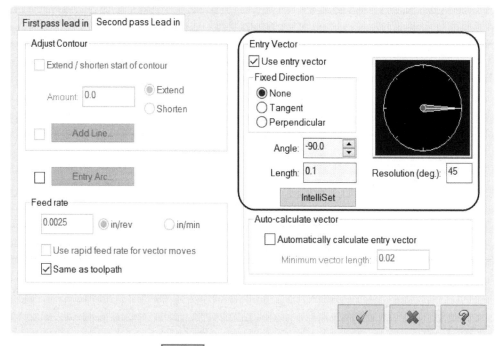

• Select the **OK** button to exit the **Lead In** dialog box.

• Select the **OK** button to exit the **Lathe Groove (Chain)** dialog box and to generate the toolpath.

16.1 Backplot the toolpath

♦ Once the operation has been regenerated **Backplot** the toolpath.
♦ See **page 49** to review the procedure.

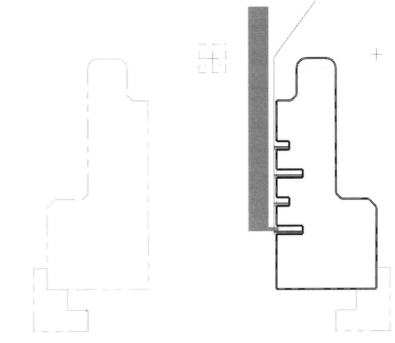

♦ Select the **OK** button to exit **Backplot**.

16.2 Verify the toolpaths

♦ To verify all toolpaths, from the **Toolpaths Manager**, choose the **Select all operations** icon.
♦ See **page 51** to review the procedure.

♦ To go back to the Mastercam window, minimize the **Mastercam Simulator** window as shown.

STEP 17: THREAD THE OD OF THE PART

In this step we will thread the outside diameter of the part to a 9" X 5 thread.

Toolpath Preview:

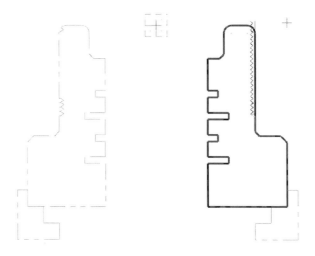

TURNING

* From the **General** group, select the **Thread** icon.

> **NOTE:** The toolpath dialog box will open automatically.

* Right click the **OD Thread Left** tool from the tool list and select **Edit tool** as shown.

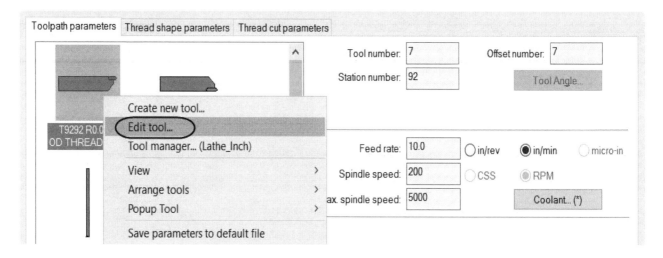

◆ When the **Define Tool** dialog box appears, select the **Setup Tool** button.

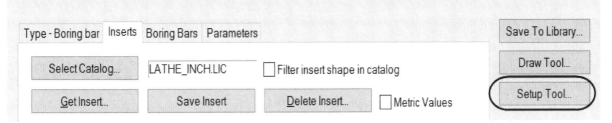

◆ Change the **Turret** to **Right** as shown.

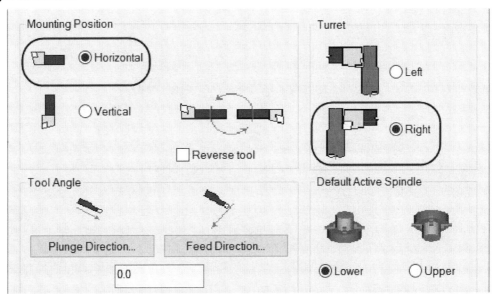

◆ Select the **OK** button to exit the **Lathe Tool Setup (VTL)** dialog box.

◆ Select the **OK** button to exit the **Define Tool** dialog box.

• The new tool should be selected. Enter the comment as shown.

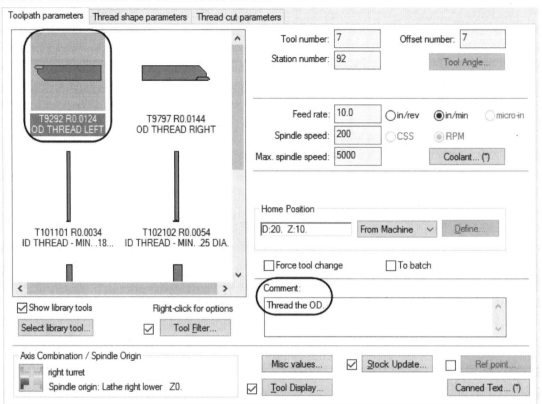

• Select the **Thread shape parameters** tab, enter the **Lead**, and click on the **Compute from formula** button.

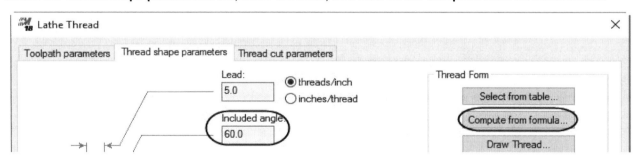

• Change the **Thread form** and enter in the **Lead** and **Basic major diameter** as shown.

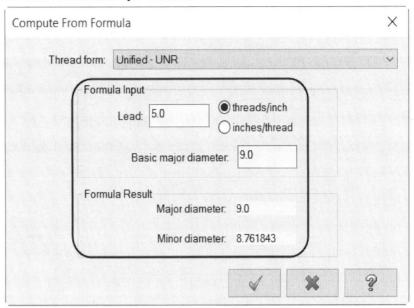

• Select the **OK** button to exit the **Compute From Formula** dialog box.
• Ensure that your parameters match the parameters as shown.

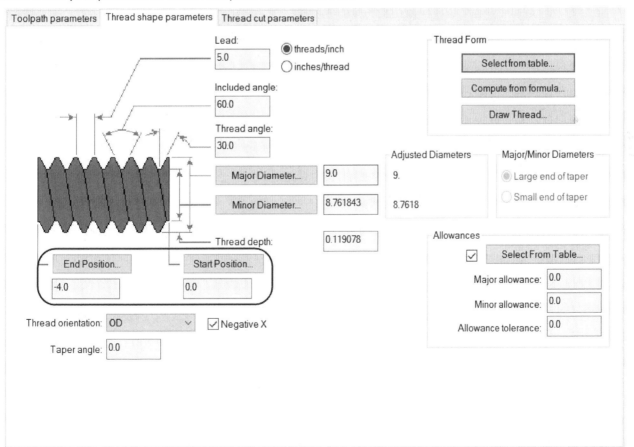

• Select the **Thread cut parameters** tab and make any necessary changes as shown.

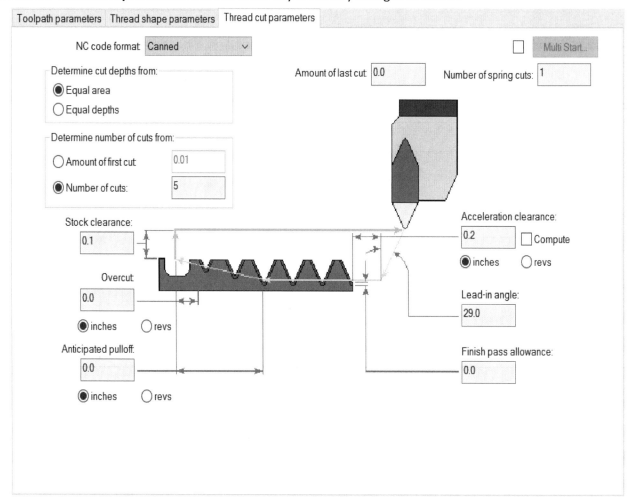

• Select the **OK** button to exit the **Lathe Thread** dialog box.

17.1 Verify the toolpaths

- To verify all toolpaths, from the **Toolpaths Manager**, choose the **Select all operations** icon.
- See **page 51** to review the procedure.

- Select the **Verify** tab, click on the drop down arrow below **3/4** and select **2nd quadrant** to see a section through the part as shown.
- The part should look as shown.

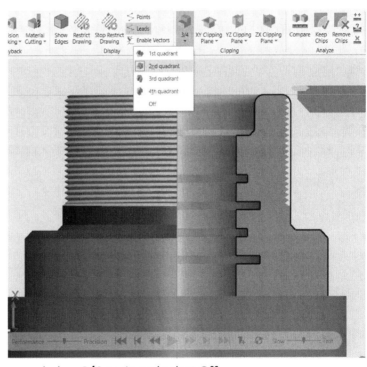

- To remove the section, click on the drop down arrow below **3/4** again and select **Off**.

- To exit the **Mastercam Simulator** window click on the **Close** icon.

STEP 18: RUN THE POST PROCESSOR TO OBTAIN THE G-CODE FILE

Post Processing refers to the process by which the toolpaths in your Mastercam part files are converted to a format that can be understood by your machine tool's control. A special program reads your Mastercam file and writes the appropriate NC code.

- Make sure that all operations are selected, otherwise click on the **Select all operations** icon.
- Select the **Post selected operations** icon from the **Toolpaths Manager.**

- In the **Post processing** dialog box, make all of the necessary changes as shown.

NC File enabled allows you to keep the NC file and to assign the same name as the MCAM file.

Edit enabled allows you to automatically launch the default editor.

- Select the **OK** button to continue.
- Save the NC file.

• The **Mastercam Code Expert** window will be launched and the NC program will appear as shown.

```
1   %
2   O0007
3   (PROGRAM NAME - TUTORIAL #7 TOOLPATH)
4   (DATE=DD-MM-YY - 20-01-17 TIME=HH:MM - 13:22)
5   (MCX FILE - C:\USERS\GONG.ZHANG\DOCUMENTS\MASTERCAM\LATHE\TUTORIAL #7 TOOLPATH.MCAM)
6   (NC FILE - C:\USERS\GONG.ZHANG\DOCUMENTS\MASTERCAM\LATHE\TUTORIAL #7 TOOLPATH.NC)
7   (MATERIAL - STEEL INCH - 1030 - 200 BHN)
8   G20
9   (TOOL - 1 OFFSET - 1)
10  (RIGHT TURRET - 80 DEG.  INSERT - CNMG-432)
11  (FACE THE PART.)
12  G28 U0. V0. W0.
13  G50 X-20. Y0. Z10.
14  G0 T0101
15  G18
16  M8
17  G97 S62 M03
18  G0 X-12.4 Z.0867
19  G50 S3600
20  G96 S200
21  G99 G1 X.0625 F.01
22  G0 Z.1867
23  X-12.4
24  Z.0483
25  G1 X.0625
26  G0 Z.1483
27  X-12.4
28  Z.01
29  G1 X.0625
30  G0 Z.11
31  X-12.4
32  Z0.
```

• Select the **"X"** box at the upper right corner to exit the editor.

STEP 19: SAVE THE UPDATED MCAM FILE

REVIEW EXERCISE - STUDENT PRACTICE

IMPORT THE GEOMETRY FOR TUTORIAL #7 EXERCISE

Import the SolidWorks file.
* Use **File Open** and make sure that you change the file extension to SolidWorks files.

Create the turn profile geometry.
* In the **Plane Manager** change the **WCS** to the **Top** plane.
* Use the **Levels Manager** to create a new level and make the new level the **Main Level.**
* **Turn Profile**.

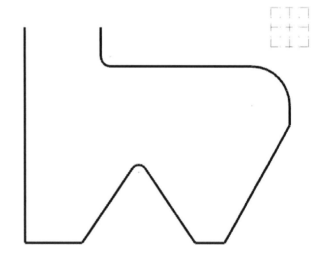

CREATE THE TOOLPATHS FOR TUTORIAL #7 EXERCISE

Create the Toolpaths for Tutorial #7 Exercise as per the instructions below.

Set the machine properties including the stock.

* Change the **Machine** to a **VTL RIGHT TURRET**.
* The geometry will be automatically rotated into position.
* Select an appropriate stock size and chuck size.
* In the Machine Properties **Files** select the **VTL tool library**.

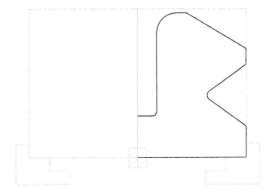

Face, Rough and Finish the OD.

* Use the stock to define the face operation.
* Use the OD Rough Right Turret tool for roughing and facing operations.
* Use an OD Finish Right Turret tool for the finish operation.

Groove the OD using a custom tool with a round insert.

* Use the chain selection method.
* Right click on the **Right Turret Ctr 0.25 Wide Groove** tool from the tool list and select **Edit tool** to create a round insert.

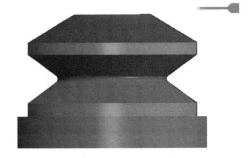

◆ Modify the **Holder** geometry to avoid collision with the stock.

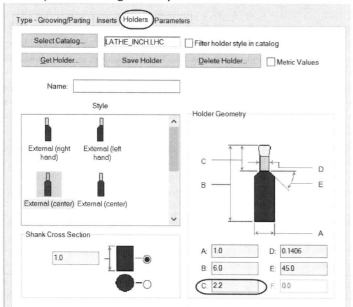

◆ Finish the groove in the same toolpath

Drill the center of the part.
◆ Select the **1.75"** Drill bit.
◆ Set the Depth as per the part.
◆ **Edit tool** to change the tool diameter to **2.0"**.
◆ Modify the **Holder** geometry to avoid holder collision with the stock.
◆ Select a suitable drill cycle.
◆ Use a Flat endmill final drill operation to remove the material left by the drill.
◆ Set the tool parameters as shown. modify the holder as shown.

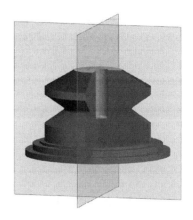

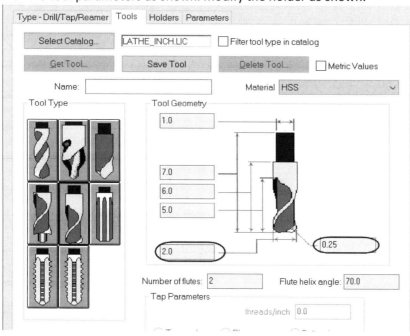

Rough and Finish the ID.

• Chain the ID fillet only using the **Single** button.
• Edit the **2" Boring Bar** by changing the **Holder** geometry to avoid collisions with the stock.
• Enable **Use stock for outer boundary** to avoid burying the tool into too much material.
• Use the same tool for the finish operation.

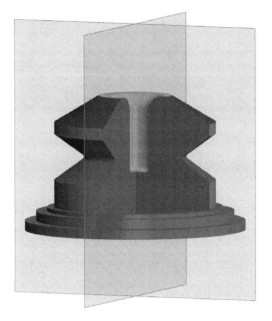

NOTES:

Mastercam. 2018

TUTORIAL #7 QUIZ

◆ What does VTL stand for?

◆ What is a VTL machine?

◆ What happens when you change the Machine definition from a default machine to a VTL definition?

CREATING A LATHE TOOL LIBRARY

Objectives:

✓ The Student will learn how to create a new tool and to save it in a library.

CREATE NEW TOOL

Objectives:
◆ To create a rough turn tool with an 80 deg. insert.

> **NOTE:** To display the Toolpaths Manager press **Alt + O.**

MACHINE
◆
◆ Select the **Default.**

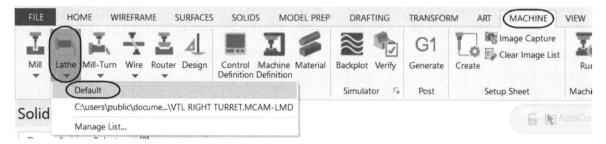

◆ Select the plus sign in front of **Properties** in the **Toolpaths Manager** to expand the **Toolpaths Group Properties.**

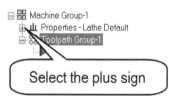

◆ Left click on **Files** to open the **Machine Group Properties** dialog box.

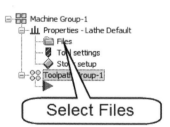

◆ Select the **Tool** icon in the **Tool Library** area.

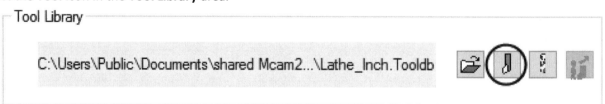

◆ Right click in the **Part display area**.
◆ Select **Create new tool**.

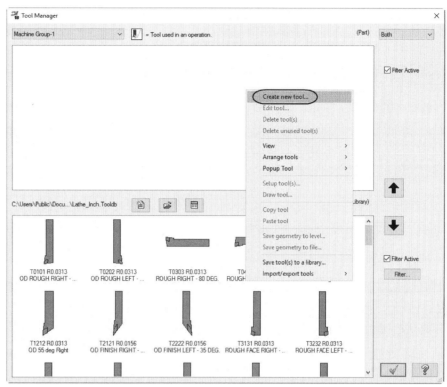

◆ Select the **General Turning** type in the tool **Type** page.

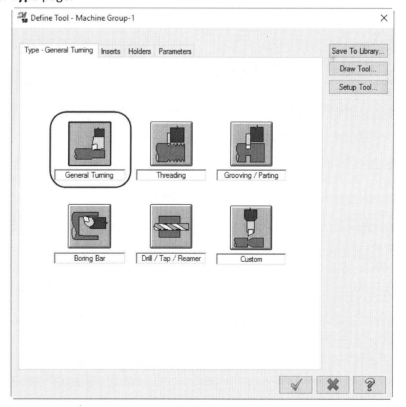

• Select the **Get Insert** button in the **Inserts** page.

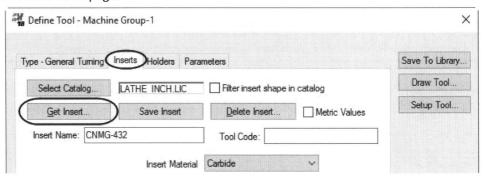

• Select the **"CNMG-321"** insert.

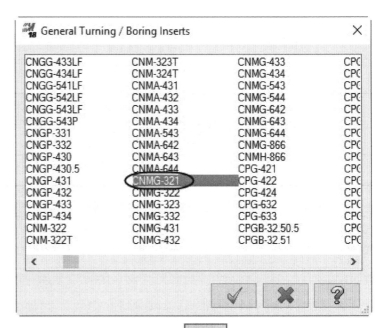

• Select the **OK** button to exit the **General Turning / Boring Inserts** dialog box.

◆ The inserts parameters are as shown in the following picture.

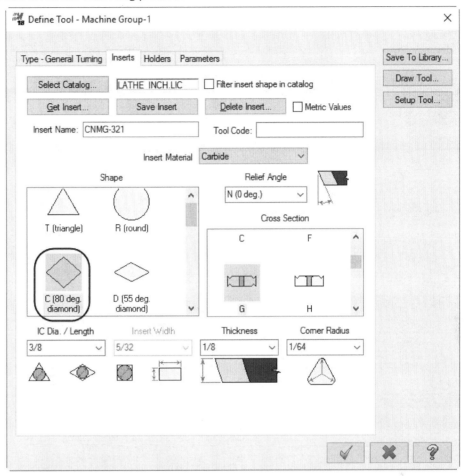

◆ Select the **Holders** tab and click on the **Get Holder** button.

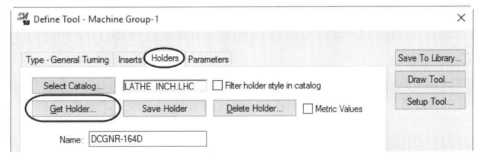

◆ Select the **"NVLCR-163D"** holder.

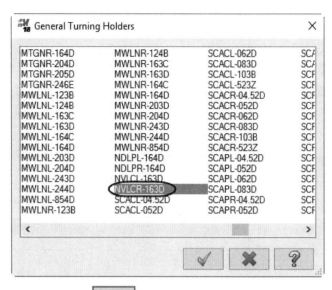

◆ Select the **OK** button to exit the **General Turning Holders** dialog box.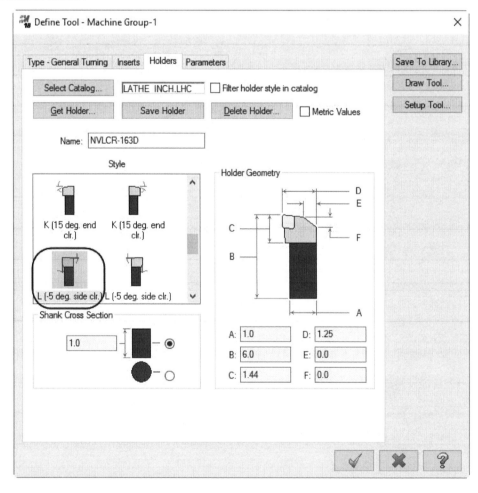
◆ The holder's parameters are shown below.

◆ Select **Setup Tool**.

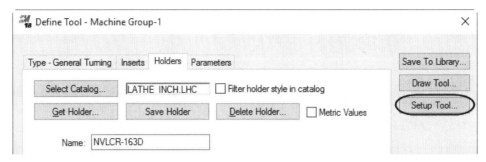

◆ Make the changes as shown and click **OK** to return back to the **Define Tool** dialog box.

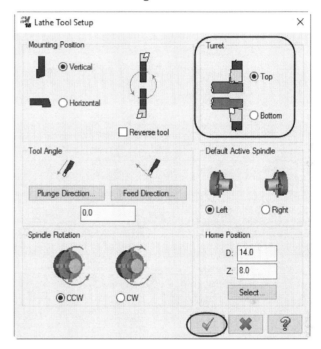

NOTE: **Setup Tool** will establish the mounting position, tool angle, spindle rotation, turret, active spindle and home position.

◆ Select **Draw Tool** to view the rough turn tool.

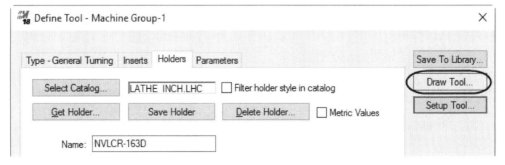

- A preview of the tool will be shown in the graphics user interface. Press **Enter** to return to the **Define Tool** dialog box.

◆ Select the **Parameters** tab and enter the **Tool name** as shown.

◆ Select the **Tool Clearance** button as outlined above.
◆ Select the **Scan Tool Geometry** button.

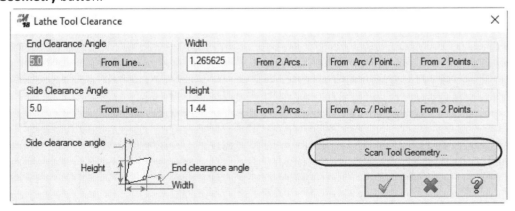

NOTE: Tool Clearance will allow you to view and edit the tool's end and side clearance angles as well as the tool's width and height.

♦ Click on the **Select All** button.

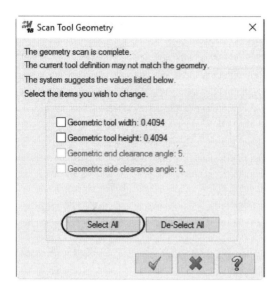

♦ Select the **OK** button to exit.
♦ The **Lathe Tool Clearance** page will look as shown.

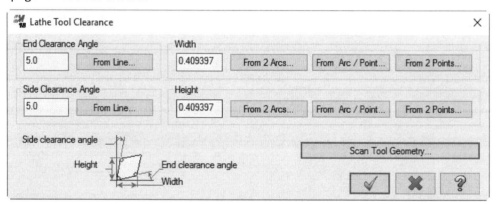

♦ Select the **OK** button to exit.
♦ Select the **Save to Library** button to save the new tool in the library.

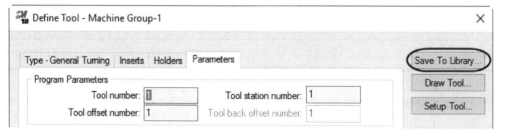

NOTE: Make sure that you save the tool to your own library to separate it from Mastercam's Library. When prompted, save it with your library name.

♦ Select the **OK** button twice to exit the **Lathe Tool Manager**.

Exercises:

Create a finish turn tool with a 35 Deg. Insert.

Create a boring bar with a 55 Deg. Insert.

Lathe Training Tutorial   *Mastercam.* 2018

EDITING A LATHE TOOL LIBRARY

Objectives:

✓ To edit an existing grooving tool, "OD GROOVING W0.375 CENTER", and change it to an "OD Cutoff RH".

EDIT A TOOL

Objectives:
* To edit an existing grooving tool, "OD GROOVING W0.375 CENTER", and change it to an "OD Cutoff RH".

MACHINE
*
* From the **Machine Type** group, select the drop down arrow below **Lathe**.
* Select the **Default**.

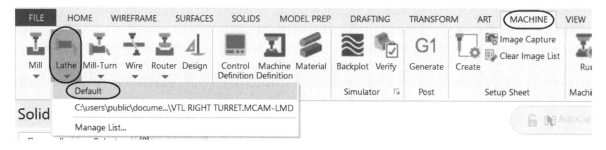

* Select the plus sign in front of **Properties** in the **Toolpaths Manager** to expand the **Toolpaths Group Properties**.

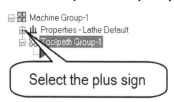

* Left click on **Files** to open the **Machine Group Properties** dialog box.

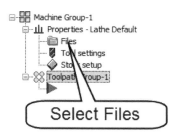

* Select the **Tool** icon in the **Tool Library** area.

◆ Find the **R0.01 W0.375 GROOVE CENTER WIDE** tool in the library list and right click on the tool.
◆ Select **Edit tool.**

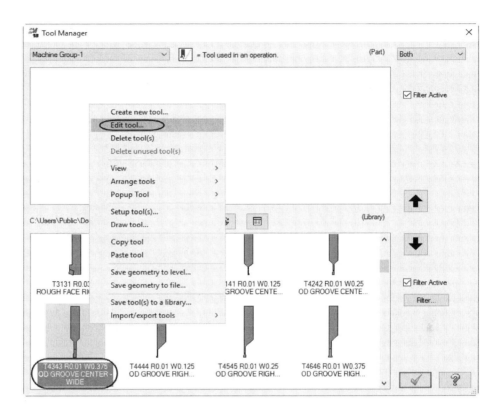

• Set the parameters of the insert as shown.

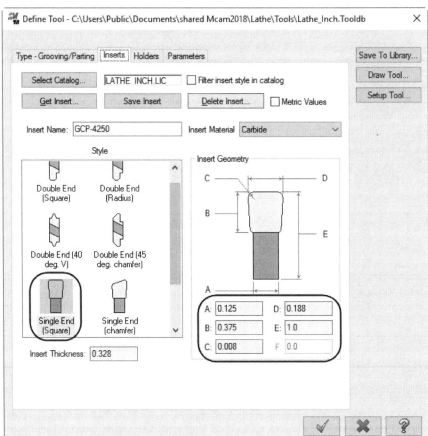

◆ Select the **Holders** tab and make any changes as shown.

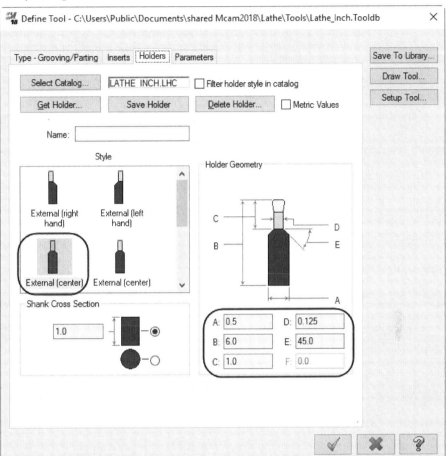

◆ Select the **Draw Tool** button as outlined above.

◆ A preview of the tool will be shown in the graphics user interface as shown.

◆ Press **Enter** to return to the **Define Tool** dialog box.

• Select the **Parameters** tab and change the parameters of the grooving tool as shown.

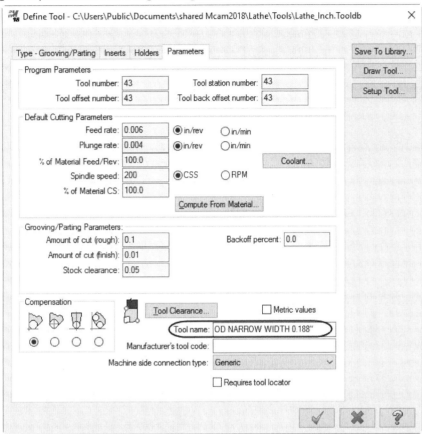

• Select the **Save to Library** button to save the new tool in the library.

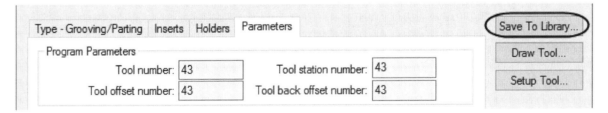

> **NOTE:** Make sure that you save the tool to your own library to separate it from Mastercam's Library. When prompted, save it with your library name.

• Select the **OK** button twice to exit the **Tool Manager** dialog box.

• Select the **OK** button to exit the **Machine Group Properties** dialog box.

Exercises

Edit a finish turn tool to have a 35 Deg. Insert.

Edit a boring bar to have a 55 Deg. Insert.

QUIZ ANSWERS

Objectives:

✓ The answers to the 7 Tutorial quizzes.

LATHE TUTORIAL QUIZ ANSWERS

Tutorial #1 Answers

* Why should you create a facing operation?
  * A facing operation is used to quickly clean the stock from one end of the part and create an even surface for future operations.

* What is a roughing toolpath used for?
  * Roughing operations are used to quickly remove large amounts of stock in preparation for finish passes.

* What does backplotting your toolpath allow you to see?
  * Backplotting shows the path of the tool and helps you spot any errors in the program before you machine the part.

* What does toolpath verification represent?
  * The toolpath verification represents the finished part simulated as a solid.

* What does a post processor do?
  * A post processor takes your Mastercam part file and converts it to a format that can be understood by your CNC's controller.

Tutorial #2 Answers

* What does a Drill Toolpath allow you to do and what is needed to create a drill toolpath?
  * A drill toolpath allows the user to drill along the part's center line. To create a drill toolpath you do not need to create any geometry. You simply need a point.

* What is a groove toolpath intended for?
  * A groove toolpath is intended to machine any recessed areas that cannot be machined by roughing toolpaths or tools.

* How do you create a grooving toolpath using the width of the tool?
  * To create a groove toolpath using the width of the tool, disable the finish pass and set the Width of cut on the roughing page to 100%.

Tutorial #3 Answers

* Why would you use a canned rough cycle?
* A canned rough cycle would be used if you wanted to define how the toolpath is cut in preparation for the finishing operation.

* What type of toolpath must precede a canned finish cycle?
* You must have a canned rough or canned pattern repeat operation in order to create a canned finish toolpath.

* Where can you edit the groove angle?
* You can edit the groove angle in the setup tool page.

Tutorial #4 Answers

* What does the X Tangent point button allow you to do?
* The X Tangent point button allows you to select a point on the geometry where the cutoff should stop.

* What does drill tip compensation do?
* Drill tip compensation automatically adjusts the depth value adding the tip of the drill to it.

* What does a cutoff operation do?
* A cutoff operation allows the user to vertically cut off pieces of the part in sections once the machining has been completed.

Tutorial #5 Answers

* What options does the Thread toolpath give you?
* The Thread toolpath allows you to create a screw, bolt or nut.

* Why would you flip the stock?
* You would flip the stock to cut the second half (backside) of the part.

* What operation would you use to cut a chamfer on the inside of the part?
* You would use a finish toolpath to cut the chamfer on the inside of a part providing there is already a hole in the part.

Tutorial #6 Answers

- What is a center drill used for?
  - A center drill is used to start a small hole for a drill or a tailstock.

- Why would you use a stock advance toolpath?
  - To advance the stock through the spindle and allow you to machine more stock without having to open the door and place stock in the chuck.

- Why would you advance a tailstock?
  - You would advance a tailstock so you could work on a long piece near its center.

Tutorial #7 Answers

- What does VTL stand for?
  - VTL stands for Vertical Turret Lathe.

- What is a VTL machine?
  - A VTL machine is a lathe with the same essential design as a horizontal lathe except this machine has the chuck rotating parallel to the floor of the machine.

- What happens when you change the Machine definition from a default machine to a VTL definition?
  - The geometry is rotated 90 degrees and the stock setup page is adjusted so that it accommodates a vertical chuck and stock setup.

Lathe Training Tutorial

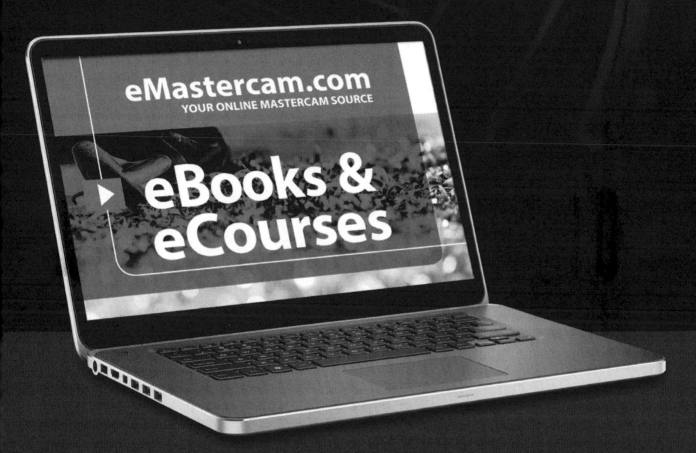